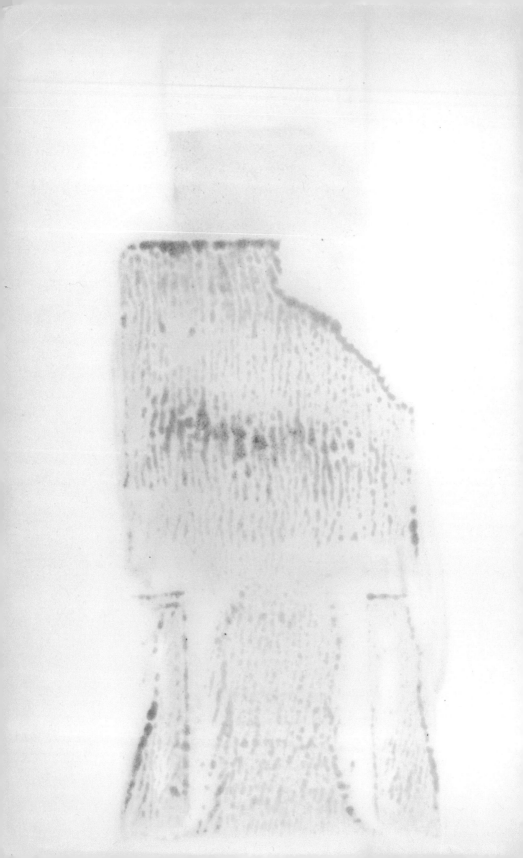

McGRAW-HILL **T**ECHNICAL
EDUCATION
SERIES

McGRAW-HILL TECHNICAL EDUCATION SERIES

Norman C. Harris, Series Editor

(Other volumes in preparation.)

INTRODUCTION TO ELECTRON TUBES AND SEMICONDUCTORS

E. C. ALVAREZ

Pierce College
Woodland Hills, California

DAVID E. FLECKLES

San Diego Junior College

McGRAW-HILL BOOK COMPANY

New York
St. Louis
San Francisco
London
Toronto
Sydney

to:
OUR FAMILIES
for their patience and understanding

INTRODUCTION
TO ELECTRON TUBES AND
SEMICONDUCTORS

01396

2 3 4 5 6 7 8 9 0   HD   9 8 7 6

PREFACE

Introduction to Electron Tubes and Semiconductors is an introductory text designed to give the user a solid background in device structure and operations. The subject of electron devices is developed in a graded approach, progressing from the simple to more complex.

In preparing this book, we have assumed that the user has a good foundation in a-c and d-c fundamentals, an understanding of the standard procedures for making simple laboratory measurements, and a working knowledge of both algebra and trigonometry.

In an approach to the subject from a graphical base, devices are treated in a nonintegrated manner; first vacuum tubes are analyzed and then semiconductors. Many of the basic principles, such as those concerning electrostatic fields and carriers, are carried over into the discussion of transistors. The newer types of semiconductors are explained and illustrated, and particular emphasis is placed on triodes and tetrodes.

No attempt has been made to analyze basic circuits such as push-pull amplifiers or oscillators. Instead, we have placed emphasis on fundamentals since it is our belief that a strong framework of basic knowledge is the best approach to circuit analysis.

We have made liberal use of graphs and illustrations with the hope that they will be helpful to the student. Also, the many practical problems at the ends of the chapters and the worked-out examples within the chapters should prove valuable tools in providing a strong background in the fundamentals needed for the study of circuit analysis.

The preparation of this book would never have been possible without the help and encouragement of many people. We are grateful to our associates for their helpful suggestions and to our students for their cooperation in helping us test the teachability of the material. Special thanks are extended to the host of device manufacturers who supplied us with curves, graphs, and data.

E. C. Alvarez
David E. Fleckles

CONTENTS

I

VACUUM DIODES

1·1 INTRODUCTION

Diode vacuum tubes divide themselves into two basic groups, those used in power circuits where the tube conducts large currents and those used in signal circuits where only nominal currents are required. In both types the operational theory is the same. The tube acts essentially as a switch where current is permitted to flow in one direction but not in the other. In power circuits this switching action serves as the basis of converting alternating currents to direct currents. In signal circuits the switching action converts modulated (a-m or f-m) signals to audio signals, clips or limits voltage waveshapes, and serves as the basic element in logic circuits.

This chapter develops the basic theories required for understanding various diode circuits. The physical construction is related to the graphical and algebraic representation of the device. The forward- and reverse-bias characteristics are related to load lines.

Semiconductor diodes will be covered as a separate topic in Chaps. 8 and 9.

1·2 PHYSICAL CONSTRUCTION

The term *diode* means two-electrode device. Figure 1 · 1 illustrates the two principal elements of the tube, the cathode and the anode. The physical structure of the device is shown in Fig. 1 · 1*a*, and its schematic equivalent is shown in Fig. 1 · 1*b*.

ANODE

The term *anode* derives from chemistry where an ion is defined as having a positive electrostatic charge capable of attracting negative charges. Such is the function of the *an* electrode (anode or plate). It generally operates with a higher (positive) potential than the cathode, thus attracting the electrons emitted from the cathode. It can also be thought of as *collecting* the electrons within the tube. The term *plate* has been adopted because of the physical shape of the anode. Sometimes the shape of an anode is a cylinder (as shown in Fig. 1 · 1*a*). It can, however, take on the shape of an ellipse, a hexagon, or a triangle. In most instances the anode completely surrounds the cathode, making possible maximum efficiency in collecting of electrons.

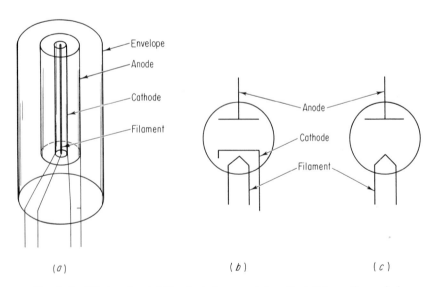

Fig. 1 · 1   Diode tube. (*a*) Physical characteristics. (*b, c*) Schematic symbols.

The anode must meet requirements of heat dissipation and physical rigidity. Some of the more common types of anode materials are tungsten, tantalum, graphite, molybdenum, and nickel. Under the conditions of rated conduction, the plate must be capable of remaining rigid with extremely high currents and should therefore be able to throw off or dissipate the heat generated by the current flow. Since the structure is housed in a glass or metal envelope and in a vacuum, very little heat is liberated through convection or by conduction. The principal method of heat dissipation is through radiation.

CATHODE

The cat ion (opposite in charge from the an ion) is the source of the term *cathode*. The cathode or emitter is the source of electrons within the tube. These electrons are liberated from the cathode surface when a sufficient amount of energy in the form of heat is supplied by the filament to the cathode. The filament is contained within the cathode sleeve and resembles the light-producing filament of an incandescent lamp. The materials used in the construction of the cathode depend upon the ultimate application of the tube.

Some electron tubes do not contain a cathode. The filament becomes the source of electrons attracted to the plate. This type of emitter is identified as a "directly heated" type and is discussed further in Sec. 1·4. The schematic symbol for a directly heated emitter is shown in Fig. 1·1c.

Small-signal Applications. If the anode is to be operated at low positive potentials, less than 400 volts, the cathode sleeve is constructed of nickel with a coating of barium and/or strontium oxide. The oxide-coated emitter provides an abundant supply of electrons at relatively low cathode temperatures. Oxide-coated emitters also provide the best available efficiency since the energy lost at the cathode is held to a minimum.

Power Application. Oxide-coated emitters are subject to damage when bombarded with positive ions. The flow of space current within a vacuum tube results in the generation of such ions. At high current values large numbers of ions are developed. The heavy bombardment of the anode with a stream of electrons liberates the ions from the anode surface. Other ions are produced because a perfect vacuum within the envelope (glass or metal covering) is impossible to achieve. The small remaining amount of gas within the envelope is bombarded with electrons, and more positive ions are produced. The presence of such gas can be noted visually within the envelope as a pale bluish haze. Normal operation for many power tubes includes a small amount of residual gas. Since the potential at the cathode is negative, these ions are accelerated toward the cathode. The impact of these ions upon the cathode increases the temperature of the

cathode, causing greater emission of electrons and also causing the libera-
tion of gases from the cathode surface. These new gases cause an even
greater generation of positive ions. The positive ions bombarding the
cathode have a mass many thousands of times that of the electrons. The
resultant increase in cathode temperature due to ion bombardment is
called *cathode back heating*. Diodes used in power applications contain
cathodes constructed of either tungsten or thoriated tungsten. With these
materials the temperature at the cathode may range as high as 2400°C
without risk of damage to the emitting surface. The efficiency of the tungsten and thoriated tungsten device is quite poor since considerable
amounts of power are lost in the energy conversion.

Tube Housing. The tube is sealed in an evacuated enclosure, either glass
or metal, for the purpose of removing all gases which would interfere with
normal conduction of the tube through ionization. Since it is impossible
to evacuate all gases mechanically, a small strip of magnesium or metallic
barium is mounted at the bottom of the tube envelope. As part of the
manufacture, the tube is then heated to a high temperature and the small
strip is "flashed" electronically. The process unites the gas molecules with
the magnesium or barium strip. This magnesium strip is called a *getter*
since it literally "gets" the positive ions. The getting operation generally
continues for the life of the tube since the getter has a high affinity for gas.
This gas molecule "grabbing" property absorbs any new gases developed
at the anode or cathode.

1·3 TYPES OF EMISSION

The operation of electron devices relies principally on a source of electrons. This available supply of electrons is produced through a number
of processes.

THERMIONIC EMISSION

The process of heating metals or metallic substances to a high temperature
causes electrons to be emitted from the surface of the metal. The amount
of energy required to cause the emission of a given number of electrons
for a given square surface of emitting area is provided by the Richardson-
Dushman equation

$$I = AT^2 \epsilon^{-b/KT} \tag{1·1}$$

The symbols used in the equation stand for the following: I equals the
current emitted per square centimeter of emitting surface. A is a constant
whose value depends upon the type of material used. (The constant for

thoriated tungsten is 30. Figure 1·2 shows a graph of filament emission for various types of materials.) K stands for the Boltzmann constant of 1.38×10^{-23} watt-sec. T is the temperature in degrees Kelvin. The quantity b is called the *work function* and is expressed in electron-volts.

Work function can be defined as a constant which represents the amount of energy needed to dislodge an electron from the surface of a metal. The unit of energy used for work function is the electron-volt. One electron-volt represents 1.6×10^{-19} joule or about 0.224 cal of heat. It is important to note that tungsten has a work function of 4.52 while oxide-coated emitters such as barium oxide have a work function of about 1.0. The tungsten therefore requires more heat energy to liberate surface electrons than does the oxide-coated emitter.

The equation along with the graph of Fig. 1·2 brings out a number of facts pertinent to thermionic emission. For example, the amount of emission from the cathode surface depends mostly upon the temperature. The two values in the exponent of ϵ greatly influence the current.

A study of Table 1·1 and Fig. 1·2 shows how the various substances are used for the construction of vacuum tubes for particular applications. It is readily seen that oxide-coated emitters emit electrons at a lower temperature than tungsten; however, the melting points of the two materials differ considerably.

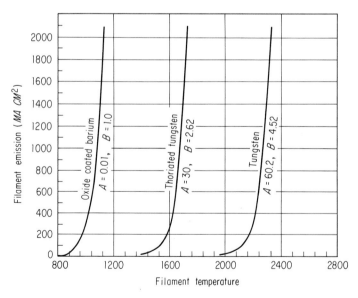

Fig. 1·2   Emission characteristics.

The choice of material used is influenced by the ultimate application of the tube. Tungsten and thoriated tungsten emitters, though requiring large amounts of power for their operation, are used in transmitting and high-power rectifying tubes. The lower-temperature emitters are used in receiving-circuit applications and small-signal circuits.

SECONDARY EMISSION

When electrons, traveling at high velocities, bombard a metal surface they force out other electrons from the surface. The electron in motion has kinetic energy and under operating conditions of the tube (positive potential on the anode) will be traveling at a high velocity. This process of dislodging electrons as a result of electron bombardment is called *secondary emission*. Secondary emission is usually undesirable since the electrons being emitted from the plate area are forced out into the electron stream moving from cathode to plate. Because the secondary-emitted electrons have the same electrical charge as the electron stream, a repelling force occurs between them and the electrons arriving from the cathode. This reduces the overall flow of electrons from the cathode to the plate and thus reduces plate current. Secondary emission is a characteristic of tetrode-type tubes and in some cases is useful.

PHOTOELECTRIC EMISSION

In thermionic emission the energy required to cause an emission of electrons was in the form of heat. This process is satisfactory for metals of the type shown in Table 1 · 1. For some materials such as cesium, potassium,

TABLE 1 · 1*

Material	A	b, ev	Melting temp., °C
Tungsten	60.0	4.52	3410
Thoriated tungsten	3.0	2.63	3400
Tantalum	60.0	4.12	2900
Barium oxide	0.01	1.0	875
Strontium oxide	0.05	1.5	750
Platinum	32.0	5.29	1769
Molybdenum	(55–60)	4.27	2622 ± 10

* McGraw-Hill Encyclopedia of Science and Technology (an international reference work), McGraw-Hill, New York, 1960.

sodium, and zinc, energy in the form of light at a specific wavelength will liberate electrons from the surface exposed to the light waves. The amount of emission from these materials is dependent upon the intensity of light wave, the frequency (wavelength), and the angle of approach of the light wave.

FIELD EMISSION

Field emission uses the principle of attraction of charges from an unheated cathode. When an extremely high positive force is brought into the area surrounding the cathode, electrons can be drawn out or pulled from the surface and attracted to the positive charge. The action is sometimes called *cold-cathode emission.*

Analysis of Eq. (1·1) shows that the energy supplied to the cathode material is in the form of heat (T). In photoelectric emission the source of energy is in the form of light, and for secondary emission the source of energy is in the form of kinetic energy resulting from the velocity of the electrons bombarding the surface. In cold-cathode emission the energy is in the form of electron-volt energy contained in an electrostatic field. If a high potential difference is placed between the cathode and the plate of a diode the result is the same as adding heat energy to the cathode material. The thermionic-emission equation can be replaced with the electric-field equation

$$I_f = BV^2\epsilon^{-K/V} \qquad (1\cdot2)$$

where I_f is current emitted per square centimeter of emitting surface, B and K are constants dependent upon the material of the emitter, and V is the potential gradient at the cathode. A typical material used for the cathode is magnesium oxide.

1·4 EMITTERS AND FILAMENTS

Cathodes are classified as either "directly heated" types or "indirectly heated" types. The indirectly heated emitter was discussed in Sec. 1·2. Here a heater is inserted into the cathode sleeve. A current passed through the filament transfers the heat from the filament to the cathode. Either an a-c or d-c source may be used for the filament supply; however, in some circuits where the alternating current might produce an objectional hum, direct current is used. Current fluctuations in the filament supply do not readily affect the emission characteristics of the cathode. The result is that the emission characteristic in indirectly heated emitters is reasonably constant.

In a vacuum tube where no cathode sleeve is present the filament becomes the emitting surface or the cathode. Such an emitter is defined as a directly heated cathode.

Filament power is supplied to the tubes through a series connection or a parallel connection. In some cases, a combination of both may be used. In either case, however, the basic power requirements of the filament must be delivered. Each tube has a filament voltage and current rating established by the manufacturer as the optimum to ensure rated tube operation. For example, a 6SA7 listed in the tube manual will show that the HEATER CHARACTERISTICS are as follows:

Heater voltage   6.3 volts
Heater current   300 ma

The first number of the tube type indicates the approximate value of the heater voltage requirement. A 12SQ7 requires 12.6 volts while a 35W4 requires 35 volts. The 6C4 requires 6.3 volts at its filament. Some tubes rated at 12.6 volts can also be operated from a 6.3-volt source. For example, the 12AU7 can be operated from a 12.6-volt source or a 6.3-volt source. Many dual-purpose tubes have a center tap connection to provide this convenience. Other exceptions can be found with the seven series of loktal tubes. The 7A7 requires 6.3 volts while the 7AU7 will operate from either 6.3 or 3.5 volts. In all cases the tube manual should be consulted for the correct heater power requirements.

SERIES CONNECTION

Modern television receivers, a-c/d-c receivers, and commercial transformerless devices employ a series string connection of filaments. With this type of connection two requirements must be met:

1. The total voltage requirements should be equal to the sum of the filament voltage ratings of the individual tubes.
2. The filament current requirements must fulfill manufacturers' specifications.

It is sometimes possible to use a tube with a lower filament-current requirement than that of the other tubes in the string. When this is done a parallel resistor must be used to bypass the unwanted current.

EXAMPLE ONE   What is the value of the resistance R of Fig. 1·3 in order to ensure proper filament operation of the tubes in the circuit? What is the power rating of the resistor? What is the total power drawn from the filament circuit?

$$R = E/I = 6.3/(150)(10^{-3}) = 42 \text{ ohms}$$
$$P = I^2R = (0.15)^2(42) = 0.945 \text{ watt}$$

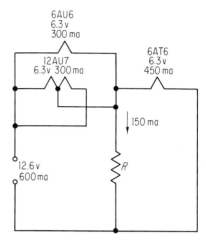

Fig. 1·3   Current by-pass for filament connection.

The resistor rating should be three or four times larger than the wattage it must dissipate. The resistor should be 42 ohms 5 watts. Five watts must be chosen because that is the nearest RETMA value available commercially.

$$P_t = IE = (600)(10^{-3})(12.6) = 7.5 \text{ watts (total)}$$

PARALLEL CONNECTION

There are two basic requirements for parallel connection of filaments:

1. All voltage ratings must be as recommended by the manufacturer.
2. The total current supplied will be equal to the sum of the individual currents drawn by the tubes.

The circuit of Fig. 1·4 shows an example of a parallel filament connection. Note that the filament windings on the transformer have sufficient current rating to provide the operating currents.

1·5 DIODE CHARACTERISTICS

The operating characteristics of a diode vacuum tube are such that when the plate is made positive with respect to the cathode, plate current flows. When the plate is made negative with respect to its cathode no current flows since the plate is not capable of emitting electrons. Even though both plate and cathode are at a negative potential, plate current will flow so long as the plate is less negative than the cathode.

PLATE-CURRENT CHARACTERISTICS

Two factors influence the amount of plate current in a diode, the amount

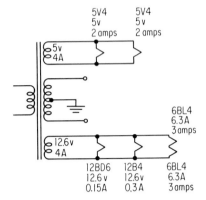

Fig. 1·4   Parallel filament connection.

of plate voltage with respect to the cathode and the temperature of the cathode. Examine the circuit of Fig. 1·5. Assume the switch is in position 1. Variable resistor R and battery E are not in the circuit. Assume that tap 1 on the transformer represents 6.3 volts a-c. A small current of a few microamperes flows in the plate circuit. This small current exists because a few electrons boiled off from the cathode attain sufficient velocity to carry through to the plate.

In order to reduce this plate current to zero, a small negative potential must be inserted at point A. The magnitude of the voltage at A which reduces the plate current to zero is known as the *contact potential*. Figure 1·6a shows contact potential graphically. Note that about 0.6 volt of contact potential is indicated.

Assume the switch is changed to position 2 and R is adjusted so that a minimum amount of plate current flows. R will be at its largest value.

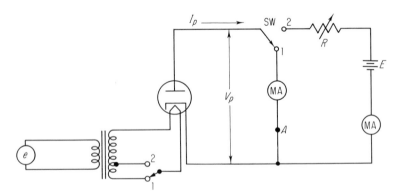

Fig. 1·5   Diode characteristics.

As R is varied the voltage between plate and cathode also varies. The resultant plot of plate-voltage and plate-current variation is shown in Fig. 1·6 as a solid line. As V_p is increased a saturation point is reached.

Assume that the filament switch is connected to tap 2 of the transformer. The resultant reduction of filament voltage and current causes a decreased operating temperature at the cathode. The reduced cathode temperature

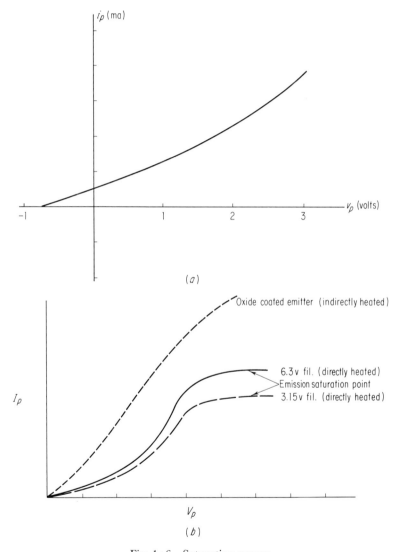

Fig. 1·6   Saturation curves.

characteristic is shown as a dashed line in Fig. 1·6b. Any further reduction of cathode temperature further reduces the point of saturation. Note that the solid-line and dashed-line characteristics represent directly heated types of emitters.

The diode shown in Fig. 1·5 and the resultant characteristics of Fig. 1·6 has a cathode and hence is an indirectly heated type. If a similar set of tests were conducted with this diode a somewhat different set of curves would result. The number of electrons emitted from an oxide-coated emitter greatly exceeds the number emitted from a tungsten or thoriated tungsten emitter at the same operating temperature and plate voltage. As a result no distinct saturation point is reached and the curve is similar to the dotted-line characteristic of Fig. 1·6. The tube would be damaged long before saturation could be reached. The action can be summarized as follows: At low plate potentials plate current is determined largely by plate voltage since the number of electrons emitted from the cathode greatly exceeds the number attracted to the plate. At high plate potentials the plate current is determined by the cathode temperature since the maximum number of electrons attracted to the plate is limited by the number emitted from the cathode.

SPACE CHARGE

The number of electrons emitted from the cathode at low plate potentials greatly exceeds the number attracted to the plate. The excess electrons not attracted to the plate tend to form a "cloud" of electrons which hover around the cathode. This cloud of electrons possesses a negative charge (called *space charge*) which exerts a repelling force upon the other electrons being emitted from the cathode. Assume the plate potential to be a fixed value. A given number of electrons leaves the space charge and is attracted to the plate. However, since the cathode is boiling off electrons faster than they flow to the plate the number of electrons accumulating at the space charge tends to increase. An equilibrium point is established which finds a fixed number of electrons in the space charge for every value of cathode temperature and plate voltage. Because of the equilibrium condition set up by the space charge the excess electrons are returned to the cathode from the space charge.

As the plate voltage is increased more electrons are attracted to the plate and fewer are returned to the cathode from the space charge. When the saturation point is reached the space charge is depleted and is not returning any electrons to the cathode. The plate is attracting electrons at the same rate that the cathode is emitting them. This condition is also known as *emission saturation*.

CHARACTERISTIC CURVE

In most vacuum tubes the plate current is limited by the space charge. A plot of the change in plate current resulting from changes in plate voltage is given in Fig. 1·7. Note that the function is not quite a linear one nor is it a parabolic one. The actual function was developed experimentally by Child and Langmuir and is known as the *Child's-law characteristic*. The law is also known as the *three-halves-power law*.

$$i_p = K e_p^{3/2}$$

where K is a constant determined by the physical construction of the tube. The equation is approximately correct and can be verified by a laboratory experiment.

The characteristic curve is essentially a plot of the resistance of the tube. Two important resistance values can be determined from the curve, the d-c or static plate resistance R_p and the a-c or dynamic plate resistance r_b. The characteristic of Fig. 1·7 is a 6AU4GT diode used in television damper circuits. If the tube is operated at a constant d-c plate potential of

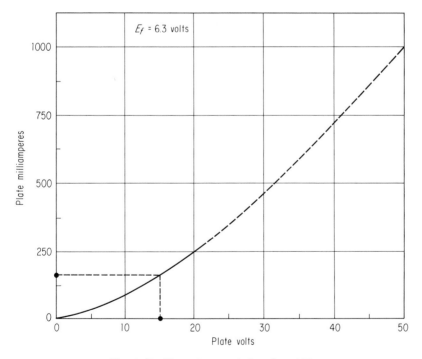

Fig. 1·7   Plate characteristics of a 6AU4.

15 volts a resultant current of 175 ma will flow at the plate. Therefore, according to Ohm's law the resistance of the tube is $R_p = E_p/I_p = 86$ ohms. If the tube were operated at a plate potential of 20 volts d-c its resistance would be 80 ohms.

Assume the tube is to be operated under dynamic conditions where the plate voltage is not a fixed value but is changing between two different values. The resistance of the tube is given as

$$r_p = \Delta e_b/\Delta i_b \qquad\qquad (1\cdot3)$$

If the plate voltage of the 6AU4 is changing from 15 to 20 volts, the resistance of the tube becomes

$$r_p = \Delta e_b/\Delta i_b = 5/0.075 = 67 \text{ ohms}$$

1·6 LOAD LINE

In order to put the diode into a practical circuit, its dynamic features must be considered. These new characteristics center around the diode load resistor R_L as illustrated in Fig. 1·8. Although E_{bb} is shown as a d-c potential, a similar analysis applies when E_{bb} is replaced by an a-c source.

In the preceding sections the factors influencing the plate current were analyzed and it was found that changes in supply voltage E_{bb} controlled plate current. With a fixed value of E_{bb} connected in the circuit, the plate load resistance also influences plate current. Refer to Fig. 1·8. If the supply voltage E_{bb} is held constant and R_L is varied, the plate current would vary inversely. The varying plate current through R_L will produce a varying voltage across R_L and thus the same variation in the voltage across the tube.

CIRCUIT VOLTAGES

When R_L is placed in the plate circuit of the diode, two voltage drops occur. One is across the tube and the other across the load resistor. Figure 1·9 is a functional schematic of the plate circuit. According to Kirchoff's law the two voltage drops must equal the applied E_{bb}.

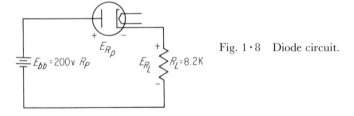

Fig. 1·8   Diode circuit.

Fig. 1·9   Equivalent diode circuit.

$E_{bb} = E_{R_p} + E_{R_L}$

PLOTTING THE LOAD LINE

The graphical representation of the dynamic characteristics involving the plate current, plate voltage, and load resistance is referred to as a *load line;* it is illustrated in Fig. 1·10. Analysis of the load-line characteristic is similar to the graphical analysis of series circuits. Examine the series circuit of Fig. 1·11a. The circuit can be analyzed by Ohm's law; the total current flow would be 3.75 ma. This circuit current can be solved graphically as shown in Fig. 1·11b.

Construction of the graph is as follows: (a) Assume R_1 alone is connected across 90 volts. The current will be 6 ma. Connect the zero current point A

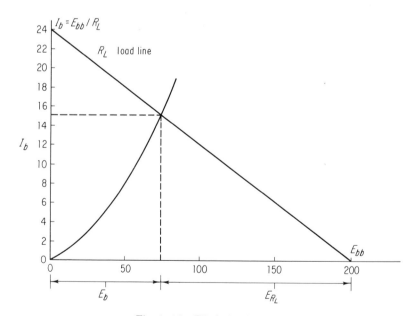

Fig. 1·10   Diode load line.

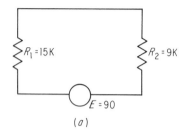

(a)

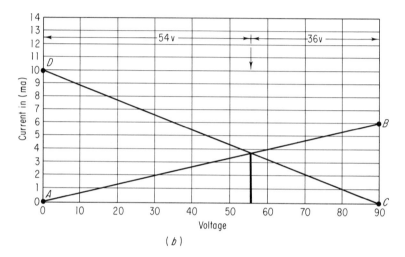

(b)

Fig. 1·11   Graphical analysis of a series circuit.

to the 6-ma current point B. Either side may be chosen. In the example of Fig. 1·11, the left-hand origin was chosen. (b) Assume R_2 alone is connected across 90 volts. The current which will flow is 10 ma. Connect the zero current point C to the 10-ma current point D. The plot of Fig. 1·11 is now a graphical solution where R_1 and R_2 are in series across 90 volts.

The point of intersection identifies all the characteristics of the circuit. The point of intersection projected to the current ordinate indicates the current flow of 3.75 ma. This same point projected to the voltage abscissa indicates the voltage distribution across the two resistors. The student should verify these values using the algebraic method of Ohm's and Kirchhoff's laws.

LOAD-LINE DATA

The method of graphical solution of a two-resistor series circuit can be applied to diode circuits. Note that the load resistor of Fig. 1·10 compares with R_2 of Fig. 1·11 and the tube resistance curve compares with R_1. The data which can be obtained from the diode load-line characteristic are useful in circuit analysis. Even though the illustration here is not directly pertinent in practice, it does illustrate fundamental theories which are important. One point of the load line is established as E_{bb} and the other point as E_{bb}/R_L (the point along the current ordinate).

When a d-c supply of 200 volts is applied to the tube of Fig. 1·10, the static potential measured across the tube will be 72 volts and the voltage across the load resistor will be 128 volts. The plate current will be 15 ma.

Assume that a diode is to be used as a rectifier as shown in Fig. 1·12. The load line is plotted along the voltage abscissa at a point equal to the maximum potential applied to the diode and load. The current point is established by dividing the maximum potential by the value of the load.

EXAMPLE TWO   What is the maximum output potential from the circuit of Fig. 1·12 when a 12-volt rms source is applied to the primary of the transformer? Draw the output waveshape.

$$E_A = \propto E_{in}(\text{max}) = (1.18)(17) = 20 \text{ volts (max)}$$

where $\propto$ equals the turns ratio of the transformer.

A load line (solid line) is plotted as shown in Fig. 1·13 using the maximum value of E_A and the 1.11-kilohm load resistance. The point of intersection of the diode characteristic and the load line is projected to the voltage axis. The maximum potential across the tube when it is conducting at maximum will be 11.8 volts and

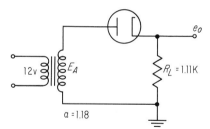

Fig. 1·12   Half-wave rectifier.

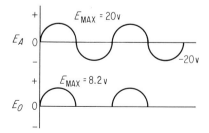

the maximum potential across the load, and hence the ouput, will be 8.2 volts. The output waveshape will reproduce only half of the input sine wave since the diode will conduct in one direction only. This output is illustrated in Fig. 1·12.

Graphical design lends itself conveniently when specific design require-ments must be met. As an illustration, assume that the circuit of Fig. 1·12 must be modified in order to produce an output peak voltage of 10 volts. Since the input requirements have not changed the maximum potential at the secondary will be the same: 20 volts. The value of the load resistor must be changed to a value which will intersect the diode characteristic at a point B of Fig. 1·13. A line (dotted) drawn through the two known points (E_{bb} and point B) indicates that the load resistance must intersect the current ordinate at the 12.5-ma point. The new value of load resistance may now be obtained by Ohm's law.

$$R_L = E_b(\text{max})/I_b(\text{max}) = 20/0.0125 = 1.6 \text{ kilohms}$$

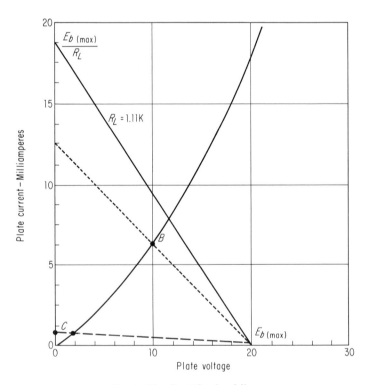

Fig. 1·13   Rectifier load line.

Problems

1·1   If a 12-volt peak-to-peak signal is applied to a 6AL5 diode working into a load resistance of 0.3 kilohm, what is the peak value of the rectified output? (The characteristic curve for the 6AL5 is given in Appendix *B*.)

1·2   If the value of load resistance in Prob. 1·1 were doubled what would be the new output voltage peak?

1·3   If the a-c supply in Prob. 1·1 is replaced with a d-c source of +5 volts, what power is developed at the load resistor?

1·4   If the bias supply in Prob. 1·3 is decreased to 3 volts, what is the d-c plate resistance of the diode?

1·5   Draw the circuit of a series string filament circuit which employs the following tubes: 12BE6, 12AV6, 35W4, and 50C5. What value of resistance must be added in series with the circuit if the applied voltage is 120 volts? What is the power rating of the resistor?

1·6   If the 50C5 of Prob. 1·5 were replaced with one 35C5, what change in the circuit would be required?

1·7   A broadband audio amplifier employs the following tubes: two 5881's, two 6SL7's, two 12AU7's, and one 6C4. The power transformer has a 6.3-volt tap. Draw the schematic of the filament circuit and indicate the current required for the filament winding.

1·8   How much power is being drawn by the filament circuit of Prob. 1·7?

1·9   If an 8-volt peak signal is applied to a 6AL5, what load resistance is required in order to develop an output of 4 volts peak?

1·10   If the circuit of Prob. 1·9 has its input potential decreased to 6 volts, what change in load resistance must be made in order to maintain an output of 4 volts peak?

1·11   Refer to the circuit of Fig. 1·8. The output characteristics of the 6H6 diode are shown in Appendix *B*. How much plate current flows if the load is 500 ohms and $E_{bb} = 20$ volts? What power is developed at the plate of the tube?

1·12   Refer to Prob. 1·11. If the E_{bb} is reduced to 15 volts, what plate current will flow? What power is developed across the load resistor?

1·13   If a given unit uses the following tubes in a series string arrangement, 12BE6, 12BA6, 12AT6, 50C5, and 35W4, and if the 12BE6 and the 12BA6 are to be replaced with a 6BE6 and a 6BA6, respectively, what is the resultant circuit? List the values of resistance and power for any resistors added to the circuit.

1·14   In the circuit of Prob. 1·13, if just the 12BA6 were replaced with a 6BA6, what circuit changes would be required?

1·15   Refer to Prob. 1·13. If just the 12AT6 were replaced with a 6AT6, what circuit changes would be required?

1·7 FORWARD AND REVERSE BIAS

The action of the diode as a circuit element can be compared with that of a switch. A switch, when it is closed, conducts a flow of current and represents a near zero resistance. When the switch is open, the resistance is infinite and no current flows. The *ideal* diode would be one which possesses no resistive property when its plate is positive with respect to its cathode, and an infinite resistive property when the plate is negative. However, when the tube conducts it represents a finite value of resistance as exhibited by the plate characteristic.

The switching property of the diode can be made to approach that of the ideal switch if the tube is operated into high values of load resistance. For example, refer to the load-line characteristic of Fig. 1·13. Note that when the 20 volts of E_{bb} was applied to the circuit only 8.2 volts appeared at the output. When the load was increased (dotted line), 10 volts appeared at the output. When the load is further increased to 40 kilohms (load line shown as a dashed line) the voltage across the load increases to 19.3 volts. The switching of the 20 volts is almost ideal when the tube is operating into a large R_L.

Diodes operating into large values of load resistance, where power transfer is not the primary requirement, are used in signal circuits, clipping and clamping circuits, and various computer logic elements. Under these conditions when the tube is ON, even though it is conducting only a small amount of current, it is said to be *forward-biased*. The diode is OFF or *reverse-biased* when the plate is negative with respect to its cathode and hence conducting no plate current.

Figure 1·14a is an example of a circuit where the diode is used as a switch. The circuit is a logic element and its purpose is to switch either signal E_1 or E_2 to the output. Assume that voltages E_1 and E_2 are both zero volts. The polarity of E_{bb} is such that both diodes are reverse-biased and no current flows through either tube. No voltage appears at the output. Figure 1·14b is a functional schematic of the V_1 circuit. Note that when E_1 equals 0, E_{bb} reverse-biases V_1. The equivalent circuit for V_2 is the same as Fig. 1·14b. When E_1 develops a positive potential of 40 volts diode V_1 switches on and a potential of 25 volts appears across the output (Fig. 1·14c). When E_1 develops a positive potential of any amount exceeding the bias voltage (in this case 15 volts), the diode will begin to conduct. A difference voltage is produced at the output since the polarities of E_1 and E_{bb} are opposite. If E_1 is switched off and E_2 is switched on, again a voltage of 25 volts appears at the output since V_2 is now forward-biased. No voltage is developed across either V_1 or V_2 when they are forward-biased since both tubes are operating into a 500-kilohm load resistor. A plot of the 500-kilohm load line on the characteristic of the tube would verify the results.

EXAMPLE THREE   In the circuit of Fig. 1·14, assume R_L equals 100 kilohms and bias voltage E_{bb} equals 20 volts. (a) What input voltage at E_1 is necessary to make V_1 conduct? (b) What voltage is necessary to produce an output of 25 volts?

SOLUTION
a. The V_1 portion of the circuit can be redrawn as in Fig. 1·14b. Assume the source impedance of E_1 is zero ohms and hence the tube is reverse-biased at 20 volts. To cause V_1 to conduct, any voltage exceeding 20 volts will suffice.
b. According to Kirchhoff's voltage law, the sum of the voltage drops in a closed circuit equals the applied voltage. Assuming V_1 to have zero resistance in the forward direction, E_1 must be 40 volts to have 25 volts dropped across R_L.

1·8 POWER OUTPUT

High-vacuum diodes align themselves into two basic groups, those used in switching and signal circuits and those used in power circuits such as rectification. In the first case the objective is to switch a voltage signal;

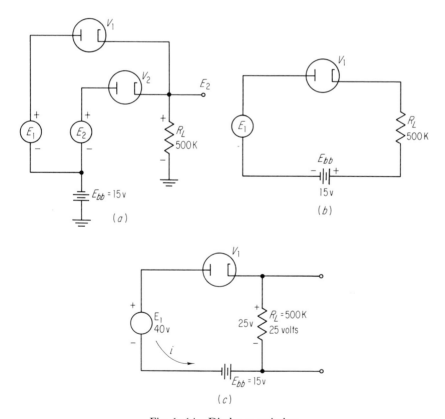

Fig. 1·14   Diodes as switches.

hence the tube should operate as close to an ideal switch as is possible. In the second case, the tube should change an alternating current into a pulsating direct current with as little consumption of power as is possible.

Consider the circuit of Fig. 1·15. The tube is to operate as a rectifier. The current flowing through the load resistor is a pulsating direct current as shown in the output in Fig. 1·15. The pulsating current has a d-c value as shown in the output in Fig. 1·15. For half-wave rectification the value of the d-c level of the output voltage is given as

$$E_{\text{d-c}} = (0.636/2)\, E_A = 0.318\, E_A \tag{1·4}$$

where E_A is the peak value of the alternating current. The d-c power developed at the load is

$$P_{\text{d-c}} = (E_{\text{d-c}})^2/R_L$$
$$E_{\text{rms}} = E_A/0.707$$
$$P_{\text{d-c}} = 0.202 E_A{}^2/R_L \tag{1·5}$$

EXAMPLE FOUR   Refer to Fig. 1·15. Assume $R_L = 60$ kilohms, what is the d-c voltage level at the output? What is the d-c power developed at the load?

$$E_{\text{d-c}} = 0.318(400) = 127.2 \text{ volts}$$
$$P_{\text{d-c}} = (0.202)(400)^2/(60)(10^3) = 540 \text{ watts}$$

1·9 DESIGN PARAMETERS

The construction and design of various diode circuits require that certain precautions be taken. In low-frequency and power circuits there are three tube ratings which must be considered: heater voltage and current, peak inverse plate voltage, and peak plate current. For diodes used in high-frequency circuits, the same three design parameters must be considered as well as the direct interelectrode capacity and electron transit time.

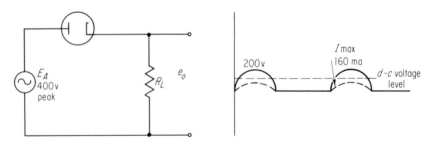

Fig. 1·15   Power rectifier circuit.

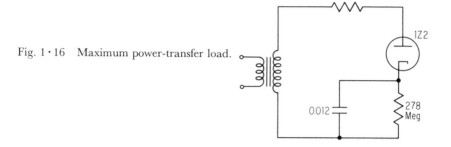

Fig. 1·16   Maximum power-transfer load.

MAXIMUM RATINGS

Vacuum-tube heater characteristics were discussed in Sec. 1·4. *Peak inverse plate voltage* rating refers to the diode under reverse-bias conditions. It defines the maximum voltage which a diode can withstand between its plate and cathode when the tube is not conducting. For example, the 1Z2 is a high-voltage low-current vacuum rectifier used in TV flyback circuits. The 1Z2 has a peak inverse plate voltage rating of 15,000 volts. Thus in a typical circuit as shown in Fig. 1·16, if the voltage on the plate, negative in relation to the cathode, exceeds 15,000 volts, an arc will occur, causing permanent tube damage.

Maximum steady-state *peak plate current* I_b is the maximum direct current the tube is capable of conducting. For the 6AL5, the tube manual lists a maximum peak plate current of 54 ma. Note from Fig. 1·17 that a forward-bias voltage of slightly more than 8 volts at the plate produces maximum peak plate current.

The *maximum d-c output current* rating defines that current which can flow continuously at the plate. For the 6AL5, this rating is given as 9 ma. Note that a direct current of 2.5 volts at the plate produces the maximum rating.

EXAMPLE FIVE   Assume that a 6AL5 is to be connected into a circuit similar to that of Fig. 1·18. If $E_{bb} = 6$ volts, what value of load must be used in order for the plate to operate at its maximum d-c rating?

Construct a load line such that it passes through point Q on the plate characteristic of Fig. 1·17 and point E_{bb} on the voltage ordinate. Point Q is the maximum d-c rating. The load line intersects the current ordinate at 14 ma. Since this point is given as $E_{bb}/R_L = I_x$,

$$R_L = E_{bb}/I_x = 6/(14)(10^{-3}) = 430 \text{ ohms}$$

INTERELECTRODE CAPACITY

A diode vacuum tube has an inherent capacitance because it contains two metal surfaces separated by an insulator. At low a-c frequencies, this

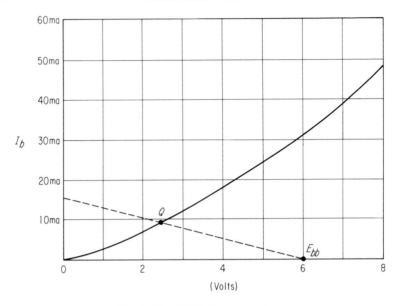

Fig. 1·17   6AL5 characteristics.

capacitance is insignificantly small. At high frequencies (30 kc plus) the effect of capacitance cannot be ignored. Consider Fig. 1·18. C remains constant and is initially determined by the physical spacing and size of the tube elements. As the frequency f increases the capacitive reactance decreases. The reduced reactance tends to produce a low-impedance a-c path, bypassing the tube and reducing plate resistance. In addition to r-f operation, diode capacitances become a significant problem when the tube is used in high-speed switching circuits. For a 6AL5 the interelectrode capacitance is about 3.5 pf.

In the circuit of Fig. 1·18, assume that E represents an a-c signal at

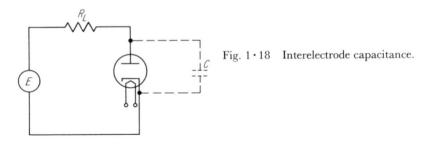

Fig. 1·18   Interelectrode capacitance.

455 kc and $R_L = 100$ kilohms. During the half-cycle when the diode is reversed-biased, ideally its resistance should be infinitely large and no current should flow. However, at 455 kc the tube is beginning to act more like a capacitor than a diode. Since $X_c = 1/2\pi f C$, the capacitance of the tube places an X_c of about 100 kilohms in series with the 100 kilohms of R_L. Instead of the applied voltage being developed across the reverse-biased tube, the voltage is divided between R_L and the capacitance of the tube.

ELECTRON TRANSIT TIME

The physical distance between the cathode and anode determines the time of travel required by space electrons. The positive anode potential also influences electron transit time; however, its effects are minor compared with the element spacing. Assume a 7-volt 800-Mc sine wave is applied to the diode of Fig. 1·19. $T = 1/f = (1.2)(10^{-9})$ sec. The distance between cathode and anode is such that 0.7×10^{-9} sec is required for an electron to travel to the anode from the space charge when 10 volts is applied. Transit time is given as

$$t = 5.05d/V_b^{1/2} \tag{1·6}$$

where d = physical distance, meters
$\quad V_b$ = anode potential
$\quad t$ = time, μsec

The anode is positive for only half the period, or 0.625×10^{-9} sec. As a result some electrons initially traveling toward the positive plate of the tube may be forced back toward the cathode since the time that the plate remains positive is less than the transit time. Higher-frequency operation is possible by reducing the spacing between the elements. When this is done, however, the inverse breakdown voltage rating decreases, limiting the tube to very low amplitude signals.

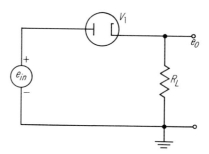

Fig. 1·19   Reverse-biased diode.

Problems

1·16 In the circuit of Fig. 1·8, assume that V_1 is a 6AL5 (Appendix *B*) and e_{in} is 3 volts d-c. What value of R_L will allow the tube to operate at its maximum d-c rating?

1·17 In the circuit of Prob. 1·16, what plate current would flow if R_L were doubled?

1·18 In the circuit of Fig. 1·19, assume e_{in} to be 5 volts d-c and $V_1 = $ 6AL5. What value of load resistance will produce an output of 2 volts across the tube?

1·19 In the circuit of Fig. 1·19, if e_{in} is 8 volts and $R_L = $ 100 kilohms, $V_1 = $ 6AL5, what voltage will appear at the output if the bias is 2 volts?

1·20 Refer to Prob. 1·19. What power would be developed at the load if the load resistance were decreased to a value which would allow the tube to operate at its maximum d-c rating?

1·21 In the circuit of Fig. 1·20, E_1 and E_2 are d-c signal voltages. What voltage must *either* E_1 or E_2 attain in order to draw current through the 1-megohm load? (V_1 and V_2 are ideal diodes.)

1·22 In Prob. 1·21 if E_1 is 26 volts positive with respect to ground, what is the output voltage?

1·23 In the circuit of Fig. 1·20, E_2 is 25 volts and E_1 is zero with respect to ground. What is the output voltage?

1·24 In Prob. 1·23, if the 20 volts supply were changed to 10 volts, what current would be drawn through the load resistance? (Diodes are ideal.)

1·25 In Fig. 1·12, the transformer has a step-up ratio of 1:2, the tube is a 6H6, and the load is 4 kilohms. With 10 volts rms applied to the input, what d-c voltage will appear across the 4-kilohm load resistor? How much power is developed across the load?

1·26 A 6H6 is to be used as a signal detector with a load resistance of 400 ohms. The peak signal applied is 4 volts. What peak voltage is developed across the load resistance?

1·27 Find the d-c power developed at the load in Prob. 1·26.

1·28 If the physical distance between the cathode and anode of a diode is 0.1 mm what is the transit time when 50 volts d-c is applied to the anode?

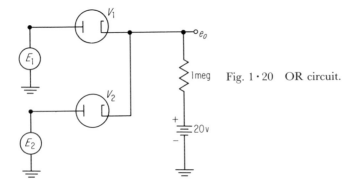

Fig. 1·20 OR circuit.

1·29 Decreasing the voltage in Prob. 1·28 to 20 volts will change the transit time to what new value?

Review Questions

1·1 A 6SQ7, 6SK7, 6SA7, 6K6, and 6X4 are to be used in a system. Which filament connection, series or parallel, will require more or less filament power?

1·2 The diode characteristic curve is actually a plot of the tube's forward resistance. How does R_p vary as the d-c voltage at the plate is increased?

1·3 Assume a signal diode has a load connected to it and a forward bias is applied to the circuit. Will the voltage across the diode be increased if the load is made larger or smaller?

1·4 Does the a-c plate resistance of a diode remain constant along the characteristic? Why?

1·5 How can a diode with finite value of plate resistance be made to act like an ideal diode?

1·6 If a diode has a thermionically heated cathode and a plate circuit which contains neither forward or reverse bias, will there be any plate current?

1·7 Explain how the vacuum tube is evacuated of gases following sealing of the glass or metal envelope.

1·8 In the physical construction of diodes, how does a wider spacing between cathode and anode influence tube capacity and transit time?

1·9 What is the difference between maximum peak plate current rating and the maximum d-c rating?

1·10 How does the plate voltage on a diode influence transit time?

II
TRIODE
TUBES

2·1 INTRODUCTION

Analysis of the triode vacuum tube as a device is presented in this chapter. Emphasis is placed on basic tube parameters and the information available from characteristic curves. The student should become as familiar with the algebraic and graphical representations of tube characteristics as he is with Ohm's law.

2·2 SPACE CURRENT

The diode, at the time it was developed, was thought to be adequate for the work intended. Its applications were nonetheless limited. For instance, a diode either conducted or it didn't, depending upon the potentials placed across it. The control of space current (the current from cathode to plate) was accomplished by controlling the positive voltage at the plate. Plate current could be varied either by varying the forward bias on the tube or by varying the value of the load resistance. In 1906, Lee De Forest inserted a third element (a meshlike structure) between plate and cathode and, by varying the potential on this *grid*, with respect to the cathode, was able to *control* the flow of space current. Figure 2·1*a* is a cutaway view of a triode. Figure 2·1*b* shows schematically the positioning of the control grid.

PLATE CURRENT

A flow of electrons from the space charge to the anode will occur when the potential on the plate is more positive than the cathode. Figure 2·2*a* is a cutaway view looking into the top of the triode. If the plate is 50 volts positive with respect to the cathode, the electrons of the space charge will be impelled in the direction of the electrostatic field. Assume a second field is introduced between the grid and cathode as shown in Fig. 2·2*b*. The direction of the field is opposite to the field between the cathode and plate. Note that the 50-volt cathode-anode field represents an energy distribution of 12.5 volts between cathode and grid and 37.5 volts between grid and anode. If the value of E_g is zero, the energy impelling electrons toward the anode is the cathode-anode potential.

Assume that a large negative voltage is applied between grid and cathode. No electrons will be impelled toward the anode since the field produced by E_g will completely cancel the 12.5-volt field between cathode and grid. Such a condition is known as *cutoff*. As the negative voltage is reduced, the field produced by E_g will decrease. For example, if the grid voltage is established as 12.0 volts there will be an *effective* field between grid and cathode of 0.5 volt. A small space current will result. Therefore, plate current in a triode is controlled by

1. The positive plate potential with respect to the cathode
2. The potential between the grid and the cathode

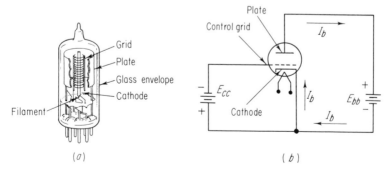

Fig. 2·1   (*a*) Cutaway view of triode. (*b*) Schematic of a triode.

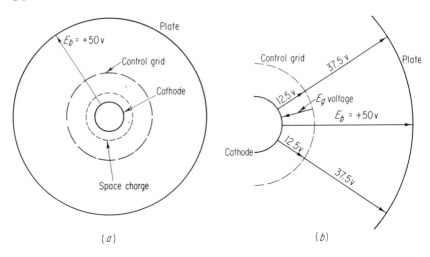

Fig. 2·2   (a) Triode—top view. (b) Electrostatic fields.

GRID CURRENT

If the control grid is maintained negative with respect to the cathode, no grid current will flow. When the grid is made positive with respect to its cathode, grid current will flow. The grid now acts as a plate, even though it is physically different from a plate. Some of the electrons en route to the plate strike the meshlike structure and flow in the grid circuit. The directions of the electrostatic fields between grid and cathode and plate and cathode are now the same; hence they are added. A greater acceleration of space-charge electrons will result. The plate current will increase as the grid is made more positive than the cathode.

Assume that the positive grid-cathode potential is larger than the plate-cathode potential. The plate current will still be the larger of the two currents since the grid is not a solid surface like the plate. Most of the electrons will pass on through to the plate.

CATHODE CURRENT

The current leaving the cathode depends on one of two conditions:

1. If the control grid is maintained negative with respect to the cathode, the cathode current equals the plate current.

$$i_k = i_b \qquad (2\cdot1)$$

2. If the grid is drawing current, the cathode current becomes the sum of the grid current and the plate current.

$$i_k = i_g + i_b \qquad (2\cdot2)$$

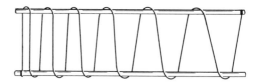

Fig. 2·3   Grid structures.

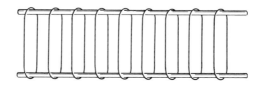

2·3 PHYSICAL CHARACTERISTICS

Figure 2·3 illustrates two common types of grids. The materials used for the grids are chosen for low emission, high tensile strength, and good ductility. Examples of such materials are steel, nickel, and alloys.

The internal mechanical structure of typical triode grids is shown in Fig. 2·4. Figure 2·5 shows typical miniature triode sizes.

2·4 CONTACT-POTENTIAL BIAS

If a positive voltage is placed on the control grid, the electrons (negative charges) emitted from the cathode will be attracted to the grid as well as

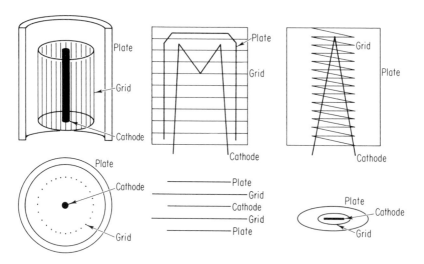

Fig. 2·4   Triodes—physical view.

the plate. Conversely, a negative control grid will do the opposite—or will tend to repel the electrons and all the emitted electrons will flow to the plate. The control grid could be likened to a faucet in that it is capable of "adjusting" the rate of flow of electrons from the cathode. In this sense, the British perhaps use a more graphic term for the triode: the valve.

If the control grid has no potential connected to it the element is left "floating" electrically. As electrons travel from cathode to plate and pass in the vicinity of the uncharged control grid, a few electrons will attach themselves to the control-grid structure by chance contact. The control grid will begin to exhibit more and more of a negative potential first with respect to the plate and, if allowed to continue, eventually in relation to the cathode. The control grid becomes less and less positive with respect to the cathode. As more and more electrons attach themselves to the grid, it assumes a more negative charge and begins to repel any additional electrons. In this "floating" condition, the grid voltage limits itself to about 1 volt. In practical circuits the control grid is never left floating. It is "tied" to ground through a resistance R_g. This *grid-load* resistor provides a path for the contacted electrons to travel back to the cathode. The circuit connection of R_g is shown in Fig. 2·6. The number of electrons flowing through the grid resistor R_g will be small (about 1 μa). The contact potential will produce a small voltage drop across R_g. If R_g is small, up to 100 kilohms, this voltage can be neglected. In this mode of operation the grid resistor acts as a "grid return." All triode tubes must incorporate some form of grid return or grid load. The grid return may not always be through a resistance. Tuned or untuned tank circuits, and even other tubes may serve to return the contact-potential electrons.

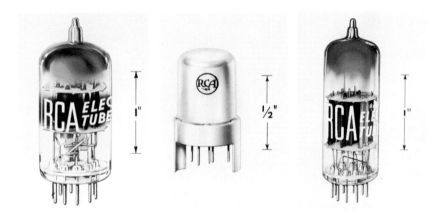

Fig. 2·5   Photo of miniature triodes.

Fig. 2·6   Grid-load resistor.

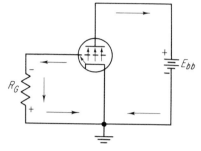

Some amplifier circuits utilize this condition as a means of establishing an operating bias. As an example, if the battery of Fig. 2·1 is 3 volts it can be replaced by a grid-load resistor of 3 megohms. The voltage developed across it as a result of 1 μa of contact-potential current is 3 volts. The polarity is the same as that shown for the battery. Only small values of bias can be achieved by this method.

2·5 OPERATING POINT

GRID BIAS

Sections 2·2 and 2·4 have illustrated that when the control grid is positive with respect to the cathode the control grid will intercept some of the electrons emitted from the cathode. In most cases the resulting grid current is an undesirable effect, since current passing through the grid-load resistor produces power losses. Although many tubes can be operated into the positive grid region, it is generally undesirable; distortion of the input waveshape will result. In order to keep the grid from consuming power a bias voltage is used, a voltage which must be negative with respect to the cathode. The input circuit of the triode is illustrated in Fig. 2·7. Assume that the signal at e_{in} is from an a-c source. During the positive alternation, the input signal is similar to a d-c voltage acting in the oppo-

Fig. 2·7   Triode input circuit.

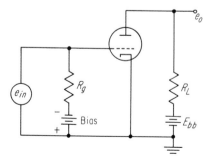

site polarity to the bias potential. Since it is important not to draw grid current, the input signal must not exceed the bias potential. In order to understand this concept more completely, study the input circuit graphically for a specific set of values. Assume that the a-c input signal varies as shown in Fig. 2·8a.

Arbitrarily assign a bias value of −6 volts to the grid in Fig. 2·7. This bias voltage is shown graphically in Fig. 2·8b. Note that the bias value exceeds the positive peak, or 4-volt value, by 2 volts to ensure that no grid current will be drawn when the signal is applied.

Figure 2·8c illustrates the actual voltage changes developed between the control grid and cathode. The changing grid potential is reflected at the plate with a changing plate current. The steady-state I_b (that is, the plate current when the input signal is 0 and just the bias of −6 volts is present) is 15 ma. As the grid signal goes positive (less negative), I_b in-

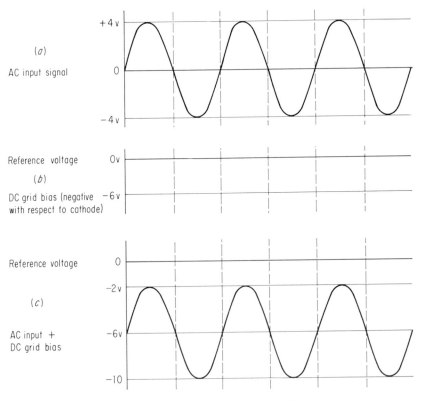

Fig. 2·8   Graphical representation of grid voltages.

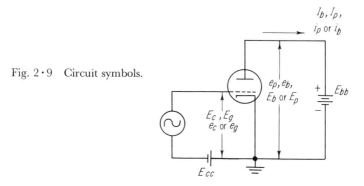

Fig. 2·9   Circuit symbols.

creases up to 25 ma; when the grid goes negative (negative to -10 volts) it decreases to 5 ma.

The grid-voltage change of 8 volts has produced a change in the plate current of 20 ma. The *direction* of the plate current is not altered (from cathode to plate); however, a variation of the magnitude has been produced.

CIRCUIT SYMBOLS

The length of some of the triode terms requires that a means of symbols and notations be used. The most important examples are given in the following list:

E_{bb} d-c plate supply voltage
e_b total a-c signal voltage between plate and cathode
e_p instantaneous a-c voltage between plate and cathode
E_b d-c plate voltage from plate to cathode
E_{cc} grid supply voltage (bias)
E_c d-c grid to cathode voltage
e_c total a-c input signal voltage grid to cathode
e_g instantaneous a-c voltage grid to cathode
I_c d-c grid current
i_c instantaneous a-c grid current
I_b d-c plate current: cathode to plate
i_b total a-c plate current: cathode to plate
i_p instantaneous a-c plate current: cathode to plate

The lowercase letters refer to a-c or instantaneous values. This convention is followed throughout all circuit notations. All notations are shown in Fig. 2·9.

2·6 CHARACTERISTIC CURVES

Plate current of a triode is controlled by three factors:

1. Plate voltage
2. Control-grid potential
3. Cathode temperature

In most applications, the triode is operated at the correct cathode temperature; hence the characteristic curves constructed are in terms of changes in plate current as the dependent variable with plate-voltage and grid-voltage variations. A circuit which can be used to obtain characteristic curves is illustrated in Fig. 2·9. Assume that the plate voltage E_b is set to a fixed value. In this case $E_{bb} = E_b$. Assume now that E_{cc} is varied from some large negative value through a positive value. This curve is considered to be a *grid transfer curve* and is obtained under no-signal conditions (Fig. 2·10). The tube here is operated under *no-load* conditions— i.e., no resistance is connected in the plate circuit. Note that the linear portion of the curve extends from approximately -3 to -1 volt on the E_g axis. Going more positive from -1 volt, the tube becomes nonlinear. Linearity is important for undistorted signal amplification. The signal will remain undistorted if operated in the linear area under conditions which allow the tube to conduct equally on each alternation of the signal voltage. If a tube such as this were used as an amplifier it would probably be biased at -2 volts. Then the peak-to-peak input signal should not exceed 2 volts.

Several important conclusions can be drawn from the graph of Fig. 2·10:

1. The curve exhibits a "linear" region.
2. The curve exhibits a "saturation" point. This point is A in Fig. 2·10. There will always be a plate-current saturation point for a given value of plate and grid voltage. Sometimes this point is unreachable since the tube may be destroyed by excessive heat and arcing before this point is reached.
3. The curve exhibits a "cutoff" region (point B). This cutoff region indicates that a sufficiently high negative potential on the grid will cause a cutoff of plate current; $I_b = 0$.

GRID CURVES

When a series of grid curves are plotted for different values of plate-voltage constants, the result is a *grid "family" of characteristic curves*. The information derived, although limited, aids in further understanding grid-voltage–

plate-current characteristics for a given tube. The grid is not usually driven into the positive-voltage area; hence the grid family of curves shows plate-current changes versus negative grid-voltage changes. Figure 2·11 illustrates a grid family of curves for a typical triode.

A considerable amount of static, or *quiescent* (conditions when no signal is applied), information may be obtained from the grid family of curves. For example, if the plate voltage E_b is at 200 volts, what grid voltage E_c will cause 10 ma of plate current to flow? The 10-ma plate-current point touches the $E_b = 200$ volts curve at point A in Fig. 2·11. Note that point A corresponds to a grid voltage of -6.4 volts. This same information can be

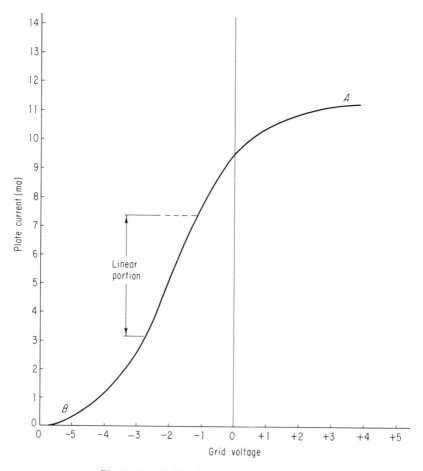

Fig. 2·10   Grid-voltage plate-current curve.

used to determine the d-c plate resistance R_p of the tube. According to Ohm's law, $R = E/I$; hence $R_p = E_b/I_b = 200/(10)(10^{-3}) = 20$ kilohms.

EXAMPLE ONE What plate current will flow in the tube whose characteristics are shown in Fig. 2·11 if the plate voltage $E_b = 100$ volts and the grid voltage $E_c = -6$ volts? What is the d-c resistance of the tube?

The $E_b = 100$ volts curve intersects the $E_c = -6$ volt point where $I_b = 4$ ma (point B of Fig. 2·11).

$$R_p = E_b/I_b = 100/(4)(10^{-3}) = 25 \text{ kilohms}$$

PLATE CURVES

Refer to the circuit of Fig. 2·9. The grid family of curves was developed with various constant values of plate voltage and gradual variations of

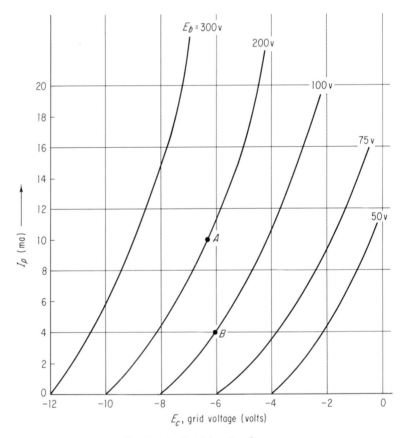

Fig. 2·11   Grid family of curves.

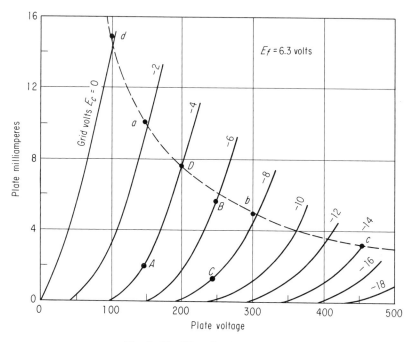

Fig. 2·12   Plate family of curves.

grid potential. If E_{cc} is held constant at different fixed values of E_c and E_{bb} is swept from zero through large positive potentials the plate family of curves results. Figure 2·12 displays a *plate family of characteristic curves* for a 6J6 triode. Consider when $E_{cc} = -2$ volts. The characteristics show that for the 6J6 the plate voltage can be varied from 45 to approximately 155 volts (up to the dotted line) to produce a plate-current change from 0 to approximately 10 ma. Above this 10-ma point, the tube would be operating into a region where excessive power is dissipated at the plate; damage to the tube could result. The limitation for I_b is 10 ma for -2 volts on the grid and 155 volts on the plate. No plate current will flow with less than 45 volts on the plate because the tube is cut off with -2 volts between grid and cathode.

The plate family of curves provides static information concerning tube operation. For example, if the plate voltage E_b is 150 volts what plate current I_b will flow when the grid is at -4 volts? Following the $E_c = -4$ volt curve in Fig. 2·12 to point A shows a plate current $I_b = 2$ ma.

EXAMPLE TWO   If the plate voltage on a 6J6 is 250 volts, what is the d-c plate resistance when $E_c = -6$ volts? What is the resistance when $E_c = -8$ volts?

Locate the 250-volt point along the voltage ordinate in Fig. 2·12. The corresponding plate current when $E_c = -6$ volts is 5.8 ma (point B of Fig. 2·12).

$$R_{p1} = E_b/I_b = 250/(5.8)(10^{-3}) = 43.2 \text{ kilohms}$$

The corresponding plate current when $E_c = -8$ volts is 1.3 ma (point C of Fig. 2·12).

$$R_{p2} = E_b/I_b = 250/(1.3)(10^{-3}) = 193 \text{ kilohms}$$

MAXIMUM-DISSIPATION RATING

The tube manual lists a maximum plate dissipation rating for most vacuum tubes. This rating lists the maximum amount of heat energy which can be dissipated at the plate of the tube. For example, the 6J6 triode has a maximum plate dissipation rating of 1.5 watts. This maximum-dissipation curve is shown as a dotted line in Fig. 2·12. The tube cannot be operated above the dotted-line region since such operation would develop excessive heat at the plate of the tube.

If the plate family of characteristics does not indicate the maximum-dissipation curve it can be superimposed onto the curves. Since $P = IE$ a series of voltage and current points can be developed. In Fig. 2·12 if the plate voltage is 150 volts a maximum current of 10 ma will produce a plate dissipation of 1.5 watts.

$$I = P/E = 1.5/150 = 10 \text{ ma}$$

A general dissipation equation can be developed where the maximum-dissipation rating is a constant.

$$I_b = P_d/E_b \qquad (2·3)$$

where P_d is the maximum rating as listed in the tube manual, E_b is an arbitrarily selected value of plate voltage, and I_b is the resulting plate-current flow.

EXAMPLE THREE   Develop a maximum-dissipation curve for the 6J6 shown in Fig. 2·12. Assume $P_d = 1.5$ watts. The $E_b = 150$ volts point has been selected and the resultant current is 10 ma. This point is shown as a in Fig. 2·12.

Assume $E_b = 300$ volts

$$I_b = 1.5/300 = 5 \text{ ma} \quad \text{(point } b \text{ of Fig. 2·12)}$$

Assume $E_b = 450$ volts

$$I_b = 1.5/450 = 3.33 \text{ ma} \quad \text{(point } c \text{ of Fig. 2·12)}$$

Assume $E_b = 100$ volts

$$I_b = 1.5/100 = 15 \text{ ma} \quad \text{(point } d \text{ of Fig. 2·12)}$$

If these four points (a, b, c, and d) are connected to produce a final curve, the dashed line of Fig. 2·12 results.

The plate family and the grid family of curves are actually the same plot of variables. Either set of curves can be used to consider plate changes for small changes in grid voltage. These curves lead to the development of *tube constants* or specifications provided by the manufacturers. The constants or parameters supply a means of comparing tubes and determining their suitability in various circuits.

2·7 TUBE PARAMETERS

Plate-current variations as a result of changes in grid voltage or plate voltage are a direct result of tube design, geometrical and hence electrical. Some examples of the physical properties which contribute to electrical operation of the tube are the spacing of electrodes (plate to cathode, grid to plate), the type of filaments (tungsten or oxide), the area of cathode surface, and the shape and dimensions. These design considerations determine the amount of plate current that will flow, how much grid voltage is needed for plate-current cutoff at a specific value of plate voltage, and what maximum voltage can be applied to the tube. The geometrical characteristics are represented as electrical characteristics identified as *tube constants* or *tube parameters*. The use of the term *parameter* is preferred since *constants* may imply something which cannot be varied. In actual practice the tube parameters do have a range of variation. These parameters are listed as

1. Plate resistance = r_p
2. Amplification factor = μ
3. Transconductance = g_m

PLATE RESISTANCE

The triode vacuum tube represents a static and dynamic plate resistance similar to the diode (Sec. 1·4). The control grid becomes an additional factor in determining the value.

EXAMPLE FOUR   What is the d-c plate resistance of a 6J6 (Fig. 2·12) when 150 volts is applied at the plate? Assume the grid is maintained at −4 volts.

According to the plate family of curves, the plate current corresponding to $E_b = 150$ volts and $E_c = -4$ volts is 2 ma (point a if Fig. 2·12). Since

$$R_p = E_b/I_b$$
$$R_p = 150/(2)(10^{-3}) = 75 \text{ kilohms}$$

Further examination of the problem of Example Four indicates that if the plate voltage is maintained at 150 volts and the grid voltage is changed to − 2 volts, the new plate current will be 8.5 ma. The static plate resistance of the tube becomes 17.6 kilohms.

Static or d-c values of plate resistance are useful in many circuits ranging from amplifiers to computer switching circuits. When the triode is operated with a varying voltage at its grid the resistance exhibited by the tube is identified as the *dynamic* or *a-c plate resistance*. The equation for the a-c plate resistance is

$$r_p \text{ (a-c plate resistance)} = \frac{\Delta e_p}{\Delta i_p}\bigg]_{e_g = K} \tag{2·4}$$

[The bracket at the end of Eq. (2·4) is a mathematical symbol which states that everything before it is true so long as e_g is held at some constant value. The constant here is shown as K.] Since a triode is most often used in circuits that are controlled by alternating currents the a-c plate resistance is a significant parameter and is always listed in the tube manuals. The value listed in the tube manual, however, is optimum. It is the correct value so long as the tube is operated at the static value shown in the listing. Any variation of operation from the listed optimum requires that the new value of r_p must be determined graphically.

DETERMINING PLATE RESISTANCE GRAPHICALLY

Solution of the a-c plate resistance requires the use of a graph of the plate family of characteristic curves. Figure 2·13 is the plate family of curves for the 7A4. By definition

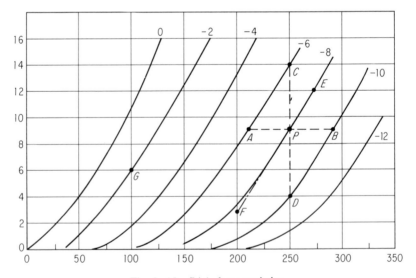

Fig. 2·13   7A4 characteristics.

$$r_p = \frac{\Delta e_b}{\Delta i_b}\bigg]_{e_g=K}$$

where e_g is held constant. Assume a value of -8 volts for e_g. The assumed value of e_g will depend on the operating conditions of the tube. For this example, consider -8 volts to be the amount of grid bias necessary for proper operation. In order to provide as much accuracy as possible, assume a tangent line at point P on the linear portion of the $E_c = -8$ volt curve. The change in E_b is from point $F(200$ volts $E_b)$ to point $E(275$ volts $E_b)$. Projecting this change to the left from the $E_c = -8$ volt curve, Δe_b causes a corresponding change in I_b of 10 ma (from 2.4 to 12.4 ma).

$$r_p = 75/10 \text{ ma} = 7,500 \text{ ohms}$$

The tube manual lists the r_p for a 7A4 as a value between 6,700 and 7,700 ohms. If a second graphical calculation were made at point G of Fig. $2\cdot 13$ the r_p would be smaller.

The *slope notation* is frequently used in vacuum-tube and transistor analysis. A detailed explanation of slope is beyond the scope of this book. As a result, proofs cannot be presented.

Refer to Fig. $2\cdot 14$. Note that in case I where $x = 3, y = -1$ and that where $x = 8, y = 6$. The change in x (Δx) with respect to the change in y (Δy) is identified as the average slope of the function between $x = 3$ and $x = 8$.

$$\text{Average slope} = \Delta y/\Delta x$$

Connecting the two points with a straight line results in a secant line which intersects the x axis at a specific angle θ. The angle is related to the slope of the secant line through the tangent function.

$$\text{Slope} = \tan \theta = \Delta y/\Delta x$$

Transferring this to the vacuum-tube parameter, r_p is related to the slope of the line (or the segment along a characteristic curve).

$$\text{Slope} = 1/r_p \tag{2.5}$$

The larger the slope the larger the angle; hence the smaller the plate resistance. $r_p = 1/\text{slope}$.

A negative slope results when θ is larger than $90°$. In Fig. $2\cdot 14$, case II results in a negative slope where $\tan \phi = -\text{slope} = -\Delta y/\Delta x = -0.4$. The actual angle can be found in trig tables or on the slide rule.

AMPLIFICATION FACTOR

The amplification factor, or the mu (μ), of a tube is the ratio of a small change in e_b to a small change in e_g when i_b is held constant; it is expressed mathematically as follows:

$$\mu = \frac{\Delta e_b}{\Delta e_g}\bigg]_{i_b = K} \tag{2·6}$$

The ratio identifies the ability of a tube to *amplify* a *change* in voltage. If the plate current is held constant, a small signal e_g impressed on the control grid causes a change in e_b at the plate of the tube. The ratio represents how much the tube has amplified the signal; i.e., it is a figure of *tube gain.* Mu is the phonetic pronunciation of the symbol for the amplification factor μ and is a dimensionless ratio, meaning that it has *no* units since the voltage units cancel out.

$$\mu = \Delta e_b/\Delta e_g = e_b/e_g = \text{a ratio}$$

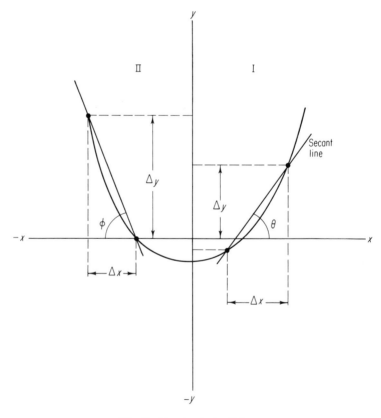

Fig. 2·14   Analysis of slope.

Analysis of a graph of the plate family of characteristic curves for the 7A4 shows a small change in e_g *on* the plane of a constant I_b value produces a corresponding change in e_b as shown in Fig. 2·13 at point *APB*.

EXAMPLE FIVE   What is the μ of the 7A4 if the tube is to operate with about 250 volts at the plate and a plate current of 9 ma with a grid bias of -8 volts? The change in e_g chosen is from -6 to -10 volts with a resultant change in E_b from 210 to 290 volts. The μ is given as

$$\mu = \frac{\Delta e_b}{\Delta e_g} = \frac{290 - 210}{(-6) - (-10)} = \frac{80}{4} = 20$$

This ratio shows that the tube has the ability to amplify a maximum of twenty times. When the tube is connected in a circuit it will not actually amplify twenty times, but some value less. The parameter indicates the hypothetical maximum gain for the 7A4 when operated at a given plate potential and grid bias. Chapter 3 shows how the introduction of a load in the tube circuit reduces the hypothetical gain of 20 down to a real *circuit* gain.

TRANSCONDUCTANCE

Transconductance, or g_m, is the ratio of a change in i_b to a change in e_g with e_p held constant.

$$g_m = \frac{\Delta i_b}{\Delta e_g}\bigg]_{e_p=K} \tag{2·7}$$

Transconductance predicts how much of a change in plate current will be produced by a change in grid signal voltage. Transconductance, or *mutual conductance,* is measured in units of mhos. Since the actual values are quite small g_m will be identified in *micromho units.*

EXAMPLE SIX   The transconductance of the 7A4 is determined from the characteristics of Fig. 2·13. Assume the tube is to be operated at about -8 volts E_g and a plate voltage of 250 volts. The increment of plate current from 4 to 14 ma is produced by a change in grid voltage of 4 volts (point *CPD*).

$$g_m = \frac{\Delta i_b}{\Delta e_g} = \frac{(10)(10^{-3})}{4} = (2,500)(10^{-6}) = 2,500 \ \mu\text{mhos}$$

Transconductance is a measure of the ability of a tube to furnish signal output. Large values of g_m are desirable for voltage amplifiers.

TUBE-PARAMETER INTERRELATIONSHIPS

The interrelationship of the three tube constants can be shown graphi-

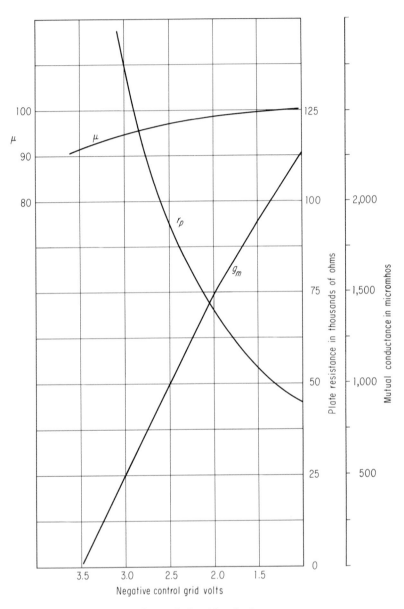

Fig. 2·15 Interrelationship of tube parameters.

46

cally and algebraically. Most tube manuals show this relationship graphically. Figure 2·15 shows how changes in negative grid bias influence the tube parameters. The set of curves shown in Fig. 2·15 are developed for a fixed plate operating potential. If the plate operating voltage is lowered a different set of curves will result. The amplification factor will remain fairly constant over a large segment of grid potentials. Note that the ratio changes only 10 percent over a range of about 3.5 volts at e_g. Plate resistance and transconductance will vary greatly with operating voltages.

Transconductance will vary inversely to the plate resistance. Lower plate current flows because of high plate resistance. When the plate current diminishes to zero (cutoff) the plate resistance is infinite. At this same point (-3.5 volts of E_g) the transconductance is zero.

A mathematical relationship for the three tube parameters can be shown as

Since $\qquad r_p = \Delta e_b/i_b \qquad$ or $\qquad \Delta i_b = \Delta e_b/r_p$

$\qquad\qquad g_m = \Delta i_b/\Delta e_g \qquad$ or $\qquad \Delta i_b = g_m \Delta e_g$

Equating, $\qquad \Delta e_b/r_p = g_m \Delta e_g \qquad \Delta e_b/\Delta e_g = g_m r_p$

However, $\qquad \Delta e_b/\Delta e_g = \mu$

and thus $\qquad\qquad \mu = g_m r_p \qquad\qquad\qquad\qquad (2\cdot8)$

$\qquad\qquad\qquad r_p = \mu/g_m \qquad\qquad\qquad\qquad (2\cdot9)$

$\qquad\qquad\qquad g_m = \mu/r_p \qquad\qquad\qquad\qquad (2\cdot10)$

EXAMPLE SEVEN The tube manual lists the transconductance for a 12AU7 operated at 250 volts E_b and a grid bias of -8.5 volts as 2,200 μmhos. The approximate r_p is given as 7,700 ohms. What is the μ of the tube? Inserting the known values into Eq. (2·8) yields

$$\mu = (2{,}200)(10^{-6})(7{,}700) = 17$$

If the tube of the example is operated at the lower potential of 100 volts E_b and zero grid bias the tube parameters become $r_p = 6{,}500$ ohms, $g_m = 3{,}100$ μmhos, and $\mu = 20$.

2·8 TUBE CAPACITANCES

Chapter 1 illustrated the effective capacitance which exists between vacuum-tube elements. In the case of the diode this capacitance is easy to visualize since there are two elements and a capacitor usually involves two surfaces. Capacitance, however, is present between any two pieces of metal regardless of their shape or structure. A grid can therefore act as a common element for two different capacitances in a triode.

INTERELECTRODE CAPACITANCE

There are three different capacitances in a triode: grid-cathode capacitance C_{gk}, grid-plate capacitance C_{gp}, and plate-cathode capacitance C_{pk}. The interelectrode capacitance of the triode is small, ranging from 0.2 to 10 pf depending upon the structure of the tube. As in the case of the diode, the capacitive effects are negligible at low frequencies. Figure 2·16 illustrates, schematically, the interelectrode capacitances of the triode.

FIGURE OF MERIT

Whenever triodes are used in high-frequency applications or in the switching circuits of digital computers, care must be taken to select a tube with low interelectrode capacitance and a high transconductance. A classification known as *figure of merit* serves to compare various triodes for high-frequency applications. This ratio is given as $K =$ figure of merit and equals

$$K = g_m/(c_i + c_o) \qquad (2·11)$$

where $c_i =$ input capacity C_{gk}, and $c_o =$ output capacity C_{pk}. In practical circuits, the c_i and c_o may be influenced by various circuit elements. In comparing one tube with another, the designer may substitute C_{gk} for c_i and C_{pk} for c_o.

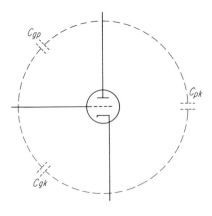

Fig. 2·16   Interelectrode capacitances.

Problems

2·1 What is the d-c plate resistance of 2CW4 if the plate voltage is 200 volts d-c and the grid is maintained at -2.5 volts? (Refer to the Appendix for the plate family of curves.)

2·2 What is the a-c plate resistance of the tube described in Prob. 2·1 at the point indicated?

2·3 In Prob. 2·1 if the plate voltage is 150 volts and the grid is at -1 volt, what current is flowing at the plate? What is the d-c plate resistance?

2·4 If the 12B4 triode has a listed r_p of 1.1 kilohms and a change of 20 volts is measured at the plate, what is the change in plate current? (Assume $E_b = 150$ volts and $E_c = 17.5$ volts.)

2·5 What is the μ of the 12B4 if the tube is operated at the quiescent point of Prob. 2·4? (Assume $g_m = 6,300$ μmhos.)

2·6 If a 6J6 triode is maintained at -4 volts at the grid, what is the R_p if the plate is maintained at 180 volts?

2·7 If the plate voltage in Prob. 2·6 is decreased to 150 volts, what increase or decrease is observed in R_p?

2·8 If the R_p of a given triode is 10 kilohms and the μ is 30, what is the transconductance of the tube?

2·9 If the tube in Prob. 2·8 has a change of 2 volts at the grid, what is the maximum possible change in plate current?

2·10 Refer to the plate family of curves for the 12BH7. What is the transconductance of the tube if it is to be operated at $E_b = 200$ volts and $I_b = 10$ ma?

2·11 A given triode has a μ of 70. If a change in grid voltage of 2 volts causes a change in plate current of 20 ma, what is the r_p of the tube?

2·12 What is the transconductance of the tube in Prob. 2·11?

2·13 If the grid-load resistor for a given triode is established as 4.7 megohms, what contact-potential bias is measured between grid and cathode?

2·14 If the 12BH7 triode (characteristics given in Appendix B) is to operate at a quiescent point of $E_b = 175$ volts and $E_c = -5$ volts, which is larger, R_p or r_p?

2·15 If the quiescent point of Prob. 2·14 is shifted to $E_b = 100$ volts and $E_c = 0$ volts, which is larger, R_p or r_p?

2·16 What is the slope of the 12BH7 resistance at the quiescent point in Prob. 2·15?

2·17 Assume the triode whose parameters are shown graphically in Fig. 2·15 is operated at -2.5 volts at the grid. What are the r_p, g_m, and μ of the tube?

2·18 If the grid bias of Prob. 2·17 is shifted to -1.5 volts, what are the new r_p, g_m, and μ?

2·19 A given triode has an r_p of 10 kilohms. If a 2-volt change at the grid produces a 40-volt change at the plate, what is the transconductance of the tube?

2·20 A given triode shows a 35-volt change in plate voltage and a 5-ma change in plate current when the grid voltage is varied. If the g_m of the tube is 3,000 μmhos, what is the change in grid voltage?

2·21 If the maximum plate dissipation rating of a 12BH7 is 3.5 watts, what is the maximum plate current which can flow if the plate voltage is at 250 volts d-c?

2·22 Refer to Prob. 2·21. If the quiescent plate voltage is to be established at 170 volts, what is the maximum grid bias permitted? (Draw a maximum-dissipation curve first.)

2·23 The tube manual lists the following interelectrode capacitances for the 12B4: $C_{gp} = 4.8$ pf, $C_{gk} = 5.0$ pf, and $C_{pk} = 1.5$ pf. What is the figure of merit of the tube? (*Hint:* Determine the g_m graphically.)

2·24 If the interelectrode capacitances for the 12BH7 are $C_{gk} = 3.2$ pf, $C_{pk} = 0.5$ pf, and $C_{gp} = 2.6$ pf, does it have a higher or lower figure of merit compared with the 12B4?

2·25 Assume the 12BH7 has an $E_b = 300$ volts. At what value of negative grid voltage will this tube go into cutoff? (Where $I_b = 0$ ma.)

Review Questions

2·1   If the μ of a tube remains reasonably constant, how does the g_m vary as r_p is increased?

2·2   What is the d-c plate resistance of a tube when it is at cutoff?

2·3   Does the negative grid bias on a triode influence the tube's figure of merit?

2·4   Which is usually larger, R_p or r_p?

2·5   What electrostatic field exists between grid and cathode and grid and plate when a triode is cutoff?

2·6   Will increasing the grid voltage on a triode (or making it less negative) increase or decrease the plate voltage if the plate current is held constant?

2·7   How does the grid voltage on a triode influence the maximum-dissipation rating?

2·8   Does the distance between the control grid and the cathode influence the μ of a tube? How? (*Hint:* Refer to the discussion on electrostatic fields.)

2·9   How does the quiescent d-c operating potential at the plate E_b influence the cutoff potential at the grid?

2·10 Two triodes have the same transconductance. The slope of the r_p for the first one is larger than the second. Which will have the larger μ?

III
BASIC
TRIODE
AMPLIFIER

3·1 LOAD RESISTANCE

Chapter 2 pointed out that the μ of a vacuum tube indicates a ratio which defines the ability of a tube to amplify a change in voltage. The amplification factor of the tube, however, is a theoretical maximum. When the tube is operated into a fixed value of load impedance the actual stage gain is less than the μ of the tube by an amount that depends on the value of the load resistance.

Consider the circuit of Fig. 3·1. The μ of a 6AV6 triode is given as 100; however, when the tube is operated into a 100-kilohm load the stage gain is 65. The change in voltage across the load resistor R_L will be 65 times larger than the change in voltage across R_g, e_g.

A considerable amount of circuit information is obtained from a plot of the load line on the plate family of curves. A major portion of this book is devoted to establishing a clear understanding of load-line character-

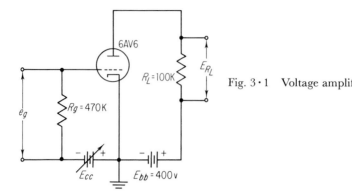

Fig. 3·1   Voltage amplifier.

istics. The student should study each example and problem carefully to obtain a good grasp of the subject.

The technique of plotting the load line is exactly the same as that outlined in Chap. 1.

EXAMPLE ONE   Assume a 100-kilohm load is to be connected across a 6AV6. The d-c supply voltage is 400 volts.

a. Construct a load line.
b. What current will flow in the plate circuit when the grid is at −1.5 volts?
c. What voltage appears across the tube when the grid is at −1.5 volts?

SOLUTION

a. Figure 3·2 is a plot of the load resistance on the plate family of curves for the 6AV6. Point A is determined by the E_{bb} and point B is determined by the boundary condition of what current would flow if the 100 kilohms were placed across 400 volts (4 ma). The two points are connected with a straight line (solid line).
b. The current flowing in the plate circuit is the projection from point Q to the current ordinate (1.7 ma).
c. The voltage across the tube is the projection from Q to the voltage abscissa (230 volts).

EXAMPLE TWO   Assume that a 265-kilohm load is connected across a 6AV6. Assume the d-c supply is 400 volts. If the grid is maintained at −3 volts,
a. What current will flow in the plate circuit?
b. What voltage will appear across the load resistor?

SOLUTION

a. The load-line plot is shown in Fig. 3·2 as a dashed line. A projection of point R to the current ordinate shows a current of 0.48 ma.
b. A projection of point R to the voltage abscissa indicates the voltage across the load as 120 volts. (Note the voltage across the tube is 280 volts.)

The graphical solution of a circuit problem is not always so easy to plot as the two preceding examples have indicated. In a few types of problems the plot of the load line extends beyond the boundaries of the graph. An example of such a case is shown in Fig. 3·2 (dotted line). Under these conditions the load line is plotted by a different method. From trigonometry

$$\tan A = \text{opp}/\text{adj}$$

The opposite side of the triangle is the length from the origin ($I = 0$) to the point where the load line intersects the current ordinate. Hence opp side $= E_{bb}/R_L$.

Similarly the adjacent side of the angle produced at A of Fig. 3·2 is the segment from the origin ($E = 0$) to the $B+$ point, E_{bb}. Hence adj side $= E_{bb}$. Tan A is identified as the slope.

$$\tan A = \text{slope} = \frac{\text{opp}}{\text{adj}} = \frac{E_{bb}/R_L}{E_{bb}} = \frac{-1}{R_L}$$

The negative sign indicates a slope which decreases to the right with increasing plate voltage. The units of the slope are given in amperes per volt.

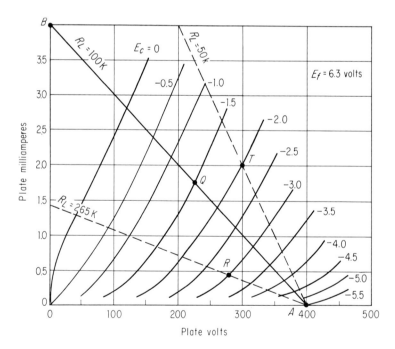

Fig. 3·2   Load-line characteristic.

EXAMPLE THREE   Construct a 50-kilohm load line on the plate characteristics of the 6AV6. Assume the d-c supply voltage to be 400 volts.

One point of the load line is established at point A of Fig. 3·2. A second point (not on the current ordinate) is determined from slope.

$$\text{Slope} = -1/R_L = 1/(50)(10^{+3}) = 20 \times 10^{-6} \text{ amp/volt}$$

This means the current changes 20 μa per volt. Assume a 100-volt change, from 400 to 300. The 100-volt change would result in a current of 2×10^{-3} amp. The 2-ma and the 300-volt point is shown in Fig. 3·2 at T. A dotted line passing through point T and the E_{bb} point describes the load line.

3·2 GRAPHICAL SOLUTION OF GAIN

Chapter 2 described the characteristics of the triode in terms of its tube constants. The vacuum-tube device has the property to amplify a change of voltage applied to its grid at a ratio defined as μ. It is important to differentiate between two definitions of gain. Whenever a discussion centers about the gain of a tube (without a load) the reference is always to the μ of the tube.

$$\mu = \text{gain of a tube}$$

Some books identify stage gain as G and others as VA. This text will use A. Both these gains, μ and A, refer to voltage amplification. Just as the tube gain μ was identified as the change in plate voltage to the change in grid voltage $\mu = e_b/e_g$, the gain of a stage is given as a similar ratio

$$A = \Delta e_o/\Delta e_{in} \tag{3·1}$$

where e_o is the change in the output voltage of the stage and e_{in} is the change in voltage at the input of the stage. In order to provide an accurate operating analysis of a stage through graphical methods, it is important that we examine three separate yet related topics: (a) operating point, (b) stage gain, and (c) dynamic transfer characteristics.

OPERATING POINT

The first consideration in designing an amplifier is application of the stage. If the purpose of the amplifier is to amplify the input signal without introducing distortion, a specific set of circuit conditions will be required. The B supply and load resistance will be selected and then the operating point will be determined. The operating point is the value of negative d-c grid bias applied at the input circuit. The input-signal voltage will vary about this operating point. An E_{cc} of -1.5 volts intersects the R_L load line at point Q and establishes the quiescent operating point of the amplifier. The term quiescent means no-input-signal conditions. If a 1-volt peak-to-peak a-c signal were developed across R_g, the actual grid voltage at the tube would vary from -1 volt during the positive half of the cycle to -2 volts during the negative half of the cycle. If no bias were provided at the input, the quiescent input would be zero volts. Then, when the same 1-volt peak-to-peak signal was applied, the grid would be driven positive during the positive half of the input cycle. The resultant drawing of grid current could produce severe distortion and loss of power.

In selecting the operating point, it is always necessary to determine the magnitude of the input signal first. In most cases the operating point chosen must be sufficiently negative to ensure that the grid is not driven positive, but it cannot be so negative as to drive the tube into the cutoff region (-5.5 volts for Fig. 3·2). The selection of operating point is considered further below under Dynamic Transfer Characteristics.

STAGE GAIN

Once the operating point is established the gain of the stage may be determined. Stage gain is best illustrated through a numerical example.

EXAMPLE FOUR   Assume that the triode section of a 6AT6 is to be operated into a load of 50 kilohms and a B supply of 400 volts. The tube is to be driven with a 3-volt peak-to-peak a-c signal. What is the operating point? What is the gain of the stage?

SOLUTION   Construct a load-line characteristic on the plate family of curves (refer to Fig. 3·3). Since the positive peak of the input signal is to be 1½ volts and the quiescent operating point must be at least $-1½$ volts. The operating point chosen is -2 volts (point Q of Fig. 3·3).

The stage gain is given in Eq. (3·1).

$$A = \Delta e_o / \Delta e_{in}$$

When the input signal passes through its positive half of the cycle the total effective grid voltage will be $-½$ volt. A projection from the positive peak to the load line establishes point a. A second projection to the voltage ordinate indicates that the plate voltage will be 180 volts when the grid is at $-½$ volt. During the negative half of the input-signal swing the grid of the tube will be at $-3½$ volts. A projection b to the voltage ordinate indicates that the plate will be at a potential of 290 volts. The gain of the stage is the ratio of the two changes.

$$A = \frac{110}{3} = 36.6$$

The signal at the plate of the tube is 36.6 times larger than the signal at the grid.

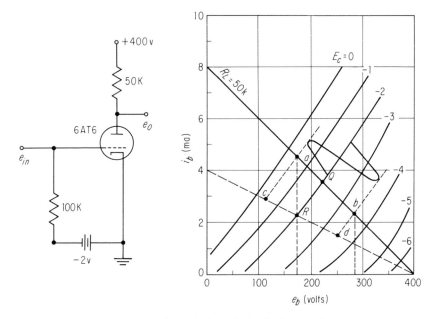

Fig. 3·3   Graphical analysis of voltage gain.

If the value of the load resistor in Fig. 3·3 were doubled, the stage gain of the stage would increase, though not twice as much. The new operating point R would result in plate-voltage changes from 115 to 260 volts (projections from c and d). Since the input change is still 3 volts the stage gain is 48.3.

DYNAMIC TRANSFER CHARACTERISTICS

The technique of choosing the operating point outlined above under Operating Point is valid for most applications. The process of estimating the grid-voltage swing which passes through the linear portions of the plate family of curves will give reliable results. Some applications require a somewhat more sophisticated process. Construction of a *dynamic transfer characteristic* provides an exact picture of the linear operating range of a tube.

Construction of the transfer curve consists of transferring plate-current grid-voltage points from a graph containing the nonlinear characteristic onto a graph with a linear scale. The resultant curve indicates the linear and nonlinear regions of operation.

EXAMPLE FIVE   If one of the triode sections of a 12BH7 is to operate as an amplifier with a minimum of distortion, what value of bias is required in order to accommodate a maximum possible input-signal voltage? Assume that the B supply is 450 volts and the load resistance is 15 kilohms (refer to Fig. 3·4).

In order to determine what maximum input voltage swing is possible without distortion, it is necessary to construct a dynamic transfer characteristic. In Fig. 3·5 the 15-kilohm load line has been plotted on the plate family of curves. A second graph has been sketched in to the left of the plate family of curves. The only requirement of this graph is that the abscissa be a linear scale showing grid voltages. (These should be similar to the ones shown on the plate family.) Note that each intersection of plate current and grid voltage (point A) has been transferred to the left-hand graph (point a). For each point on the plate family of curves (points A through G) there exists a corresponding point (a through g) on the transfer graph. Points a through g are then connected and the transfer characteristic is complete. Note that the curve remains linear from point a to just past point c. The grid voltage corresponding to this point of tangency is about -12 volts. The maximum input voltage swing can be 12 volts peak-to-peak without the introduction of distortion due to nonlinearity. The bias should be midway between this range, or about -6 volts d-c.

Problems

3·1 Construct a graphical solution for a series circuit which consists of a 10-kilohm resistor and 40-kilohm resistor across 50 volts. What is the circuit current? What is the voltage across the 40-kilohm resistor?

3·2 If the 10-kilohm resistor of Prob. 3·1 is doubled, what is the current in the circuit? What is the voltage across the 10-kilohm resistor?

3·3 Draw the load line for the circuit of Fig. 3·6 on the plate family of characteristic curves for a triode portion of a 12AU7. Assume R_L to be 3 kilohms and E_{bb} to be 350 volts. (The plate characteristics for the 12AU7 are given in the Appendix.) (a) From the load-line and plate-family information,

Fig. 3·4 Voltage amplification.

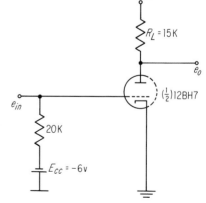

how much i_b will flow with an E_{cc} of -5 volts? (b) How much voltage between plate and cathode will be measured when $e_g = -8$ volts? (c) How much i_b will flow when $e_g = 0$ volts? (d) What will be the voltage across the tube when $e_g = 0$ volts? (e) What is the voltage across R_L when $e_g = 0$ volts?

3·4   If the value of the load in Prob. 3·3 is decreased to 2.5 kilohms, answer questions a, b, d, and e of Prob. 3·3.

3·5   On the plate family of curves for the 6C4 triode tube, draw a 2.5-kilohm load-line characteristic. Assume the tube is connected to a power source of 300 volts d-c. (a) When the grid is at -6 volts, what potential exists across the load resistor? (b) In order for the plate voltage in the above circuit to be at $+250$ volts, what negative voltage is required at the grid? (c) What is the voltage across the load when the grid-to-cathode voltage is at -25 volts?

3·6   If the tube in Prob. 3·5 were replaced with a 12AV7 triode, answer questions a, b, c, and d of Prob. 3·3.

3·7   If a 6SN7 triode is operated with $E_{bb} = 350$ volts and a load of 22 kilohms, what is the μ of the tube if the grid is maintained near -2 volts?

3·8   Refer to Prob. 3·7. If the grid is maintained at -8 volts, what is the μ of the tube?

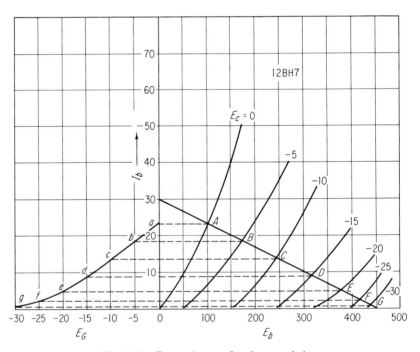

Fig. 3·5   Dynamic transfer characteristic.

3·9   If the triode portion of a 6AV6 has a load of 50 kilohms and a supply of 150 volts, at what negative grid potential will the tube be cut off?

3·10   Find the stage gain and the a-c output voltage for the following triode amplifier: tube type 6J5, load resistance 18 kilohms, grid bias E_{cc} − 4 volts, plate supply E_{bb} + 300 volts, input signal e_g = 2 volts (peak-to-peak).

3·11   What is the steady-state plate current in Prob. 3·10 with quiescent conditions?

3·12   Using the same triode tube as in Prob. 3·10, what is the gain of the amplifier with the following circuit values: E_{bb} = 200 volts, R_L = 10 kilohms, E_{cc} = − 2 volts, e_{in} = 3 volts peak-to-peak.

3·13   Assuming that the stage gain of a certain triode amplifier is taken to be 22, what will the effect of a small increase in E_{bb} be if R_L is kept at a constant value? (*Hint:* How do the load-line slopes compare?)

3·14   A stage of triode amplification has a load resistance of 120 kilohms across a 5691 which has an amplification factor of 70. When the grid voltage is decreased from − 1 to − 4 volts, the plate voltage increases from 160 to 295 volts. What is the stage gain?

3·15   Draw a load line for the circuit of Prob. 3·14 using the values indicated. (*a*) What is E_{bb}? (*b*) At what grid potential will the tube cut off? (*c*) What is the r_p of the tube?

3·16   If the grid of the tube in Prob. 3·14 is held at − 3 volts, what voltage exists across the load resistor?

3·17   If a 2-volt peak-to-peak signal is applied to the circuit of Fig. 3·3 and the load resistance is increased to 75 kilohms, determine the following: (*a*) quiescent plate current, (*b*) gain of the stage, (*c*) signal voltage across R_L, (*d*) quiescent plate voltage, (*e*) maximum range of imput-signal swing for undistorted output.

3·3 ALGEBRAIC SOLUTION OF GAIN

The preceding section outlined the processes for solving circuit or stage gains using geometric methods. Similar conclusions can be drawn using algebraic methods. In reality the geometric method and the algebraic method are one and the same. In one the characteristic curves are used and in the second the tube parameters are used. Chapter 2 pointed out that the characteristic curves of the tube are graphical representations of the tube parameters.

VOLTAGE AMPLIFICATION

Since it has been stated that the gain of a stage is

$$A = \Delta e_o / \Delta e_g \qquad (3·2)$$

it seems reasonable to ask why this equation cannot suffice. In many cases it does; however, any equation involving voltages is impractical since the circuit would first need to be wired and then the appropriate measurements completed. A more practical equation would be one involving constants such as the tube parameters and resistances. With such an equation the gain could be approximated before the circuit was wired. The result would be a reliable prediction of the circuit operation.

Compare the circuit of Fig. 3·6 with its equivalent circuit of Fig. 3·7. The B supply and the bias supply have been removed from the equivalent circuit. Since the signal applied at the grid changes to both sides of the grid bias and the signal at the plate changes to both sides of the direct current at the plate, these d-c or reference potentials can be neglected in the equivalent circuit. The d-c potentials serve only to make the tube "operational." Here we are concerned with signal conditions only and we *assume* that the correct operating potentials have been supplied to the tube. The tube is represented as a series combination of a voltage and a resistance. The voltage, $-\mu e_g$ volts, is considered a zero internal impedance source whose voltage is μ times larger than the instantaneous voltage applied at the grid (e_g). The internal impedance of the tube is shown separately as r_p. The minus sign in $-\mu e_g$ denotes a phase shift of $180°$ from the voltage at e_g.

The output voltage e_o will be the voltage developed across R_L when i_b flows through it.

$$e_o = i_b R_L \tag{3·3}$$

Substituting into the gain equation [Eq. (3·2)]

$$A = e_o/e_g = i_b R_L/e_g \tag{3·4}$$

Since according to Ohm's law $I = E/R$, plate current in the plate circuit of Fig. 3·7 is

$$i_b = -\mu e_g/(r_p + R_L) \tag{3·5}$$

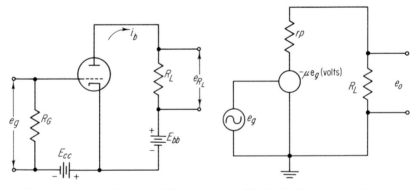

Fig. 3·6 Low-voltage amplifier.   Fig. 3·7 Equivalent circuit.

where $-\mu e_g$ is the voltage of the circuit [the grid voltage is μ times larger in the equivalent plate circuit] and $(r_p + R_L)$ is equal to the plate circuit's total opposition. Substituting Eq. (3·5) into Eq. (3·4) results in

$$A = -\mu R_L/(r_p + R_L) \qquad (3\cdot6)$$

where μ and r_p are tube parameters and R_L is the proposed load.

Equation (3·6) defines the voltage gain of the stage just as the plot of the load line on the plate characteristics does. The advantage of Eq. (3·6) is that gain can be determined quickly without actually wiring and testing a circuit. All the factors in the equation are constants.

EXAMPLE SIX   A 6SL7 triode operates into a 100-kilohm load. The μ of the tube is given as 70 and the transconductance as 1,600 μmhos. What is the gain of the stage?

It is first necessary to calculate the tube's r_p from Eq. (2·9).

$$r_p = \mu/g_m = \frac{70}{(1,600)(10^{-6})} = 44 \text{ kilohms}$$

from the gain equation [Eq. (3·6)]

$$A = (70)(10^5)/[(44)(10^3) + 10^5] = 48.5$$

EXAMPLE SEVEN   The output from a phono cartridge is 50 mv. If a stage amplification is to be used to increase the voltage to 1 volt, what value of load resistance is required for the triode section of a 6AV6? (The tube manual lists the parameters as $r_p = 62.5$ kilohms, $g_m = 1,600$ μmhos, and $\mu = 100$.) First determine the gain of the stage to be designed.

$$A = e_o/e_{in} = 1/0.05 = 20$$

Solve the gain equation for R_L.

$$R_L = r_p/(\mu/A - 1)$$
$$= (62.5)(10^3)/[(100/20) - 1] = 15.6 \text{ kilohms}$$

POWER

The design of voltage amplifiers is only partially completed when the correct values of B supply and load resistance are determined. The load-resistor wattage rating must also be determined. The load resistor must conduct the quiescent d-c plate current as well as signal currents. The signal power developed at the load is given as

$$P_o = i_b{}^2 R_L \qquad (3\cdot7)$$

where I_b is the effective value of the plate current. Substituting Eq. (3·5) into Eq. (3·7) yields

$$P_o = (\mu e_g)^2 R_L/(r_p + R_L)^2 \qquad (3\cdot8)$$

It should be noted that the signal power output is determined not only by tube parameters and the value of load resistance but by the magnitude of the driving signal e_g as well. The grid-driving voltage must be the rms value.

Refer to the circuit of Fig. 3·3. Note the circuit and its corresponding plate characteristics. The 3-volt input signal is superimposed on the −2-volt grid curve. The plate current changes from 3.8 to 5.2 ma during the positive half-cycle of the input. The change in plate current during the negative half of the cycle is about the same. The net result, however, is that *the average change in plate current over the entire cycle is zero.* Therefore, the average current flowing in the plate circuit is the d-c quiescent plate current. The power developed in the load resistor in Fig. 3·3 is

$$P_o = I_b{}^2 R_L \qquad (3·9)$$
$$P_o = [(3.8)(10^{-3})]^2(50)(10^3)$$
$$P_o = 0.722 \text{ watt}$$

The power delivered to the circuit is determined by the quiescent current and the B+ supply. Note in Fig. 3·3 that the average current drawn from the d-c source is 3.8 ma (point Q). The total voltage applied to the circuit is E_{bb} (400 volts). The d-c power delivered to the circuit is

$$P = I_E$$
$$P_{\text{d-c}} = I_b E_{bb} \qquad (3·10)$$
$$= (3.8)(10^{-3})(400)$$
$$= 1.52 \text{ watts}$$

3·4 PHASE RELATIONSHIPS AND CIRCUIT CONFIGURATIONS

The equivalent circuit of the triode amplifier of Sec. 3·3 included only those components which influence the signal characteristics of the amplifier. The d-c grid bias and plate potentials were not included because their values do not enter directly into the calculation for gain. Note that the equivalent circuit of Fig. 3·7 has a ground point indicated even though no d-c potentials are shown. The ground connection shown here is identified as *signal ground* or *signal reference.* Signal ground should not be associated with the negative terminal of the B supply. These two points need not be at the same circuit point electrically. The definition for signal ground is that point in a circuit to which input and output signal voltages are referenced.

Although the circuits in Sec. 3·3 were not formally identified, they are correctly called *grounded-cathode* or *common-cathode* amplifiers. The circuit is identified in this manner since the cathode of the tube is at signal ground. There are three basic circuit configurations for triode vacuum-tube amplifiers: (*a*) common-cathode amplifiers (the most often used), (*b*) common-grid, and (*c*) common-plate.

COMMON CATHODE

Figure 3·8*a* is a schematic symbol for the common-cathode amplifier. Part *b* is the equivalent circuit. Note that in this case the B— terminal of the d-c supply is at the same circuit point as signal ground. The algebraic solution for the gain of the stage was developed in Sec. 3·3.

The three different circuit configurations will each exhibit a voltage-gain characteristic. The letter *A* signifies gain, and a subscript notation will be used to signify type of gain and circuit configuration. For example, in A_{vc} the *A* represents gain, the small *v* represents voltage gain, and the small *c* identifies the common-cathode type of circuit. Hence Eq. (3·6) becomes

$$A_{vc} = -\mu R_L/(r + R_L) \qquad (3·11)$$

Assume that a signal applied to the grid of the common-cathode amplifier causes the grid to become positive with respect to the cathode. Such a signal could be the positive half of a sine wave (e_{in}) as shown in Fig. 3·9. The resultant increase in plate current would indicate that as *grid voltage increases, plate current increases* in a positive direction. Since R_L is a fixed value the increased plate current causes an increased voltage drop across R_L. It is important to note that the current through R_L

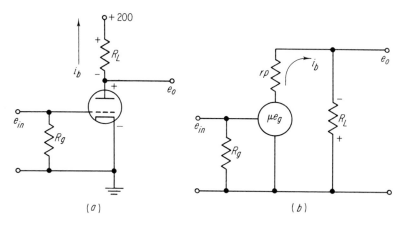

(*a*) (*b*)

Fig. 3·8 Common-cathode amplifier.

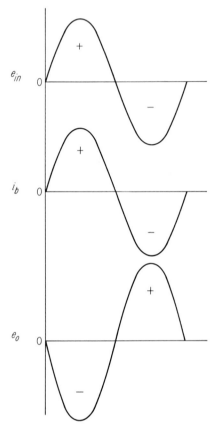

Fig. 3·9 Common-cathode phase relationships.

causes a polarity across R_L as shown in Fig. 3·8. Since the voltage across R_L is increasing, point e_o is becoming more negative with respect to signal ground (our reference point). The polarity of the output wave shown in Fig. 3·9 is displaced from the input wave by 180°. Summing up, *the common-cathode amplifier produces a* 180° *phase shift to the applied voltage.* The negative sign of Eq. (3·11) indicates the 180° phase shift.

COMMON GRID

Figure 3·10a is an example of a grounded-grid amplifier. The circuit is used frequently in television and high-frequency low-signal-level amplifiers where noise is a significant problem.

Figure 3·10b is the equivalent circuit for the common-grid amplifier. The signal applied at the input of the stage is developed across the cathode resistor. If the applied signal is positive, it will make the cathode positive with respect to ground. A positive-going cathode with respect to ground (the grid connection) produces the same effect as a negative-going grid. The negative-going grid causes the plate current to decrease. The decreasing plate current across R_L causes the voltage across R_L to decrease. The voltage at e_o is therefore becoming less negative, or going in a positive direction. The final phase relationship for the grounded-grid amplifier is a zero phase shift. The input and output signals will be in phase with each other (Fig. 3·11).

The voltage gain for the common-grid amplifier can be determined from the equivalent circuit of Fig. 3·10b. There are two loops to the equivalent circuit: loop A (the grid-cathode circuit) and loop B (the plate-cathode circuit). Note that the voltage developed across R_K is the input voltage e_{in}. In the equivalent circuit this is shown as a series circuit of e_{in} and R_K. The output voltage across R_L is given as

$$e_o = i_b R_L \qquad (3·12)$$

The voltage around loop A is

$$e_{in} = e_g + i_b R_K$$
$$e_g = e_{in} - i_b R_K \qquad (3·13)$$

The voltage drops around loop B of Fig. 3·10b are

$$0 = i_b R_L + i_b R_K + i_b r_p - \mu e_g - e_{in} \qquad (3·14)$$

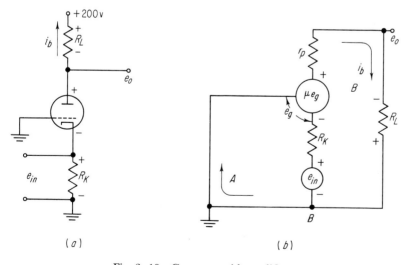

Fig. 3·10 Common-grid amplifier.

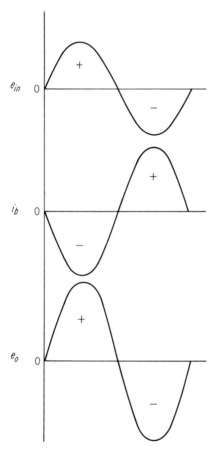

Fig. 3·11   Common-grid phase relationships.

Substituting Eq. (3·13) into Eq. (3·14),

$$e_{in} - i_b R_K + \mu(-i_b R_K + e_{in}) = i_b(r_p + R_L)$$

Rearranging,

$$e_{in}(\mu + 1) = i_b(r_p + R_L + R_K + \mu R_k) \qquad (3·15)$$

Solving Eq. (3·15) for i_b and substituting it into Eq. (3·12) results in

$$e_o = \frac{e_{in}(\mu + 1)R_L}{r_p + R_L + R_K(\mu + 1)} \qquad (3·16)$$

If Eq. (3·16) is solved for e_o/e_{in} the resultant ratio represents the voltage gain of the stage A_{vg}. (The subscript g represents the common-*grid* circuit configuration.)

$$A_{vg} = \frac{(\mu + 1)R_L}{r_p + R_L + R_K(1 + \mu)} \tag{3.17}$$

EXAMPLE EIGHT   The 6BF6 triode operates with 250 volts d-c at its plate in a common-grid circuit. If the load resistor 5 kilohms and the cathode resistor is 800 ohms, what is the voltage gain of the stage?

SOLUTION   The tube manual lists the μ of a 6BF6 as 16 and the r_p as 8.5 kilohms. Substituting these constants into Eq. (3.17),

$A_{vg} = (16 + 1)(5)(10^3)/[(8.5)(10^3) + (5)(10^3) + (0.8)(10^3)(1 + 16)]$
$A_{vg} = 3.14$

COMMON-PLATE AMPLIFIER

The common-plate amplifier is more commonly known as a *cathode follower*. The circuit is illustrated in Fig. 3·12a. The circuit is used primarily as an impedance-matching device rather than a voltage amplifier. In some applications the cathode follower is used as a power amplifier. The equivalent circuit for the common-plate amplifier is shown in Fig. 3·12b. If a sine-wave voltage is applied at the input across R_g, the plate current will increase during the positive half of the input cycle. The increasing plate current will cause the voltage across R_K to increase. Since e_o is taken across R_K, the output becomes more positive. The phase relationships are shown in Fig. 3·13. The output signal is in phase with the input signal.

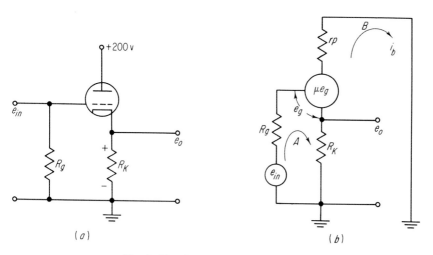

Fig. 3·12   Common-plate amplifier.

The voltage-gain equation for the common-plate amplifier is derived from the equivalent circuit of Fig. $3 \cdot 12b$. The gain of the stage is given as

$$A_{vp} = e_0/e_{in} \qquad (3 \cdot 18)$$

where
$$e_0 = i_b R_K \qquad (3 \cdot 19)$$

The voltage drops around loop A of Fig. $3 \cdot 12b$ result in

$$e_{in} = e_g + i_b R_K$$
$$e_g = e_{in} - i_b R_K \qquad (3 \cdot 20)$$

The voltage drops around loop B are

$$0 = i_b R_K - \mu e_g + i_b r_p \qquad (3 \cdot 21)$$

Substituting Eq. $(3 \cdot 20)$ into Eq. $(3 \cdot 21)$,

$$0 = i_b R_K - \mu e_{in} + \mu i_b R_k + i_b r_p$$

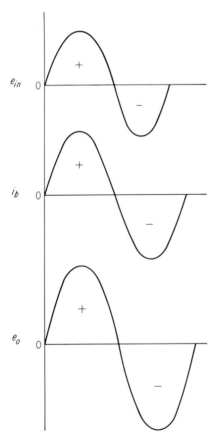

Fig. $3 \cdot 13$ Common-plate phase relationships.

Solving for i_b,

$$i_b = \frac{\mu e_{in}}{r_p + R_K(\mu + 1)} \tag{3 \cdot 22}$$

Substituting Eq. (3 $\cdot$ 22) into Eq. (3 $\cdot$ 19),

$$e_o = \frac{\mu e_{in} R_K}{r_p + R_K(\mu + 1)} \tag{3 \cdot 23}$$

Solving Eq. (3 $\cdot$ 23) for the ratio of e_o/e_{in} and substituting in Eq. (3 $\cdot$ 18)

$$A_{vp} = \frac{\mu R_K}{r_p + R_K(\mu + 1)} \tag{3 \cdot 24}$$

EXAMPLE NINE   If the load resistance R_L of Example One were reduced to zero the resultant circuit would be a cathode follower. What would be the voltage gain of the stage?

SOLUTION   Substituting the known constants into Eq. (3 $\cdot$ 24) results in

$$A_{vp} = (16)(800)/[(8.5)(10^3) + (0.8)(10^3)(16 + 1)]$$
$$A_{vp} = 0.58$$

Problems

3 $\cdot$ 18   A vacuum tube has a transconductance of 1,600 μmhos and has a load resistance of 80 kilohms connected to the circuit. If the μ of the tube is 70, what is the gain of the overall stage of amplification if the circuit is connected as a common-cathode configuration?

3 $\cdot$ 19   A single stage of amplification is to provide a gain of 12. Two tubes are available. One has a μ of 20 and a transconductance of 3,300 μmhos, and the other has a μ of 30 and an r_p of 10 kilohms. Which of the tubes would require the smaller load resistance if they were used in a common-cathode stage of amplification?

3 $\cdot$ 20   A stage of amplification utilizes a tube which has a μ of 100 and a load resistance of 35 kilohms. If the gain of the stage $A_{vc} = 60$, what is the transconductance of the tube?

3 $\cdot$ 21   In the circuit of Prob. 3 $\cdot$ 20 by how much would the stage gain be decreased if the load resistance were changed to 20 kilohms?

3 $\cdot$ 22   A common-cathode stage of triode amplification has a tube with a μ of 40 and a transconductance of 3,000 μmhos. What signal plate current will flow if a load resistance of 50 kilohms is connected into the circuit and 1 volt peak-to-peak is applied at the grid?

3 $\cdot$ 23   How do changes in value of B+ control the gain A of a stage of amplification (algebraically)?

3 $\cdot$ 24   A stage of triode amplification has a gain of 20 when a 60-kilohm load resistor is connected across a tube whose plate resistance is 38 kilohms. How

much increase in the load resistance is required to increase the gain of the stage to 25?

3·25   In the circuit of Prob. 3·24, what is the μ of the tube?

3·26   A common-cathode stage of triode amplification has a load resistance of 50 kilohms across a tube which has a μ of 100. When the grid voltage is decreased from -3 to -5 volts, the plate voltage increases from 120 to 194 volts. Assume that a B+ of 250 volts is used, what is the plate resistance of the tube?

3·27   In Prob. 3·26 what is the transconductance of the tube?

3·28   A common-grid amplifier similar to Fig. 3·10 has the following values: $R_K = 3.3$ kilohms, $R_L = 10$ kilohms, $r_p = 8$ kilohms, $g_m = 3,000$ μmhos. Find the gain A_{vg}.

3·29   In the circuit of Prob. 3·28, if R_K increased 10 percent what would be the percentage of change in A_{vg}?

3·30   A common-plate amplifier (cathode follower) uses a 12AT7 which has a μ of 50 and a plate resistance of 10 kilohms. If the input voltage is 20 volts peak-to-peak, what value of R_K is necessary to produce an output-voltage change of 16 volts peak-to-peak?

3·31   What is the change in plate current for the circuit of Prob. 3·30?

3·32   If a 12AU7 were substituted for the 12AT7 in Prob. 3·30, what would be the new voltage gain? ($\mu = 17$, $r_p = 7.7$ kilohms.)

3·33   Assume a 2DS4 triode is to be used in a common-grid configuration and the cathode resistor must be 1,000 ohms. The voltage gain of the stage must be 5. What value of load resistance would be required?

3·34   Refer to the circuit of Prob. 3·33. Decreasing the load resistance to zero would result in a common-plate amplifier; what would its gain be?

3·5 CATHODE BIAS

GEOMETRIC SOLUTION

The bias voltage at the grid of a triode can be produced in a number of ways. In the preceding chapters, a battery inserted in the grid cathode circuit established the correct operating point. The impractical aspects of batteries require another approach. Since the cathode leg of the stage is common to both the input and output circuits, the cathode current can be used to develop a bias voltage. Examine the plate circuit of Fig. 3·14a. With no signal applied a fixed value of plate current flows through the tube. The polarity of the voltage across R_K is as shown in the figure. The grid circuit has an equivalent circuit as shown in Fig. 3·14b. The voltage E (developed across R_K as a result of i_b flowing through it) is shown as a battery. The input of the tube (grid to cathode) is shown as a resistor equal to infinity.

Since voltages in a series circuit distribute by the ratio of the resistances, all the voltage E will be developed across the infinitely large resistance.

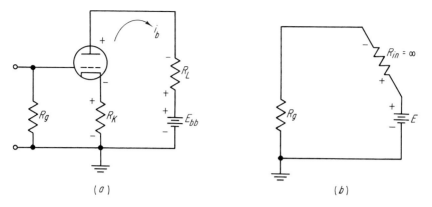

Fig. 3·14   Cathode bias and equivalent circuit.

The polarity will be such that the grid is negative with respect to its cathode at a potential equal to that developed across R_K. The value of R_K can be adjusted in order to provide the correct bias potential at the grid and thus the correct operating point.

A plot of the load resistance on the plate family of characteristic curves is shown in Fig. 3·15. The bias resistor in the cathode circuit is plotted in a similar manner to that of the load resistor (load line). The junction of the *bias-line characteristic* and the load line is the quiescent operating point of the circuit. The following are numerical examples of how a bias-line characteristic is plotted.

EXAMPLE TEN   Construct a bias-line characteristic for a 680-ohm cathode resistor on the 6SN7 plate characteristics.

SOLUTION

a. Assume that a grid voltage of -2 volts is to be developed across the cathode re-sistor. The current required to develop 2 volts across a 680-ohm resistor is 2.95 ma (Ohm's law, $I = 2/680$). Place a point on the -2-volt grid-bias curve at the 2.95-ma plate current point (point a of Fig. 3·15).

b. Assume that a grid voltage of -4 volts is developed across the cathode resistor. The current required according to Ohm's law is 6 ma. Place a point on the -4-volt grid-bias curve at the 6-ma point.

c. Draw a line which passes through the two points. The bias line at point Q. Point Q is now established as the quiescent operating point of the circuit. It identifies the plate current i_b, the plate voltage E_b, and the amount of bias voltage between grid and cathode.

EXAMPLE ELEVEN   Assume a 6SN7 triode is operating into a load resistance of 30 kilohms and has a 680-ohm bias resistor in the cathode. The B supply is

300 volts. What are (a) the quiescent plate current flowing, (b) the negative grid potential, (c) the d-c potential across the load resistor?

SOLUTION   Construct a 30-kilohm load line on the plate family of curves containing the 680-ohm bias-line characteristic (Fig. 3·15).
a. Point Q is the intersection of the load line and the bias line. It represents a plate current of 5.5 ma.
b. The negative grid potential must be extrapolated to about -3.6 volts (between the -2- and the -4-volt grid curves).
c. The d-c potential across R_L is 165 volts (point Q projected to the voltage ordinate).

The cathode resistor method of providing operating bias for the tube is the most commonly used in practical circuits. It is inexpensive, lightweight, durable, and reliable. One qualification must be introduced. Since the bias voltage is dependent upon plate current and plate current varies with an incoming signal, a bypass capacitor must be included in the circuit to filter out the $i_p R_K$ fluctuations. The capacitor is usually a large electrolytic type (20 to 100 μf).

In some circuits where a small amount of feedback is desired the bypass capacitor is removed. The result is a decreased voltage gain and an improved distortion characteristic.

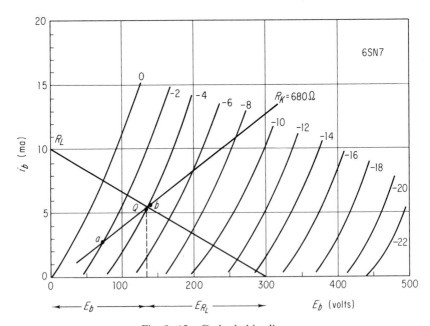

Fig. 3·15   Cathode bias line.

ALGEBRAIC SOLUTION FOR CATHODE BIAS

The process of selecting an operating point generally identifies the
necessary grid bias for the stage. It is usually some fixed value. The bias
line affords a graphic representation which permits changes and com-
promises in determining the operating point, the gain of the stage, and
the input-signal swing. When the operating point is a fixed value Ohm's
law may be used to determine the correct resistance.

As an example assume the circuit of Fig. $3 \cdot 16a$ is to act as a voltage
amplifier. The cathode resistor is to provide the correct operating bias
of -3 volts. Point Q is established on the load-line plot as shown in
Fig. $3 \cdot 16b$. The current required to flow through R_K is the projection of
Q on the current ordinate and is 6.5 ma.

From Ohm's law the resistance required is

$$R_K = E_g/I_b = 460 \text{ ohms}$$

The process outlined in the above example is actually the algebraic
solution for cathode bias, which is the same as the geometric solution.

EXAMPLE TWELVE   Assume that a 6X8 triode is to operate into a load res¹
of 5 kilohms in a circuit where the B+ supply is 200 volts. What value c′
resistance will provide a -2-volt grid bias?

SOLUTION
a. Draw a 5-kilohm load line (dashed) on the plate charac⁺   ʌig. $3 \cdot 16b$.
b. Establish point P on the load line along the -2-volt   . The current
   flowing in the plate circuit, and therefore in the ʳ   ircuit, is 10 ma
   according to Ohm's law:

$$R = \frac{E}{I_b} = \frac{2}{(10)(10^{-3})} = (0.2)(1\cap \qquad \text{ohms}$$

$3 \cdot 6$ TRIODE AS A LINEAR MOL   ʌOPTIONAL)

Graphical solutions of triode circuits provide a reasonably accurate
analysis and prediction of circuit performance. However, vacuum-tube
parameters may deviate from 10 to 15 percent from the listed characteristics. This error, coupled with the inherent error of any graphical
analysis, means that most circuit calculations are at best 80 percent
accurate.

A similar judgment can be placed upon algebraic solutions involving
the tube parameters. The preceding sections show how the actual values
of the parameters vary with different static operating conditions. Tube
manufacturers point out in their manuals that a significant difference in

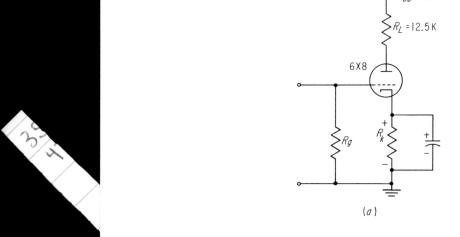

(a)

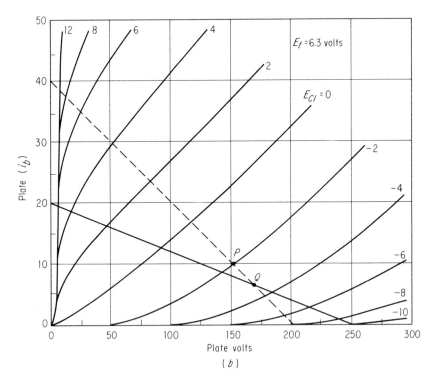

(b)

Fig. 3·16   Cathode-biased amplifier.

the parameters will result if the tube is operated at low or high values of B supply potential. Hence circuit calculations involving tube parameters are also about 80 percent accurate.

Despite the accuracy limitations of both methods of analysis they remain the simplest approach when the circuit involves one vacuum tube. The two methods, algebraic and geometric, become time-consuming and cumbersome when applied to circuits involving two or more stages. The linear-model method of analysis provides an accuracy of about 80 percent and simplifies the complexity of analysis of multiple tube circuits. It is also used in analyzing advanced and complex types of circuits. The circuit calculations are simplified because the equivalent circuits of individual stages are reduced to equivalent circuits which contain linear and predictable circuit elements.

IDEAL TRIODE

The plate characteristics for the 6SN7 triode of Fig. 3·15 exhibit nonlinear characteristics at the bottom of each of the curves. When the tube is operated in these nonlinear areas, the circuits exhibit properties of distortion and widely changing tube parameters. The ideal triode characteristic would consist of a set of linear curves originating at the voltage axis and spaced μ volts apart along the voltage axis. Figure 3·17 shows the actual characteristics of a 6SL7 superimposed on a set of ideal 6SL7 curves (linear). Note that the ideal curves all have the same slope and the spacing between the curves is the same, μ volts.

The advantage of converting a set of nonlinear characteristics to their equivalent linear models becomes apparent in the equivalent circuit. Consider the amplifier of Fig. 3·18a. The plate circuit can be redrawn to the circuit of Fig. 3·18b. Then Fig. 3·18b can be reduced to the equivalent circuit of Fig. 3·18c. The values of R_L, E_{bb}, μ, and e_g are known quantities. The r_p can be determined from any one of the ideal characteristics. The r_p will be the same regardless of which curve is used since they are all parallel. The r_p is given as

$$r_p = \Delta e_p / \Delta i_b$$

EXAMPLE THIRTEEN If no input signal is applied to the circuit of Fig. 3·18a, what is the d-c output potential? What is the Thévenin equivalent generator (d-c) of the output?

SOLUTION Under quiescent conditions the voltage at the grid is -2 volts. The μ of the tube is given as 70. A functional equivalent circuit can be drawn as shown in Fig. 3·19. Using the ratio method the voltage across r_p becomes

$$e_{rp} = [r_p/(r_p + R_L)](350 - 140)$$
$$e_{rp} = (44)(10^3)(210)/[(44)(10^3) + (100)(10^3)]$$
$$e_{rp} = 64 \text{ volts}$$

Since the output voltage is taken across points A and B the output potential becomes

$$e_o = \mu e_g + e_{rp} = 140 + 64 = 204 \text{ volts}$$

According to Thévenin's theorem the equivalent circuit consists of a voltage source and a series impedance. The circuit is as shown in Fig. $3 \cdot 20$. The Thévenin

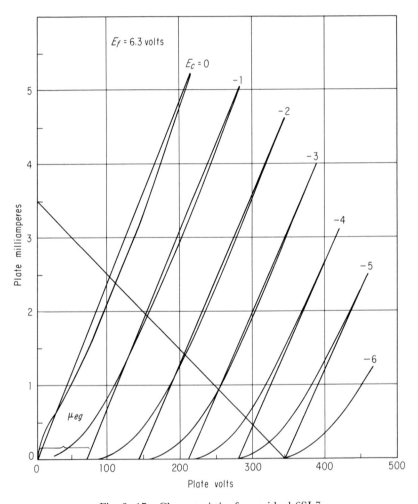

Fig. $3 \cdot 17$ Characteristics for an ideal 6SL7.

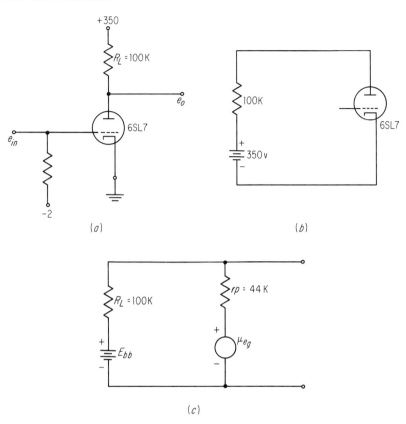

Fig. 3·18 Amplifier as a network element.

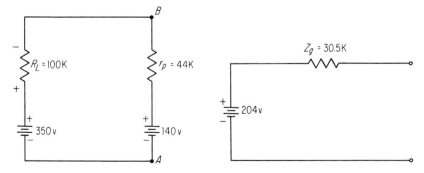

Fig. 3·19 Functional equivalent circuit.

Fig. 3·20 Thévenin equivalent of Fig. 3·18c.

voltage is the voltage across the open circuit terminals of the output (204 volts). The impedance is the impedance looking back into the terminals with the voltage sources short-circuited. Short circuiting the voltage sources effectively parallels r_p and R_L, and the resultant is 30.5 kilohms.

The example indicates the static output (e_g equal to a d-c value) and the equivalent circuit. The circuit can be reduced to a simple circuit for any input at e_g.

Since the output is always

$$e_o = e_{rp} + \mu e_g \qquad (3\cdot25)$$

and the voltage across r_p is always the ratio

$$e_{rp} = [r_p/(R_L + r_p)](E_{bb} - \mu e_g) \qquad (3\cdot26)$$

The output voltage becomes

$$e_o = E_{bb}r_p/(R_L + r_p) - \mu e_g r_p/(R_L + r_p) + \mu e_g \qquad (3\cdot27)$$

$$e_o = (E_{bb}r_p + \mu e_g R_L)/(r_p + R_L) \qquad (3\cdot28)$$

where e_g is the independent variable. The resultant equivalent circuit for any e_g is shown in Fig. 3·21.

Problems

3·35   On the plate family of curves for the 6SN7, draw a 900-ohm bias-line characteristic. (*a*) If the B+ were 350 volts and a 33-kilohm load resistor were used in the plate circuit, what value of bias would be developed between the grid and the cathode with no signal applied? (*b*) Under quiescent conditions, what voltage will appear across the cathode resistor?

3·36   On the plate family of characteristic curves for the 6SL7, draw a 1,000-ohm bias-line characteristic. (*a*) If the value of B+ were 250 volts and a 50-kilohm load resistor were used in the plate, what value of bias would be developed at the grid of the tube with no signal applied? (*b*) At what grid potential will this tube cut off? (*c*) In the quiescent conditions of *a* above, what value of voltage will appear across the load resistor of the circuit?

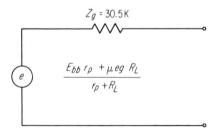

Fig. 3·21   Equivalent circuit.

(*d*) In the quiescent conditions of *a* above, what value of voltage will appear across the cathode resistor? (*e*) In the circuit described in *a* above, what increase or decrease in plate quiescent voltage would result if the load resistor in the plate circuit were decreased to 30 kilohms? (*f*) At what grid potential will the circuit described in *e* above cut off?

3·37 Draw a dynamic-transfer-characteristic curve for the circuit of Prob. 3·35. (*a*) What is the desired operating point for this circuit for a nondistorted output? (*b*) What is the maximum peak-to-peak input signal for undistorted operation?

3·38 A triode stage of common-cathode amplification has a tube whose transconductance is 6,000 μmhos and whose μ is 35 working into a load resistance of 50 kilohms. What is the gain of the stage?

3·39 A common-cathode stage of triode amplification has 1 volt peak-to-peak applied at its input. If the characteristics of the tube and the circuit are the same as those of Prob. 3·35, what is the plate-current peak-to-peak value?

3·40 If a common-cathode triode stage of amplification utilizes a tube which has a plate resistance of 10 kilohms working into a load of 35 kilohms, and the circuit develops 10 volts peak-to-peak when ½ volt peak-to-peak is applied at the input, what is the μ of the tube?

3·41 A common-grid triode stage of amplification has a load resistance of 60 kilohms and a cathode resistance of 1,000 ohms. If the μ of the tube is 50 and the plate resistance is 40 kilohms, what is the voltage gain of the stage?

3·42 A triode stage of amplification has a B+ of 350 volts applied to it. If 180 volts is measured across the tube and the plate load resistor is 40 kilohms, what value of cathode resistance will be necessary to develop 4 volts bias?

Review Questions

3·1 How do changes in the value of load resistance influence the gain of a common-cathode amplifier?

3·2 What information can be derived from a dynamic transfer characteristic?

3·3 What influence does the magnitude of the input signal have on the power output of a common-cathode amplifier?

3·4 Does the common-grid amplifier change the phase of the input signal? If so, by how many degrees?

3·5 What is another name for the common-plate amplifier?

3·6 How do changes in the cathode load resistance of a common-plate amplifier influence the voltage gain of the stage?

3·7 In a cathode bias arrangement, how does increasing the value of the cathode resistor influence the voltage between grid and *ground*?

3·8 How do the voltage gains for the three circuit configurations, common grid, cathode, and plate, compare?

3·9 How do changes in the value of load resistance on a common-cathode amplifier influence the d-c voltage between plate and cathode?

3·10 List the main limitations of triode amplifiers.

IV
TETRODES

4·1 TRIODE LIMITATIONS

In the discussion of the triode amplifier, no mention was made concerning the frequency range of operation. If the triode is operated at mid-range audio frequencies, the operation is predictable through the examples of the preceding chapter. However, as the operating range of frequencies applied to the triode increases, new higher-frequency characteristics must be considered.

In the early days of the development of vacuum tubes, experimenters encountered two major limitations of the triode. The first dealt with oscillation. A given circuit, when operated at high frequencies, would act not as an amplifier but as an oscillator. A tuned circuit would generate its own signal instead of amplifying the incoming signal. Special circuitry had to be devised to "neutralize" this effect. Neutralization is still used today, though many new developments have minimized the need for it.

The second problem encountered dealt with triodes in untuned amplifier circuits. In this case it was found that the calculated gain was considerably higher than the actual gain received in a practical circuit: As an example, a given triode may provide a gain of 14 to a signal of 20 kc. However, the gain of the same triode with the same resistive load may be as low as 6 when the signal frequency has increased to 200 Mc.

INPUT CAPACITANCE

Figure 4·1 illustrates one reason for the loss of stage gain at high frequencies. The signal applied to the grid of the tube "sees" a capacitance. The parallel combination of this input capacitance and the grid input resistor causes a decrease in the input impedance, and hence less actual voltage appears at the input of the tube. Assume the capacitance for a 6J5 triode is in the range of 3.5 pf; neglecting other factors the input reactance at 200 Mc is about 230 kilohms.

We might assume that the first impulse of the early experimenters was to consider changing the relative position of the grid and the cathode. Figure 4·1 shows the position of the control-grid element between the plate and the cathode. Physically moving the grid farther away from the cathode should reduce the capacitance since the equation for capacitance is

$$C = 0.224KA/d \qquad (4·1)$$

where C = capacitance, pf
K = dielectric constant
A = plate surface area
d = spacing between elements, in.

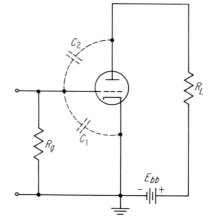

Fig. 4·1   Input capacitance of a triode.

As the distance d becomes larger, the capacitance should become smaller; then from the equation for reactance,

$$Xc = 1/2\pi fc$$

the decreasing c should increase the reactance. Experiments proved exactly opposite.

Instead of the gain's increasing, the stage gain decreased. The process of moving the grid farther away actually increased the total *effective* input capacitance and hence caused more attenuation at the high frequencies. The characteristic responsible for this condition is known as "Miller effect."

MILLER EFFECT

Miller effect can best be analyzed by first examining all the capacitances present in a triode. The input capacitance C_{gk} is capacitance due to the physical characteristics between the grid and cathode. A schematic symbol is shown in Fig. 4·2. The capacitance between grid and plate is shown as C_{gp} and the output capacitance is shown as C_{pk}. If an equivalent circuit of Fig. 4·2 is drawn to show all the tube characteristics, the Miller effect can be analyzed. Figure 4·3a is an equivalent circuit of Fig. 4·2.

The E_i of Fig. 4·3a is the voltage applied to the entire circuit. E_i appears across C_{gk} and is also applied to the remaining parallel circuit. It is the capacitance of this remaining circuit C_x which we shall consider as it is in parallel with C_{gk}. The input capacitance to the stage is therefore

$$C_{in} = C_{gk} + C_x$$

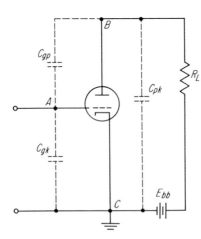

Fig. 4·2   Tube capacitances.

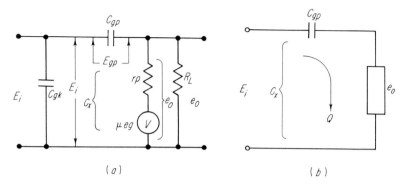

Fig. 4·3   Miller equivalent circuit.

Given that the quantity charge around a series circuit is the same at all points in the circuit (Fig. 4·3b) the total quantity charge is $q = C_x E_i$. The voltages around the loop are $E_i = E_{gp} + e_o$. However, e_o is E_i after it is amplified and phase-inverted.

$$E_i = E_{gp} - AE_i$$

Since the quantity charge across C_{gp} is $q = C_{gp}E_{gp}$ and is also $q = C_x E_i$, the equation reduces to

$$q/C_x = q/C_{gp} - Aq/C_x$$

Dividing through by q,

$$1/C_x = 1/C_{gp} - A/C_x$$
$$1/C_x + A/C_x = 1/C_{gp}$$

factoring

$$(1 + A)/C_x = 1/C_{gp}$$

and cross-multiplying

$$C_x = C_{gp}(1 + A)$$

The combination of C_{gk} in parallel with C_x is the total effective input capacitance to the stage.

$$C_{in} = C_{gk} + C_{gp}(1 + A) \qquad (4·2)$$

Equation (4·2) represents the physical capacitance between grid and cathode C_{gk} and Miller-effect capacitance $C_{gp}(1 + A)$.

EXAMPLE ONE   Assume that a 6J5 triode is to operate with a 24-kilohm load and a B+ of 200 volts. What is the total effective input capacitance of the stage?

SOLUTION   The tube manual lists the C_{gk} as 4.2 pf and the C_{gp} as 3.8 pf. From the gain equation $A = \mu R_L/(r_p + R_L)$ the gain of the stage is calculated to be $A = 15$. Substituting into Eq. (4·2),

$$C_{in} = (4.2)(10^{-12}) + (3.8)(10^{-12})(1 + 15)$$
$$C_{in} = (4.2)(10^{-12}) + 60.8 \times 10^{-12}$$
$$C_{in} = 65 \text{ pf}$$

If the load resistance for a given amplifier is increased the gain of the stage increases. The increased gain causes an increased input capacitance. If the load resistance in Example One were doubled the gain would increase to 17.1 and the input capacitance would increase to 73 pf.

4·2 SCREEN GRID
Inserting a second grid between the control grid and the anode provides a partial solution to the problem of input capacitance. The additional

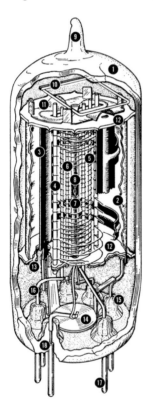

1—Glass Envelope

2—Internal Shield

3—Plate

4—Grid No. 3 (Suppressor)

5—Grid No. 2 (Screen)

6—Grid No. 1 (Control Grid)   Fig. 4·4   Screen grid.

7—Cathode

8—Heater

9—Exhaust Tip

10—Getter

11—Spacer Shield Header

12—Insulating Spacer

13—Spacer Shield

14—Inter-Pin Shield

15—Glass Button-Stem Seal

16—Lead Wire

17—Base Pin

18—Glass-to-Metal Seal

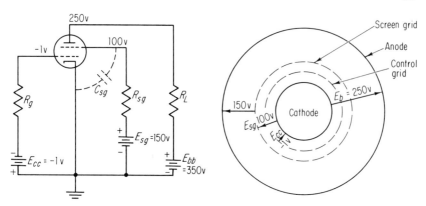

Fig. 4·5   Tetrode circuit.   Fig. 4·6   Tetrode: cutaway view.

grid divides the existing capacitance C_{gp} into two separate capacitances. These capacitors are in series; hence the total effective physical capacitance is less than the smallest of these two capacitors. The physical position of the screen grid is shown in Fig. 4·4. This new four-element tube is called a *tetrode*.

The operating circuit of the tetrode is shown in Fig. 4·5. Two new factors are involved: The screen grid must be operated with a positive potential with respect to the cathode, and a new capacitance C_{sg} is introduced into the circuit. The addition of the screen grid in the vacuum tube results in a change in the electrostatic field characteristics within the tube. After examining the circuit of Fig. 4·5, refer to the cutaway schematic representation of the tube in Fig. 4·6.

The small inner circle represents the cathode and the outer circle the plate of the tetrode. The two dashed circles between the plate and cathode represent the grids. An electron, represented as a black dot, in the vicinity of the space charge is subjected to the electrostatic forces present in that region. An electrostatic field exists between the cathode and plate shown as $E_b = 250$ volts. Another field between cathode and screen grid has a voltage distribution of $E_{sg} = 100$ volts. A reverse field, $E_{cc} = -1$ volt, between the control grid and the cathode is produced by the bias voltage E_{cc}. (This field is in an opposite direction to the other two.) In addition to these electrostatic fields, a field of 150 volts exists between the screen grid and the plate. These are the most important field configurations within the tetrode. An electron subjected to this configuration will be accelerated to the plate. The operation is similar to that described for the triode.

SECONDARY EMISSION

Many of the electrons subjected to the electrostatic forces within the tube achieve very high velocities upon arrival at the plate. These high-velocity electrons bombard the crystal structure of the plate material. The energy transfer from the high-velocity electrons is sufficient to cause many electrons to be emitted away from the plate material. Such emission, termed *secondary emission,* causes the existence of low-velocity electrons (emitted from the plate) in the vicinity of the plate. These low-velocity electrons are now subjected to the electrostatic forces present between the plate and the screen. Since these forces are in a direction extending from the screen to the plate, the electrons will quickly return to the plate. Under these circuit conditions secondary emission causes few problems other than increased dissipation at the plate.

When the circuit conditions are changed, however, so that the plate supply voltage is reduced to 40 volts (lower than the potential on the screen) and all other potentials are maintained at the same values, a different set of circuit conditions prevails. The electrostatic forces within the tube have changed and are as shown in Fig. 4·7. Notice that the electrostatic field between the screen grid and the plate is now in a direction from the plate to the screen grid (60 volts). In addition the electrostatic field between the cathode and the plate is considerably reduced (40 volts).

It is the electrostatic field between the screen grid and the cathode (100 volts) which causes the acceleration of the electrons toward the screen and plate. Those electrons which do not strike the positive screen (and therefore are not collected) continue on to the plate. If their velocity is sufficient, they will cause secondary emission, which will produce low-velocity electrons in the region between the screen and the plate. Most of these secondarily emitted electrons will now be subject to

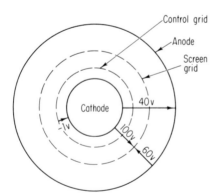

Fig. 4·7   Tetrode: low plate potential.

the field between the screen and the plate and will be accelerated toward the screen. The end result could be a screen current higher than the plate current.

OUTPUT CHARACTERISTICS

The addition of the screen grid to the triode vacuum produces an output characteristic curve similar to the one shown in Fig. 4·8. The solid curve shown is for a negative grid voltage of 1 volt and a constant screen grid supply voltage of 100 volts. Note that with low voltages on the plate of the tube (from zero to 30 volts) a steady increase in plate current results. However, when the voltage on the plate reaches 35 volts, the plate current begins to decrease. At this point many of the electrons accelerated toward the plate have sufficient velocities to cause some secondary emission. Increasing the plate potential from 35 to 65 volts causes an increased secondary-emission effect. When the plate voltage has increased beyond 100 volts, the electrostatic field between the screen grid and the plate shifts in a direction toward the plate.

The dashed line of Fig. 4·8 indicates the change in output characteristics when the screen potential is increased. The control-grid potential is maintained at −1 volt, and the plate voltage is varied. With the screen now at 200 volts, the plate current reaches a higher initial value before it begins to decrease. The secondary-emission-characteristic part of the curve extends over a wider range of plate-voltage change. Once the plate voltage is past 110 volts, the plate-current characteristic follows a rising curve. Figure 4·9 illustrates the plate-current plate-voltage characteristic family of curves for a 2EV5 tetrode.

The humped-curve characteristic of the tetrode tube for the most part is an undesirable condition if the tube is to be used for amplification. As an amplifier, the tube must be operated at very high plate potentials and in regions well past the secondary-emission effects. One of the load resistors shown has a value of 15 kilohms. Note the large supply (300 volts) required in order to place the load line to the right of the secondary-emission portion of the curves. The tube parameters must be calculated at the higher operating potentials and to the right of the secondary-emission characteristics.

4·3 TETRODE PARAMETERS

The tetrode tube parameters are calculated in the same manner outlined in Chap. 2. A geometric analysis of these parameters from the characteristics shown in Fig. 4·9 shows that $g_m = 6,600$ μmhos, $r_p = 150$

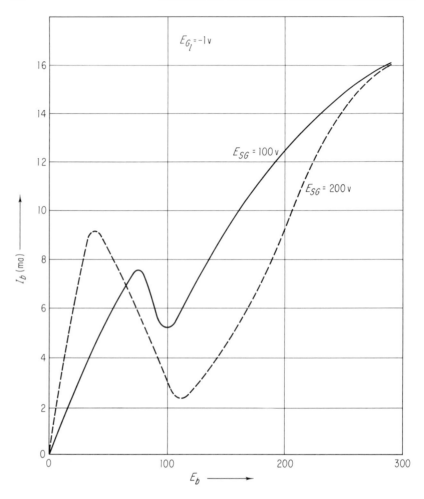

Fig. 4·8   Tetrode output characteristics.

kilohms, and $\mu = 990$. One additional parameter must be considered for the tetrode tube.

The dynamic or a-c plate resistance is given as

$$r_p = \Delta e_b / \Delta i_b]_{e_g = k}$$

In the tetrode, however, if this value is measured at low plate voltages, a negative plate resistance results. As an example, refer to Fig. 4·9. If a plate-voltage change from 25 to 35 volts is used as the increment along the $e_g = -2$ volt curve, there exists a corresponding change in plate current of 0.5 ma. The current change is a decrease or a negative change; hence the equation becomes

$$r_p = 10/(-0.5)(10^{-3}) = -20 \text{ kilohms}$$

The resultant -20 kilohms is a *negative resistance* and is derived from the secondary-emission characteristics of the tetrode. Such a negative resistance characteristic can become useful in oscillator and feedback circuits.

D-C EQUIVALENT CIRCUIT

The circuit of Fig. 4·10 shows the static conditions of a tetrode stage. By application of Ohm's and Kirchhoff's laws to the three circuits, grid, screen grid, and plate, all static conditions of the circuit can be calculated.

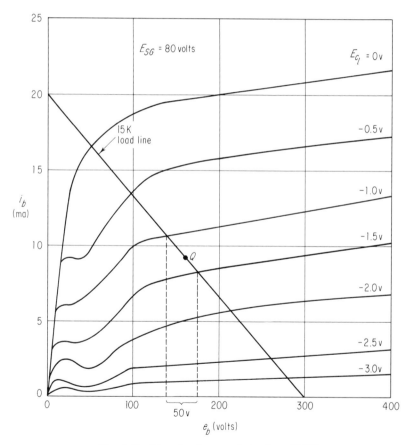

Fig. 4·9   Tetrode characteristics for a 2EV5.

EXAMPLE TWO   What direct current is flowing from the cathode in the circuit of Fig. 4·10?

SOLUTION   The total current leaving the cathode must be the sum of the screen current and the plate current.

$$I_k = I_{sg} + I_b$$

(Since the control grid is negative, it is drawing no current.)

The plate current will flow through the 17-kilohm load resistor. From Kirchhoff's law, if 250 volts is applied to the plate circuit and 116 volts appears at the plate, the voltage across the load must be 134 volts. Plate current equals

$$I_b = E_{RL}/R_L$$
$$I_b = 134/(17)(10^3) = 7.88 \text{ ma}$$

The voltage applied to the screen circuit is 150 volts. If 100 volts is developed at the screen, the remaining 50 volts is developed across the screen resistor. Screen current, by Ohm's law, is

$$I_{sg} = 50/(100)(10^3) = 0.5 \text{ ma}$$

The sum of the plate and the screen current is the cathode current.

$$I_k = (0.5)(10^{-3}) + (7.88)(10^{-3}) = 8.38 \text{ ma}$$

EXAMPLE THREE   In the circuit of Fig. 4·10, what is the d-c screen resistance R_{sg}? What is the static plate resistance?

By Ohm's law the screen resistance is the quotient of the screen voltage and the screen current.

$$R_{sg} = E_{sg}/I_{sg} = 100/(0.5)(10^{-3}) = 200 \text{ kilohms}$$

The same reasoning may be applied to the plate circuit.

$$R_p = E_b/I_b = 166/(7.88)(10^{-3}) = 14.7 \text{ kilohms}$$

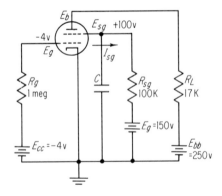

Fig. 4·10   Tetrode circuit: d-c characteristics.

STAGE GAIN

The gain of a tetrode circuit is calculated by either graphical or algebraic methods. The techniques are the same as outlined in Chap. 3. The screen circuit can be disregarded since a large bypass capacitor decouples the screen from the signal circuit (Fig. 4·10). The screen, therefore, is effectively at signal ground. The voltage gain is

$$A_v = \frac{\mu R_L}{r_p + R_L}$$

EXAMPLE FOUR   Assume that a 2EV5 tetrode has a load resistance of 15 kilohms, an $E_{sg} = 80$ volts, and a control-grid bias of -1.25 volts. If a 17.5-mv a-c signal is applied to the circuit, what is the peak-to-peak magnitude of the signal across the load? What is the gain of the stage?

SOLUTION   Point Q of Fig. 4·9 represents the quiescent operating point. The peak-to-peak magnitude of the input signal is

$$(E_g)(2.828) \approx 0.5 \text{ volt}$$

If 0.5 volt is plotted as an increment along the 15-kilohm load line, the resultant increment in plate voltage is 50 volts. The increment of the voltage across R_L is the same as that at the plate; therefore, the peak-to-peak voltage across R_L is 50 volts.
    The gain is given as

$$A = \Delta e_o / \Delta e_{in} = 50/0.5 = 100$$

A tetrode tube as an amplifier finds little use at audio frequencies. For a number of years the tube was considered extinct. Only very few receivers which utilized the old 24A or 36 are still in operation. In recent years, however, manufacturers have developed new types, such as the 6EV5, for use in television receivers and uhf amplifiers.
    The beam-power tetrode is discussed in Chap. 5.

Problems

4·1   Data for the tetrode type 6EV5 can be found in the Appendix. (*a*) If the plate and screen voltage are held constant at 180 and 80 volts, respectively, approximately how much will the plate current increase if the control-grid voltage E_{c1} is increased from -3 to -1 volt? (*b*) If the control-grid and the screen-grid voltages are maintained constant at -0.5 and 80 volts, respectively, how much change will occur in plate current if the plate voltage is increased from 275 to 325 volts? (*c*) What is the tube's transconductance based on the data of question *a*? (*d*) What is the tube's plate resistance based on the data of question *b*?

4·2   A 2EV5 is operated into a 10-kilohm load, and the B supply is 200 volts, the screen supply is 80 volts, and the grid bias is -2 volts. (a) What is the gain of the stage? (b) What is the quiescent plate current? (c) What is the quiescent plate voltage?

4·3　The B supply in Prob. 4·2 is increased to 350 volts and the load increased to 20 kilohms. (a) What is the gain of the stage? (b) What is the quiescent plate current? (c) What is the quiescent plate voltage?

4·4　Refer to the output characteristic of the 6EV5. What value of grid voltage and what increment of plate voltage will produce maximum negative resistance?

4·5　The tetrode circuit of Fig. 4·10 has a plate supply voltage of $E_{bb} = 300$ volts, screen supply voltage $E_s = 200$ volts, load resistance $R_L = 60$ kilohms, screen load resistance $R_{sg} = 100$ kilohms, and a voltmeter records plate voltage as 180 volts and screen voltage as 120 volts. (a) What is the plate current? (b) What is the cathode current? (c) What is the voltage across the screen load resistor?

4·6　In the circuit of Fig. 4·10, $R_L = 45$ kilohms, $R_{sg} = 150$ kilohms, $E_b = 350$ volts, E_s 150 volts, the cathode current is 4.4 ma, and the screen voltage is 90 volts. Find (a) the plate voltage, (b) the plate resistance of the tube, (c) the screen resistance of the tube.

4·7　In the circuit of Fig. 4·10, $E_b = 250$ volts, $E_s = 200$ volts, $R_{sg} = 200$ kilohms, the cathode current is 1.25 ma, the screen voltage is 150 volts, and the plate voltage is 150 volts. Find (a) the plate load resistance, (b) the screen current, (c) the power dissipated at the plate of the tube.

4·8　In the circuit of Prob. 4·5, increasing the value of the plate load resistance while maintaining the plate supply voltage constant will increase, decrease, or not change the (a) plate voltage of the tube, (b) cathode current of the tube, (c) screen voltage of the tube?

Review Questions

4·1　What are the limitations of a triode at high audio frequencies? How do these limitations influence the gain of the stage?

4·2　Assume a given triode has a calculated Miller input capacitance of 70 pf. If the load resistance on the tube is increased, how will the input capacitance be influenced?

4·3　Two tubes have nearly the same C_{gp} and C_{gk} and tube resistance r_p. Tube 1 has a higher g_m than does tube 2. If both are operated into the same value of load resistance, which will have a lower Miller input capacitance?

4·4　Define secondary emission. What are the effects of secondary emission on the plate characteristic curve for a tetrode?

4·5　If a tetrode is operated with 100 volts at its screen and the amount of negative resistance is to be reduced, should the d-c screen potential be increased, decreased, or unchanged?

4·6　Name two applications of the negative-resistance region of a tetrode.

4·7　In a tetrode circuit, consider the d-c characteristics. Do changes in the screen potential influence the cathode current? If so, how?

V
PENTODES

5·1 SUPPRESSOR GRID

The principal factor limiting the tetrode's application is secondary emission. If an electrostatic field is introduced between the screen grid and the plate, the effects of secondary emission are eliminated. Figure 5·1 illustrates how the addition of a grid, the suppressor grid, can be used to provide the proper field. In order to repel the secondary electrons back to the plate it is necessary that the suppressor grid be operated at a lower potential than the plate. This condition can be achieved in one of two ways. (A third method will be discussed in a later section.) Either the suppressor grid can be connected to an external pin at the base of the tube and the proper potential applied, or the suppressor can be connected to the cathode internally. Figure 5·2 shows a schematic representation of both cases. Maintaining the suppressor at cathode potential will automatically ensure that the electrostatic field between

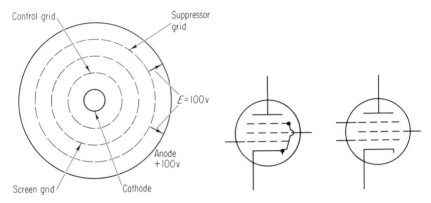

Fig. 5·1   Pentode: cutaway view.   Fig. 5·2   Pentodes: schematic symbols.

the suppressor and the plate will be toward the plate (as in Fig. 5·1), at a value equal to the plate-to-cathode potential. At low values of plate potential the field between the suppressor and the plate will be a low-intensity field. At these potentials, however, the low-velocity electrons will produce only a small amount of secondary emission, and hence the repelling effect will act as a shield from the screen.

5·2 OUTPUT CHARACTERISTICS

COMPARISON OF TUBE PARAMETERS

Figure 5·3 is a typical stage of pentode amplification. Assume that the control grid is adjusted to a fixed value of −3 volts, the screen grid to

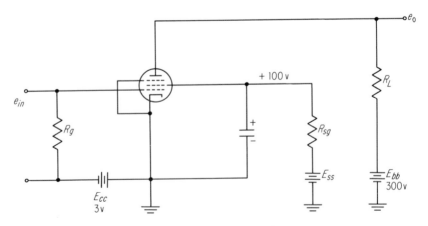

Fig. 5·3   Pentode circuit.

100 volts, and that the suppressor is at cathode potential. If the plate voltage is varied from 0 to 300 volts, the plate current will vary as shown in Fig. 5·4 (solid line). The dashed line shows how this variation compares with a similar tetrode arrangement. The dotted line compares the triode with the other two. Comparison of these curves allows a relative analysis of the plate resistances of the three types of tubes. If an increment of plate voltage from 50 to 75 volts is considered, the triode curve provides an increment in plate current of 2.0 ma.

$$r_p \text{ (triode)} = 12.5 \text{ kilohms}$$

The corresponding increment of plate current for the 25-volt increment of plate voltage for the tetrode yields a resistance of

$$r_p \text{ (tetrode)} = 32 \text{ kilohms}$$

Similarly the pentode's a-c plate resistance equals

$$r_p \text{ (pentode)} = 250 \text{ kilohms}$$

A similar comparative graph could be used to examine the relative values of amplification factor for the three tubes. Such a comparison would indicate that triode tubes generally have low values of μ (in the order of 20 to 70) while pentode tubes have μ values ranging as high as 6,000.

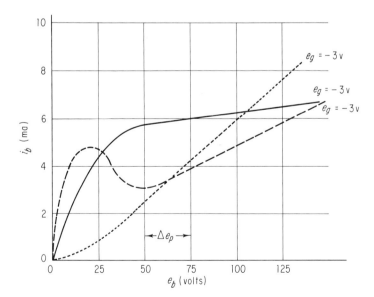

Fig. 5·4 Comparison of output characteristics.

PLATE FAMILY OF CURVES

Figure 5·5 is a plate family of curves for a 6AN8 pentode section. These curves point up some of the basic limitations of the pentode tube.

High Plate Resistance. As has been shown in the comparative graph, the a-c plate resistance for pentodes is considerably higher than for triodes. Typical pentode values range from 200 to 800 kilohms. If a vacuum tube is to be considered as a generating source of power then the high plate resistance is the internal resistance of the generator. The maximum-power-transfer theorem states that the load impedance connected to a generator should equal the internal impedance of the generator for maximum power transfer. With this restriction the pentode would have to work into a very high load impedance. The high load impedance combined with the high plate resistance means the plate current would be limited to only a few milliamperes, and hence very little power would be developed at the load. For example, the load connected to a pentode whose $r_p = 600$ kilohms would have to be 600 kilohms. If the increment of plate voltage is 200 volts as a result of applying a signal at the control grid, the increment of plate current would be

$$\Delta i_p = \frac{\Delta e_p}{r_p + R_L} = \frac{200}{(1.2)(10^{+6})} = 0.166 \text{ ma}$$

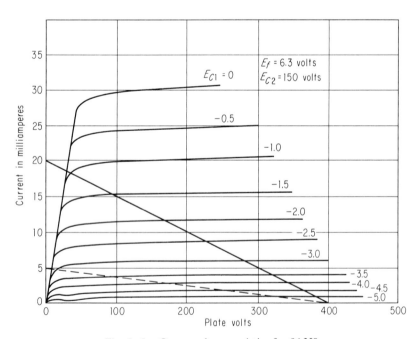

Fig. 5·5   Output characteristics for 6AN8.

The resultant power developed at the load would be on the order of a few milliwatts. It is clear, therefore, that the maximum-power-transfer theorem has little meaning for pentode voltage amplifiers.

Distortion. Harmonic distortion is essentially changing the waveshape of the original wave. Because of inherent characteristics of the pentode as an amplifier, a large percentage of harmonic distortion is introduced to a wave applied at the grid. This distortion is graphically visible by the uneven spacing between the individual plate-voltage curves. This condition is considerably less prevalent when the pentode is operated as a small-signal amplifier. Because of the high r_p and correspondingly high load resistance, the resultant dynamic transfer characteristic is quite linear; hence the harmonic distortion is low.

Examine the typical plate characteristics of a 6SN7 triode tube. Notice that a grid-voltage change from -2 to 0 volts causes a given plate-current change. For the same triode, a change of grid potential from -2 to -4 volts causes about the same change in plate current. If the grid voltage for the pentode in Fig. 5·5 is changed from -2 to 0 volts (along a perpendicular to a plate potential of 200 volts), the plate current changes from 12 to 30 ma (18 ma). When the grid is changed from -2 to -4 volts, the plate-current change is 9 ma. The positive swing in input voltage caused a larger change in plate current than did the negative swing. Note, however, how much the percentage of difference is decreased when the change from -2 to -1.5 volts is compared with the change from -2 to -2.5 volts.

5·3 PENTODE AMPLIFICATION

GRAPHICAL SOLUTION

Gain calculations for pentode circuits can be computed using the same procedure developed for triodes. The graphical solution is completed by constructing a load line on the output characteristic as shown in Fig. 5·5. A 6AN8 pentode operating into a 20-kilohm load will yield a gain of about 115. An increment of grid voltage from -1.5 to -3.5 yields a $\Delta e_p = 230$ volts. Even though a gain of 115 seems large compared with a triode operating into a similar-sized load, it is small when one considers that the μ of the 6AN8 is 1,800. Greater voltage gain is possible by increasing the size of the load resistor (dashed line of Fig. 5·5). However, the increased load resistance restricts the input-voltage swing to the stage. With a 20-kilohm load the grid voltage can vary from about -1 to -5 volts. With an 80-kilohm load the grid swing is limited to about 2 volts. This limitation on the grid input swing limits the power sensitivity of the stage. Power sensitivity is defined as the ratio of the a-c power output to the a-c grid voltage.

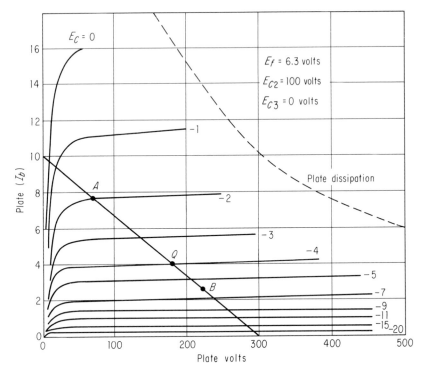

Fig. 5·6   Analysis of a pentode amplifier.

EXAMPLE   A 6BA6 pentode stage of amplification is to employ a d-c supply of 300 volts and a plate load of 30 kilohms. The grid bias supply is −4 volts. Find (a) the quiescent voltage on the plate, (b) the gain of the stage if a 4-volt peak-to-peak signal is applied, (c) the power lost at the plate at quiescence.

SOLUTION

a. The quiescent voltage at the plate is determined from the load-line characteristic of Fig. 5·6.

$$E_b = 180 \text{ volts}$$

b. According to points A and B in Fig. 5·6 a 4-volt grid swing causes a plate-voltage change of 155 volts. The voltage gain A is defined as $A = \Delta e_o/\Delta e_i$; hence

$$A = \frac{155}{4} = 38.5$$

c. The d-c plate dissipation is given as

$$P_p = I_b E_b = (4)(10^{-3})(180) = 0.72 \text{ watt}$$

(The maximum plate dissipation for the 6BA6 is 3 watts and is shown in the dashed line of Fig. $5 \cdot 6$.)

ALGEBRAIC SOLUTION OF GAIN

The output circuit for the pentode amplifier yields the same gain equation as for the triode.

$$A = \mu R_L / (r_p + R_L)$$

However, in pentode amplifier circuits ordinarily the value of r_p is much larger than the load resistance; hence the denominator of Eq. $(3 \cdot 15)$ is essentially r_p.

$$A = \frac{\mu R_L}{r_p}$$

Since $g_m = \mu / r_p$ the gain of a pentode stage is approximately

$$A = g_m R_L \qquad\qquad (5 \cdot 1)$$

$5 \cdot 4$ PENTODE LINEAR MODEL (OPTIONAL)

Figure $5 \cdot 7$ represents a set of ideal pentode output characteristics. Since the pentode is essentially a constant current source, its equivalent circuit is shown as a Norton generator (Fig. $5 \cdot 8a$). The schematic

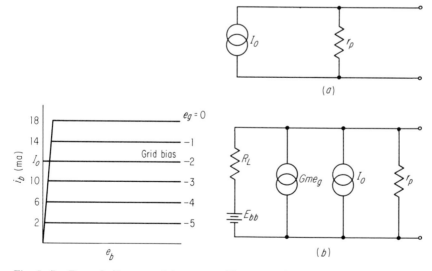

Fig. $5 \cdot 7$ Pentode linear model.   Fig. $5 \cdot 8$ Pentode equivalent circuits.

representation shown in Fig. 5·8a is taken from the ideal characteristics of Fig. 5·7. Note that the current source of 11.2 ma is the result of a 2-volt grid bias. When the tube is operated into a load resistance and a signal is applied to the grid, the complete equivalent circuit is shown in Fig. 5·8b.

Problems

5·1   If a 20-kilohm resistor is connected as the load on a 6BA6 pentode, and the screen is maintained at 100 volts, what is the quiescent plate voltage if the grid bias is −3 volts? (Assume a B+ supply of 300 volts and that the suppressor is tied to the cathode.)

5·2   If the load in Prob. 5·1 is increased to 30 kilohms, what quiescent voltage will appear across the load resistor? What power is dissipated at the plate of the tube?

5·3   If a 2-volt peak-to-peak signal is applied to the circuit of Prob. 5·1, what is the peak-to-peak change in the output voltage of the stage?

5·4   According to the tube manual, if the 6BA6 were operated at a plate potential of 250 volts and a screen potential of 100 volts, the transconductance would be 4,400 μmhos and the plate resistance 1 megohm. What would be the μ of the tube? What would be the gain of the stage if the load resistor were 60 kilohms?

5·5   The 6X8 is a triode-pentode type of tube. If the available B+ supply is 250 volts, the load resistor is 10 kilohms, and the grid bias supply is −2 volts, which of the two sections, the triode or the pentode, would provide a greater voltage stage gain if the input signal to each were 2 volts peak-to-peak? (Assume the screen for the pentode would be operating at 150 volts.)

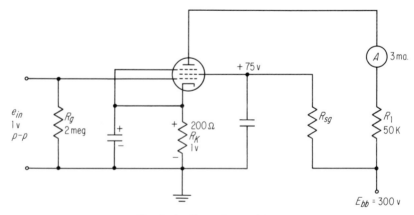

Fig. 5·9   Pentode amplifier.

5·6   Assume that the 6BA6 described in Prob. 5·4 had a plate load of 500 kilohms instead of 60 kilohms, and the a-c signal at the grid were 1 volt peak-to-peak. What a-c plate current would flow in the circuit? What is the maximum grid swing permissible for the circuit?

5·7   What is the d-c voltage from plate to ground for the circuit of Fig. 5·9? What is the value of the screen resistor to give the voltage indicated?

5·8   What direct current is flowing in the screen for the circuit of Fig. 5·9?

5·9   For the circuit of Fig. 5·9, if the input signal is 1 volt peak-to-peak and the change in plate current is 2 ma peak-to-peak, what is the amplification (gain) of the stage?

5·10 A pentode tube is to be used as a voltage amplifier. A sensing device produces a 3-mv a-c signal which is coupled to the control grid of the tube. If the tube is to develop 1 volt across a load of 150 kilohms, what should be the transconductance of the pentode?

5·5   BEAM-POWER TUBES

The pentode tubes described in Sec. 5·4 exhibit two important short-comings: (a) the excessively high plate resistance renders the tube less desirable as a power amplifier, and (b) the characteristic curves exhibit a knee at low plate potentials which limits the plate-voltage swing as well as the input grid swing. The previous discussions involving maximum power transfer emphasize a; however, a few special-purpose pentodes do have large plate resistances and are used as power amplifiers. These special-purpose types are designed to operate with extremely high B-supply values.

Item b can be observed in Fig. 5·5. Note that the knee for the $E_{c1} = 0$ volt curve occurs at about 50 volts at the plate. This means that the plate voltage should not decrease below 50 volts. Note further that the 6BA6 (shown in Fig. 5·6) has an $E_c = 0$ volt knee occurring at a plate voltage of about 50 volts as well. It should be noted that a greater plate-voltage swing is possible at lower (more negative) grid values, but at the expense of a very small grid input swing of voltage.

The beam-power pentode partially eliminates these undesirable characteristics by modifying the characteristics as compared with the standard pentode. The screen grid is located physically in line with the control grid. The effect of "hiding" the screen causes the screen to collect fewer electrons. The space current flows in streams toward the plate. Figure 5·10 is a cutaway view of the *inline grids*. Resultant effects are a decreased plate resistance and an increased amount of power-handling capacity. A further increase in the amount of plate current is possible by removing the suppressor grid and replacing it with beam-forming plates. These beam-forming electrodes are connected internally

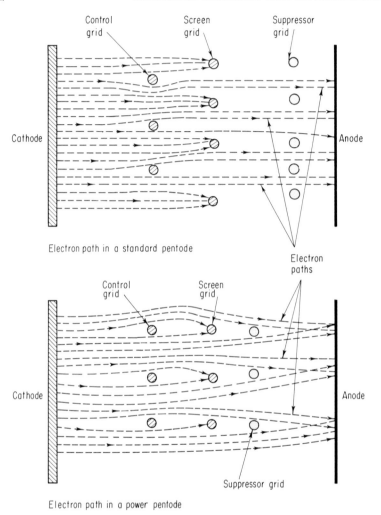

Electron path in a standard pentode

Electron path in a power pentode

Fig. 5·10   Inline grids.

to the cathode of the tube. Figure 5·11 shows schematic representations of the beam-power pentode. Manufacturers do not agree on a uniform symbolism for the power pentode. Some even identify the tube where the suppressor has been replaced with beam-forming plates as a tetrode. Figure 5·12 shows two schematic symbols for beam-power pentodes.

DYNAMIC TRANSFER CHARACTERISTIC

Figure 5·13 represents the output characteristics for a typical beam-power tube. Note the increments along the plate-current ordinate

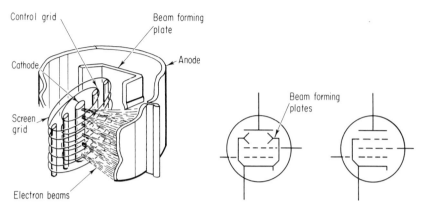

Fig. 5·11   Beam-forming plates.   Fig. 5·12   Schematic symbols.

represent larger currents than those of the standard pentode. The plate
family of curves is extended to include positive grid voltages as well. All
load-line and gain calculations for the beam-power tubes are similar to
those for triodes and pentodes.

5·6 PENTODE DYNAMIC CHARACTERISTICS

DYNAMIC TRANSFER CHARACTERISTIC

Transfer characteristics are useful for determining operating bias and
maximum-input-signal specifications. Figure 5·14 shows the dynamic
transfer characteristics for various values of load resistance connected to
a 6SJ7 pentode. A load resistance of 500 kilohms would require that the

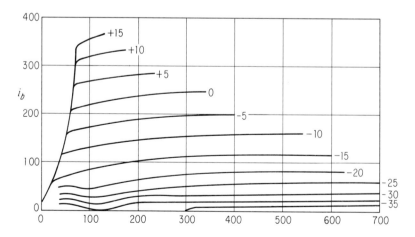

Fig. 5·13   Beam-power characteristics.

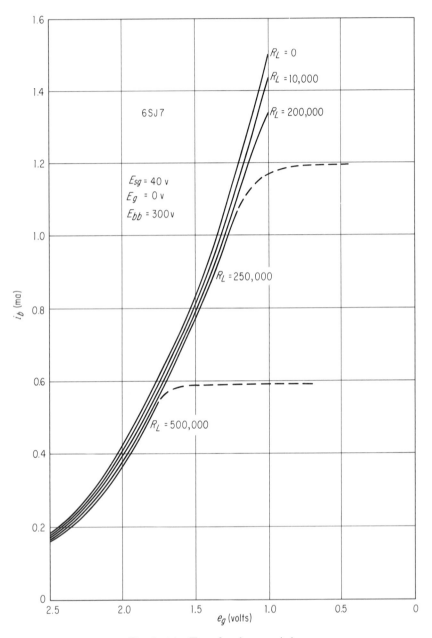

Fig. 5·14   Transfer characteristics.

tube be biased at about 2.1 volts and the signal input limited to about 500 mv. The grid could then vary up to about -1.75 volts. Any further increase in grid voltage would drive the plate into saturation. (With a 500-kilohm load plate current saturates at about 0.6 ma.) Decreasing the load resistance would permit a larger peak-to-peak input signal (about 1.5 volts).

In a comparison of these transfer curves with those of the triode it should be noted that no portion of the pentode curve is linear. The transfer curves of all pentode tubes exhibit some nonlinearity. The nonlinear transfer characteristic means that all pentodes contribute harmonic distortion to the input signal.

POWER-OUTPUT DISTORTION CURVES

Since most beam-power tubes are used as power amplifiers in audio circuits both distortion and power output become critical circuit parameters. Tube manufacturers supply important data concerning these two characteristics in their published manuals. Figure 5·15 illustrates two comparative graphs. Graph a shows that the most desirable value of load resistance for that tube is about 5,200 ohms. The optimum load resistance will produce a maximum power at minimum distortion. Graph b illustrates that both power output and harmonic distortion increase with increasing input driving signal.

5·7 REMOTE-CUTOFF TUBES

In standard pentodes and beam-power tubes the amplification factor will remain reasonably constant over the operating range of plate voltage. The grid cutoff characteristic is determined physically by the relative position of the elements. The operating plate supply voltage will also define a cutoff voltage at the grid. The larger the plate supply, the more negative the grid cutoff potential. Figure 5·16b is an illustration of a grid used in sharp-cutoff tubes. Note the uniform spacing of the individual grid wires. The electrostatic field produced by such a grid is reasonably uniform in density between grid and cathode; thus the cutoff characteristic is defined.

Many pentodes have been designed for use in control circuits where feedback is incorporated in the system. A sharp-cutoff characteristic, though used in some circuits, is undesirable in many of these circuits. Manufacturers have developed a large number of remote-cutoff (also called variable-μ or variable-cutoff or supercontrol) tubes. In ordinary operation these tubes require large negative grid voltage to cut off the tube completely. Figure 5·16a illustrates the grid of a remote-cutoff

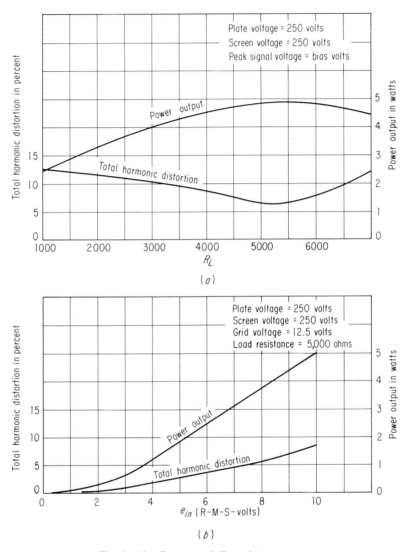

Fig. 5·15   Power and distortion curves.

tube. The nonuniform spacing of the grids produces a varying density field between grid and cathode; minimum density occurs at the center of the grid structure. Such a condition ensures that at ordinary grid (cutoff) potentials, some electrons will be attracted to the plate and that a large negative field is necessary for complete cutoff of the tube. Figure 5·17 is a graph comparing cutoff characteristics for a sharp-cutoff pentode and a remote-cutoff one.

Fig. 5·16   Grid comparison.

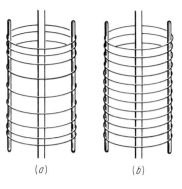

(a) (b)

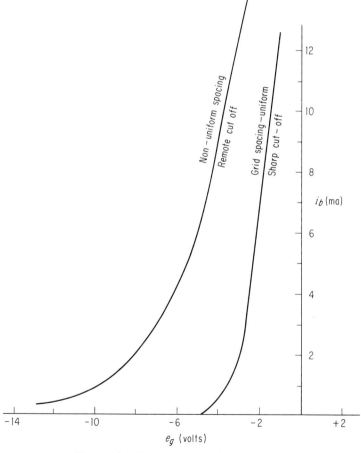

Fig. 5·17   Pentode cutoff characteristics.

Review Questions

5·1   What tetrode deficiency does the suppressor grid minimize?

5·2   How do the a-c plate resistances of the triode, tetrode, and pentode compare? Which is largest and why?

5·3   What type of distortion does a nonlinear dynamic transfer characteristic produce?

5·4   How do changes in the value of load resistance influence the voltage gain of a pentode amplifier?

5·5   How is plate current increased through physical characteristics in the power pentode?

5·6   How do the characteristics of the beam-power pentode and the power pentode differ?

5·7   What relation exists between the power output of a pentode and the amount of distortion the tube produces?

5·8   How are remote-cutoff conditions achieved in the supercontrol tube? How does this tube compare with a variable-μ-type tube?

5·9   How does the dynamic transfer characteristic of the pentode compare with that of the triode? The tetrode?

5·10   How does the stage gain of a pentode compare with the stage of a triode?

VI

CATHODE-RAY TUBES

6·1 ELECTROSTATIC CATHODE-RAY TUBES

Cathode-ray tubes, or picture, tubes find a wide variety of uses in the field of electronics science. Television receivers, test equipment, radar systems, computer systems, and fire-control devices all utilize the display characteristics of the tube. Though tubes made by different manufacturers differ in small details all CRTs operate on the same basic theory. Figure 6·1 illustrates the basic parts of the tube.

CONSTRUCTION

Electron Gun. The cathode (Figs. 6·1 and 6·2) is a cylindrical sleeve similar to the type contained in vacuum tubes. One end is enclosed and consists of a coating of strontium or beryllium oxide. The control grid consists of a larger cylinder which fits over the cathode and has a small hole in the end. The electrons emitted from the button of oxide pass

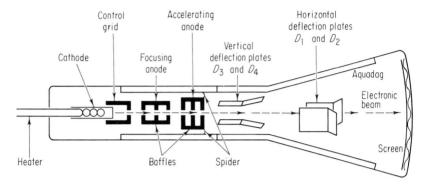

Fig. 6·1   Basic cathode-ray tube.

through the opening and are ultimately accelerated toward the screen. The focusing anode consists of a still larger cylinder open at both ends. One or more baffle plates are included within the focus anode. The baffle is a disk with a small hole in its center. When the focus anode is operated with a positive potential with respect to the control grid, an electrostatic-focus lens is created and the electrons are formed into a beam. The accelerating anode is a second large cylinder also open at both ends. A large positive potential creates an accelerating field which impels the electron beam toward the screen. The accelerating anode is generally connected to the Aquadag by a springlike spider.

The Aquadag (sometimes called the ultor) is a thin graphite coating on the inside of the tube which extends back from the screen to the accelerating anode. Electrons bouncing off the screen are attracted to the positive Aquadag.

Screen. The screen consists of a curved or flat glass face the outside of

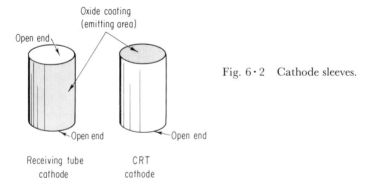

Fig. 6·2   Cathode sleeves.

which is polished to a special optical finish. The inside consists of a coating of crystals such as zinc sulfide or zinc beryllium silicate. The high-velocity electrons striking the crystal give up their kinetic energy to the crystals. The vibrating crystals convert this energy into light.

Deflection Plates. The set of deflection plates closest to the gun assembly are the vertical deflection plates. These plates are identified as D_3 and D_4 and are flared at the screen end to permit freedom of deflection of the beam. The horizontal deflection plates are exactly like the vertical plates and positioned in front of the total assembly. In some types of large-screen tubes the deflection system is external to the tube. The plates are replaced by a yoke assembly which is positioned along the neck of the CRT.

BEAM FORMATION

The electrons emitted from the oxide-coated cathode form a space charge similar to that of the standard thermionically heated receiving tube. The electrons are attracted toward the screen as a result of the electrostatic field produced by the accelerating anode (and Aquadag). Figure 6·3 shows the field and its direction as E_1. The control grid acts as a preliminary means of beam formation by forcing the electrons attracted to the accelerating anode to pass through the small opening of the cylinder. The electrons emerge from this opening in much the same way water sprays from the nozzle of a hose.

The pattern of the electrostatic field produced by the control grid and the focus anode causes the electrons to focus into a point of convergence. Varying the potential difference between these two elements controls the beam focus.

In order to examine the theory of the electrostatic lens refer to Fig. 6·4. Figure 6·4a shows the electrostatic configuration between two flat plates. The field direction extends from the negative plate to the

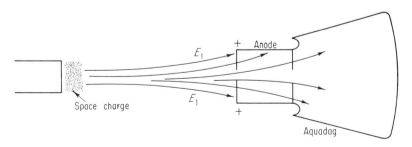

Fig. 6·3   Beam formation.

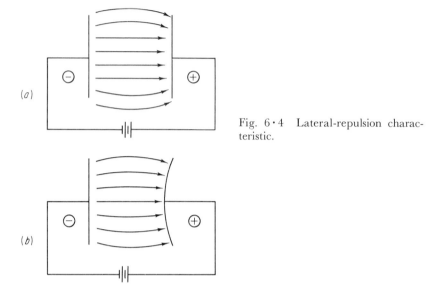

Fig. 6·4   Lateral-repulsion characteristic.

positive plate. Note that the field "bows out" at the ends of the plates. The lateral-repulsion characteristic of electrostatic waves causes a spreading of the space between the lines. Figure 6·4*b* illustrates the change in configuration of the electrostatic field resulting from curving one of the plates. If two cylinders are placed next to each other, the electrostatic field will be linear only at the adjoining rims. Figure 6·5 shows the configuration of the field. Note that the lateral-repulsion characteristic causes a group of curving electrostatic lines between the two centers of the cylinders. Figure 6·5*b* shows a cutaway view of the

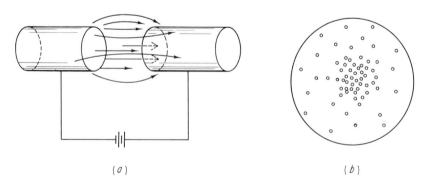

(*a*)   (*b*)

Fig. 6·5   Field concentration between two cylinders.

field coming toward the observer. The greatest concentration of field occurs in the center portion between the cylinders. Electrons entering the field parallel to the direction of the field are uninfluenced by the field. However, these electrons entering the field must enter in a straight line down the center of the cylinder in order to be uninfluenced.

Figure 6·6 shows electron A entering the field. It will continue through the field to point X with no deflection since the angle of entry is zero degrees. Electron B entering the field at an angle θ will be subjected to the forces which direct electrons to travel a path parallel to an electrostatic field. Electron B will be deflected sufficiently to cause it to arrive at point X. Electron C entering the field at an angle α will be deflected by a greater force (if α is larger than θ) and hence will also arrive at the point of convergence X. If the point of convergence X coincides with the screen phosphor a bright focused dot will appear.

ELECTROSTATIC DEFLECTION

An electrostatic field is used to deflect the beam to any point on the screen. If a voltage E is placed on the horizontal plates, the electrostatic field causes the electron beam to be deflected toward the positive plate. The velocity of the beam is sufficiently high that none of the electrons strike the positive deflecting plate; instead they are deflected toward it. If the polarity on the plates is switched the beam can be deflected in the other direction. In actual operation a sawtooth voltage (or sine wave) passing through zero is used for establishing a reference sweep.

Deflection Sensitivity. The amount of beam deflection on the screen is governed by a number of factors. The two most important, however, are the voltage on the deflecting plates and the voltage on the accelerating anode. The length of the field and the distance between the plates also

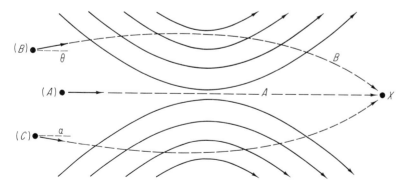

Fig. 6·6   Electron convergence.

influence the beam deflection. These factors are fixed at the time of manufacture and cannot be a source of control. Clearly the higher the anode potential, the greater the velocity of the electrons as they pass the region of the deflection plates. The result is that higher deflecting potentials are required at higher values of accelerator anode potential. The following equation defines this relationship and is approximately correct. It may be used for most design calculations.

$$S = e_d/e_a \qquad (6\cdot1)$$

where $S = $ distance of beam deflection
$e_d = $ deflection plate voltage
$e_a = $ anode potential

Tube manufacturers list deflection sensitivity as a cathode-ray tube parameter. The 5CP4 is rated with a vertical plate deflection sensitivity of 37 volts per cm per kv (the number of deflection volts required for 1 cm of deflection per kilovolt on the anode). This same tube has its horizontal deflection plates rated at 32 volts per cm per kv.

EXAMPLE ONE   If the deflection for a 5LP4A is rated at 40 volts per cm per kv, what deflection voltage on the horizontal plates is required for full screen deflection? Assume the anode is to operate at 2,000 volts. The tube manual lists the usable screen width as 5⁄16 in.; therefore, the total deflection is 5.312 in. or 13.5 cm (2.54 cm per in.).

40 volts/(cm)(kv)
80 volts/(cm)(2 kv)
1,080 volts/(13.5 cm)(2 kv)

Refer to Fig. 6·7. If no voltage E were applied to D_1 and D_2, the beam would produce a spot in the center of the screen. According to the example, a total of 1,080 volts would be required for full screen deflec-

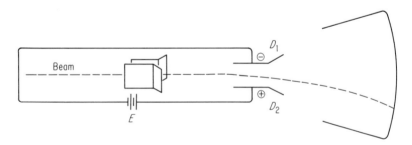

Fig. 6·7   Deflection plates.

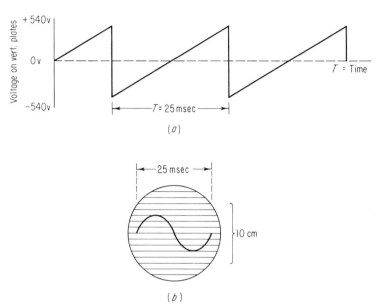

Fig. 6·8 Screen display.

tion. The voltage E of Fig. 6·7 would require a peak-to-peak change of 1,080 volts for full screen deflection as shown. If the cathode-ray tube of Fig. 6·7 is to be used in an oscilloscope, the horizontal deflection plates would be driven by a sawtooth waveshape potential similar to Fig. 6·8. If the scope is to display a sine-wave voltage of 4 kc applied to the vertical plates, the sweep time (or the period) of the sawtooth wave would have to be 0.25 msec with an assumed zero rise-time figure. Increasing the period and thus decreasing the frequency of the sawtooth wave to 12.5 msec would result in a display of two complete sine waves.

Note that the display on the screen is 4 cm peak-to-peak and the horizontal input to the scope is 20 volts peak-to-peak. Since 20 volts is insufficient to deflect the beam 4 cm, an amplifying system within the scope must be used. Since the horizontal deflection sensitivity for 5LP4A is 18 volts per cm per kv the amplifying system of the scope would require a gain of 7.2 because

$$cm = 18 \text{ volts/kv}$$
$$4 \text{ cm} = 144 \text{ volts/kv}$$
$$A = 144/20 = 7.2$$

Most manufacturers follow the same convention for identifying the vertical and horizontal deflection plates. D_3 and D_4 identify the vertical plates and D_1 and D_2 the horizontal. Some manufacturers use the letter J to identify the plates. Manufacturers differ in identifying deflection as well. Some identify it as the number of centimeters per volt. A tube may be rated at 2 mm per volt d-c. Here 1 volt of change on the deflection plates produces 0.2 cm of beam deflection with an anode potential of 1,000 volts.

Deflection Factor. Many tube manufacturers utilize the deflection-factor rating to indicate deflection characteristics. Deflection factor and deflection sensitivity are two different ways of saying the same thing. The vertical deflection factor for the 3GP4 is given as 120 volts d-c per in. Here the sensitivity is given as the number of volts required for 1 in. of deflection per kilovolt of anode potential.

EXAMPLE TWO   A given cathode-ray tube requires 1,800 volts for a screen deflection of 4 in. If the anode potential is 3,000 volts, what is the deflection factor?

$$4 \text{ in.} = 1{,}800 \text{ volts}/3 \text{ kv}$$
$$4 \text{ in.} = 600 \text{ volts}/\text{kv}$$
$$S \text{ (in.)} = 150 \text{ volts}/\text{kv}$$

The deflection factor is 150 volts d-c per in.

SCREEN PHOSPHORS

The beam of electrons released from the cathode is impelled toward the screen. As a result of acceleration on the mass of the electron, it develops kinetic energy. Upon impact with the crystal formation of the screen phosphor, the energy is transferred to the crystal. The bombarding electrons cause a vibration of the valence shell of electrons of the crystal atoms. The energy released is in the form of light. This energy conversion is termed *luminescence* or emanating light. The luminescence takes on two forms. During the time of excitation, the time when electrons are striking the screen, the light given off is termed *fluorescence,* the direct conversion to light energy. After the source of excitation is removed (no beam of electrons striking the screen) the light given off is termed *phosphorescence.* Wristwatches which glow in the dark in reality are phosphorescing. The length of time of phosphorescence varies with the type of crystal used and type of impurities added to the crystals in manufacture. A measure of how long a crystal will phosphoresce is called its *persistence.* Persistences are generally rated as short, medium, and long. A persistence from a few microseconds to 1 msec is considered short. Medium persistence has a time range from a few milliseconds to 1 or 2 sec. Screens which phosphoresce for longer than 2 sec are considered long. Memory-type oscilloscopes which hold a display on the screen have apparent persistences ranging into hours.

TABLE 6 · 1

Phosphor No.	Fluorescence	Phosphorescence	Persistence
P1	*Green*	*Green*	*Medium*
P2	*Blue-green*	*Green*	*Long*
P4	*White*	*White*	*Medium*
P5	*Blue*	*Blue*	*Very short*
P7	*Blue-white*	*Greenish-yellow*	*Very long*
P11	*Blue*	*Blue*	*Short*
P12	*Orange*	*Orange*	*Medium long*

The color emitted from the screen is dependent upon the type of screen phosphor used. Manufacturers identify the color as well as the persistence in their tube catalogs. A tube rated as 5BP4 indicates a phosphor P4. Such a phosphor has a white fluorescence, a white phosphorescence, and a medium persistence. P4 phosphors are used in television-receiver cathode-ray tubes. A P7 phosphor emits a color of about 5,500 A during phosphorescence and has a very long persistence. Tubes with P7 phosphors are used in radar work. Table 6·1 is a partial listing of screen phosphors.

Problems

6·1   If a 5-in. electrostatic CRT has a deflection sensitivity of 10 volts per cm per kv, how much deflection voltage is necessary to cause the beam to move 8 cm, if the anode voltage is 5 kv?

6·2   If the anode voltage in Prob. 6·1 were reduced to 4 kv, how much would the deflection voltage have to be increased or decreased to achieve the same 8 cm of deflection?

6·3   What vertical deflection voltage is required for one complete sweep of the electron beam for a 5CP4 cathode-ray tube if the accelerating anode is at 3,000 volts?

6·4   Refer to Prob. 6·3. If the anode potential is increased to 4,000 volts and all other factors remain the same, how long will the deflection line be?

6·5   An electrostatic cathode-ray tube has a deflection sensitivity of 85 mv per cm per kv. If the anode is operated at 7,000 volts and the focus anode has 300 volts, how much deflection voltage is required to cause the beam to move 2 in.?

6·6   What is the deflection sensitivity of a 5-in. cathode-ray tube which normally operates with 8 kv on its anode and requires 1,200 volts for full screen deflection, (*a*) in centimeters, (*b*) in inches?

6·7   What is the deflection factor for the cathode-ray tube described in Prob. 6·5?

6·8   An oscilloscope employs a 5-in. CRT which lists a deflection factor of 100 volts per in. per kv. If the signal applied to the horizontal input is 6 volts peak-to-peak and the gain of the horizontal amplifier is adjusted to 50, what will be the height of the scope display? Assume an anode potential of 4 kv.

6·9   If the horizontal amplifier of Prob. 6·8 were equipped with a multiplier and the next available gain position were 300, would the scope display extend beyond the range of the screen?

6·10   Assume a given CRT has a 5-in. screen with a screen phosphor Pl and a short persistence of 0.1 msec. What is the lowest horizontal sweep time which will provide a phosphorescent line across the full screen?

6·2 ELECTROMAGNETIC CATHODE-RAY TUBES

The main limitation of electrostatic cathode-ray tubes is the deflection system. The position of the plates in the electron-gun assembly requires that large potentials be used for full screen deflection. The potentials on these plates are limited by the physical gap between the plates since an arc between the plates would destroy the tube. The result is that conventional electrostatic cathode-ray tubes are limited in screen size to about 7 in. A few specialized types have screen sizes as large as 16 in.; however, these are not in common usage because of their cost.

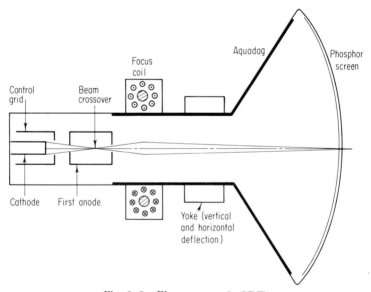

Fig. 6·9   Electromagnetic CRT.

BASIC ELECTROMAGNETIC CRT

The basic electromagnetic CRT gun assembly is similar to the electro-static type. Figure 6·9 illustrates a basic triode CRT as its schematic symbol. Note that beam deflection is caused by external means and the beam is focused by an external coil instead of an anode. The CRT of Fig. 6·9 is considered a triode because the gun assembly consists of a cathode, a grid, and an anode.

The physical shape of the electromagnetic CRT also differs from the electrostatic ones. The neck is generally smaller because of the simplified gun arrangement, the screen sizes are larger (10 to 36 in.), and the anode and Aquadag are returned externally through a button on the envelope. The theory of operation differs slightly from the electrostatic-type tube.

ACTION OF ELECTRONS IN AN ELECTROMAGNETIC FIELD

A magnetic field is set up about an electron when it is in motion. The beam of electrons emitted from the gun assembly is similar to a wire carrying a current. The left-hand rule can be applied to determine the direction of the magnetic flux around the beam. If the beam is passed through a coil energized by a direct current, an interaction between the field of the coil and the field of the beam takes place.

Focus. Assume that the focus coil around the neck of an electromag-netic CRT has a total field as illustrated in Fig. 6·10. An electron entering at *A* will continue on a straight path since its direction is parallel to the coil's magnetic flux. The vectors for the velocity, the electron's magnetic flux, and the coil's magnetic flux are all 90° with respect to each other (orthogonal); hence there is no change in the direc-tion. The electron will strike the screen at point *D*. If an electron enters the field at *B* with an angle *θ*, it will be deflected as a result of the non-orthogonal addition of the forces. Its velocity and travel pattern will follow a helical path (stretched-out spring), and it will strike the screen at point *D* at about the same time the electron entering at *A* does. Changing the angle of entry (*α* for the electron at *C* of Fig. 6·10) does not alter the convergence pattern. All electrons will converge at point *D*.

The point of convergence (hence the focus) can be changed by one of two methods: (*a*) A change in the current through the focus coil will change the density of the electromagnetic field. Decreasing the current will decrease the density and the convergence point will be farther away from the gun assembly. (*b*) A decrease in the anode potential will decrease the acceleration of the electron as it is passing through the focus field. A decreased anode potential effectively decreases the magnetic flux density about the electron beam.

Deflection. If an electron enters a uniform magnetic field perpendicular to the direction of the field, it will be deflected in a perpendicular plane.

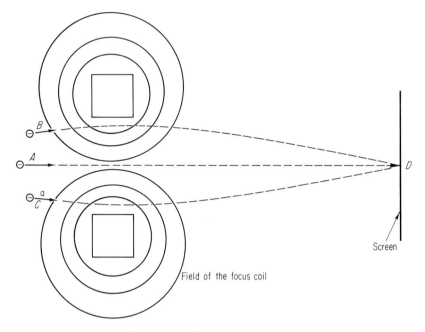

Fig. 6·10   Electromagnetic focus.

The action is similar to the theory of motor forces in the study of motors and generators. Figure 6·11 shows a linear magnetic field and an electron with its associated magnetic field moving away from the observer. Note that above the electron the two magnetic fields are additive because they are in the same direction. Below the electron the forces are in opposite directions. The resultant force on the mass of the electron is downward. The right-hand two finger and thumb rule can be applied. Point the index finger in the direction of the field's flux and the middle finger in the direction of electron motion, and the thumb will point in the direction of deflection. Changing the direction of the linear field (reversing the current through the coil) will change the direction of deflection.

The deflection yoke is positioned around the neck of the CRT and is essentially two perpendicular electromagnets. The electromagnets are positioned at 90° with one pair serving as horizontal deflection and the other as vertical. Figure 6·12 shows a typical deflection yoke as its schematic symbol.

ION TRAPS

The electron beam in a CRT contains not only electrons but ions as well. Some of the beam ions are emitted directly from the cathode while others

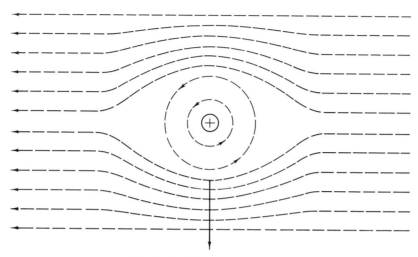

Fig. 6·11 Magnetic deflection.

are the result of gases within the envelope because of an imperfect vacuum.

In electrostatically deflected tubes the ions do not present a serious problem. The electrostatic field deflects ions as well as electrons, and hence the ion bombardment is diffused across many different points on the screen. In tubes where electromagnetic deflection is employed, ions present a serious danger of ion burn in the center of the screen. Since ions

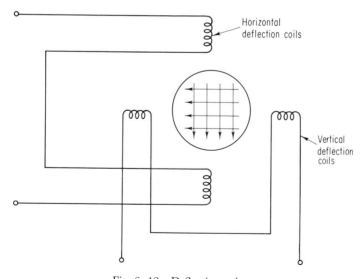

Fig. 6·12 Deflection yoke.

are many hundreds of times heavier than electrons, they are not influenced by the magnetic deflection system; without compensation they would travel in a straight path and continuously bombard the center of the screen. If this condition were allowed to continue, severe damage to the crystal structure of the screen phosphor would result. The damaging ions are removed from the electron beam by ion traps and modified gun assemblies.

Figure 6·13*a* illustrates a straight-gun or slashed-field assembly with an associated ion trap. The first and the second anodes are cut at a slight angle. Since the field produced by the two anodes is electrostatic, both electrons and ions are angled upward. The ion trap is a permanent magnet positioned along the neck so that the electrons of the beam are redeflected through the gun assembly (shown as a dashed line in

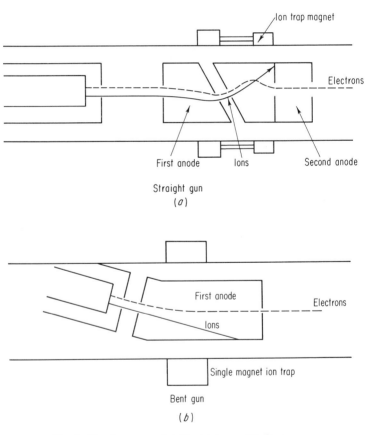

Fig. 6·13   Ion traps. (*a*) Straight gun. (*b*) Bent gun.

Fig. 6·13*a*). The ions are collected (solid line) at the anode since its potential is positive. Figure 6·13*b* illustrates a second method of trapping ions. The "bent-gun" assembly directs ions and electrons toward one wall of the anode. An ion-trap magnet bends the electron beam to a horizontal path through the anode.

COMPARISON OF CATHODE-RAY TUBES

The chief advantages of the electromagnetic CRT are:

1. Larger screen sizes
2. Brighter screen patterns (the accelerating anode potentials may range as high as 30,000 volts)
3. Simple electron-gun construction
4. Shorter overall length

The chief disadvantages are:

1. Greater power consumption
2. Cumbersome focus and deflection coils
3. Complex associated circuitry

6·3 MULTIPLE-GUN CATHODE-RAY TUBES

Both electrostatic and electromagnetic cathode-ray tubes utilizing a single gun assembly are used in television, PPI scan radar systems, oscilloscopes, A and J scan radar displays, and computing systems. The military and the television industry utilize specialized types of cathode-ray tubes where more than one gun assembly is housed in the neck of the tube. Some multiple displays of radar and fire-control systems employ CRTs that contain as many as 10 gun assemblies. The most common multiple-gun tube is the television tricolor picture tube.

Review Questions

6·1 Explain the difference between deflection factor and deflection sensitivity.

6·2 In an electrostatic CRT if the potential on the Aquadag is increased, will the velocity of the electrons increase, decrease, or remain unchanged?

6·3 If a given electrostatic CRT has 3 cm of deflection for a given change in deflection plate voltage, will the amount of deflection change if the anode potential is increased? If so, how?

6·4 Do changes in the Aquadag voltage influence the focus of the beam on the face of the CRT?

6·5 Define the difference between luminescence, fluorescence, and phosphorescence.

6·6 About how long in seconds is a medium persistence?

6·7 What color will the crystal P5 "glow" during excitation?

6·8 What are some of the disadvantages of electrostatic-type cathode-ray tubes which employ electrostatic deflection?

6·9 Why is an ion trap needed in an electromagnetic CRT, whereas it is not in an electrostatic CRT?

6·10 Compare electromagnetic CRTs with electrostatic CRTs.

6·11 Give two examples where multiple-gun CRTs are used.

6·12 Why are larger screen sizes more practical with electromagnetic deflection compared with electrostatic?

VII
SPECIAL-PURPOSE TUBES

7·1 PHOTOSENSITIVE DEVICES

Photosensitive devices operate on the principle of changing the energy of light waves into electrical energy. The devices can be classified into two categories. Those which depend on an emission of electrons from a photocathode surface are called *photoemissive cells*. There are two basic subgroups of this type, high-vacuum phototubes and gas phototubes. Photoemissive cells are used in sound-film-reproduction systems, light-control relay systems, and amplifiers.

The second group is classified as *photovoltaic cells*. The basic principle of operation is that the light energy striking the cell produces a potential at the terminals of the cell. The photovoltaic cell has many applications, the most common of which is in photographic light meters.

A third category, which is discussed in Chap. 9, is a semiconductor device. It works on the principle of converting light energy into resistance changes of the cell.

125

TERMINOLOGY

The human eye responds to a specific band of wavelengths in the electromagnetic spectrum. This range of wavelengths, identified as light, extends from 7.6×10^{-7} to 4.0×10^{-7} meter. The light region of the electromagnetic spectrum is generally expressed in angstrom units. One angstrom unit (A) is equal to 10^{-10} meter. The term *luminous flux* (symbol ϕ) is the rate of flow of light energy detectable by the human eye. A few microwatts of infrared energy would have a zero ϕ since it cannot be detected by the human eye. A similar amount of energy at 6,000 A would represent a specific amount of flux because 6,000 A is seen as a reddish color.

The fundamental unit of light intensity $\mathcal{I}$ is the international candle or *candle*. The unit is developed from a standardized lamp operating in a set of specified conditions. By definition 1 candle equals 4π lumens where the lumen is the unit of luminous flux. One lumen equals the ϕ emitted at a specified angle from 1 international candle.

The number of lumens striking a given square area of surface is called *illumination*. Illumination is measured in foot-candles. It is defined as the illumination on a surface 1 ft away from and perpendicular to a standard candle. The symbol for the foot-candle is E. It is just barely possible for the average person to read at illuminations of 1 ft-c. A 100-watt household bulb produces about 100 ft-c approximately 4 in. from it.

$$E = \text{lumens/sq ft}$$

PHOTOEMISSION

A material is considered photoemissive if it emits electrons when light shines upon it. The quantity and energy of electrons emitted from the surface are dependent upon the intensity of the light striking the surface and the wavelength of the light. A phototube can be made sensitive to a given wavelength by coating the cathode with various combinations of photosensitive materials such as cesium, potassium, and sodium. For example, a cathode of oxidized silver coated with a monatomic layer of cesium will emit electrons when exposed to light frequencies. Figure 7·1 shows the response-radiation pattern for three different types of photocathodes. Curve A represents a cathode response in the visible-light region. Curves B and C illustrate responses to ultraviolet and infrared, respectively.

HIGH-VACUUM PHOTOTUBES

Figure 7·2 shows the construction of a typical high-vacuum phototube and its schematic symbol. The plate or anode is operated at a positive

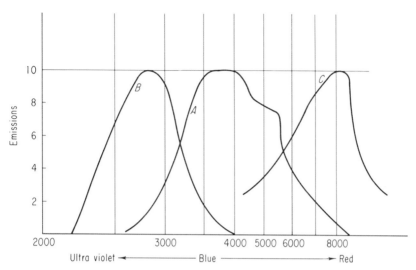

Fig. 7·1   Frequency-response curves.

potential with respect to the cathode in order to collect the emitted electrons. The output characteristics (Fig. 7·3a) resemble somewhat those of a standard pentode. The characteristics are similar because the phototube like the pentode has a very high plate resistance r_p. A representative circuit is shown in Fig. 7·3b.

Circuit analysis is usually completed graphically. The techniques are the same as those outlined for receiving tubes. A load line is plotted on the output characteristics and from it quiescent conditions are developed. The following numerical example illustrates how a high-vacuum phototube is used as a switching device.

Fig. 7·2   High-vacuum phototube.

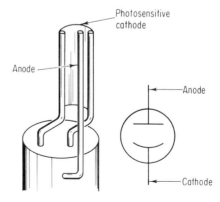

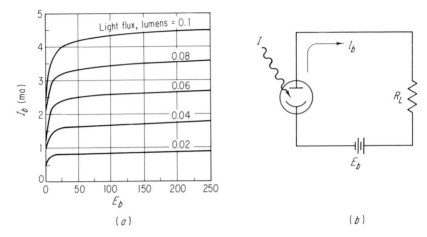

Fig. 7·3   Output characteristics.

EXAMPLE ONE   Refer to the circuit of Fig. 7·4. Assume the light intensity $\mathcal{I}$ is 0.2 lumen; what is the bias potential applied to V_2? What current is flowing through the solenoid of relay R_1? If $\mathcal{I}$ is reduced to zero, what current flows through the solenoid?

SOLUTION   The voltage developed across R_1 is the bias for V_2 and is determined from the load-line characteristic for V_1 (Fig. 7·5). The intersection of the 0.2-lumen characteristic and the load line establishes point Q. The voltage across R_1 is 30 volts. The bias on V_2 is sufficient to cut off the tube; hence no current is flowing through the solenoid. When $\mathcal{I}$ is reduced to zero the bias on V_2 reduces to zero. The plate current through V_2 with a 1.35-kilohm d-c load is determined from the load-line characteristic. $I_b = 17.5$ ma.

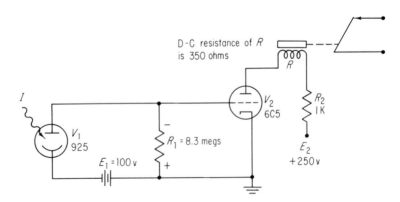

Fig. 7·4   Phototube switching circuit.

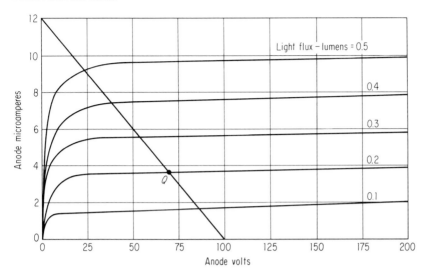

Fig. 7·5   925 characteristics.

The preceding example illustrated a relay circuit which is actuated when the light source is interrupted. Figure 7·6 illustrates a circuit which is actuated when a light source is impinged on the cathode of the phototube. With no signal applied to the phototube the relay remains deenergized since V_2 is held at cutoff by the bias voltage developed across R_3. No plate current flows through the solenoid of the relay.

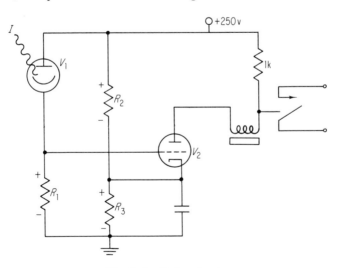

Fig. 7·6   Relay circuit.

When a light source strikes the cathode of V_1, the tube conducts and a potential is developed across R_1. Since this potential opposes the bias potential across R_3, V_2 will conduct and the relay will be energized.

HIGH-VACUUM PHOTOTUBE AMPLIFIER

High-vacuum phototube amplifiers are used in reproducing sound from movie film. A d-c "exciter" lamp incorporated in the projector is focused on the sound track. Varying degrees of light pass through the sound track to the cathode of a phototube. These changes in light are amplified through conventional circuits.

The most important consideration in the design of phototube sound amplifiers is linearity. If the anode-current response for given changes in light intensity introduces distortion the quality of reproduction will be garbled and "muddy." Proper selection of load resistance and d-c supply can ensure a linear dynamic transfer characteristic. Figure 7·7 illustrates a typical phototube sound-reproduction system. The sound-track portion of the film passes the window, thus varying the light impinged on the cathode of V_1. The variations in light carry audio intelligence to the circuit as voltage changes across R_1 and R_2. A high-gain pentode is used to amplify the audio.

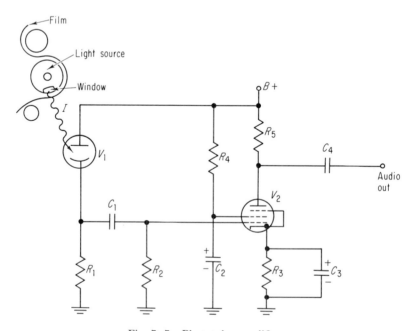

Fig. 7·7   Phototube amplifier.

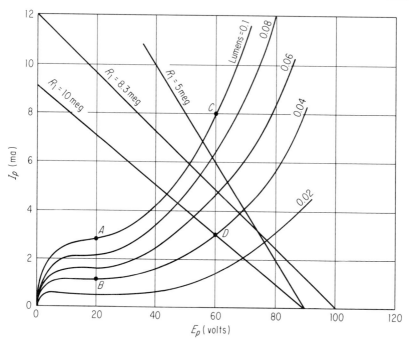

Fig. 7·8   Output characteristics of a 930 phototube.

GAS PHOTOTUBES

The high-vacuum phototube's chief advantage was demonstrated by linear characteristics. The principal disadvantages are its high plate resistance and low sensitivity. The addition of a small amount of inert gas into the tube envelope serves to increase current capacity of the tube for a given amount of lumen excitation. It also improves the tube sensitivity. Figure 7·8 illustrates the output characteristics for a 930 phototube. When the tube is operated at plate potentials below 20 volts its operation is identical to the high-vacuum phototube. Compare point A, which represents a 0.1-lumen, $e_b = 20$ volts point, with a high-vacuum phototube (929) whose excitation is 0.1 lumen at a plate voltage of 20 volts. Both plate currents are about 3 μa. When the gas phototube is operated at plate voltages above 20 volts, the electrons attracted to the plate reach sufficient velocities to ionize the gas and bring the tube into its normal glow region. The resulting plate characteristics to the right $e_b = 20$ volts indicate a greater change in plate current for a given change in ℱ. The symbol for the gas phototube is exactly like the high-vacuum type. The addition of a large black dot within the envelope signifies the presence of gas. Note the gas phototube V_1 of Fig. 7·9.

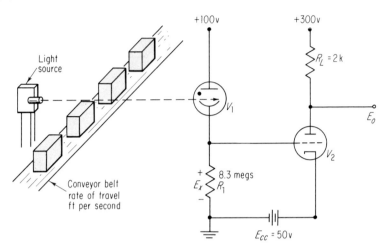

Fig. 7·9   Gas-phototube amplifier.

Gas Amplification. A ratio of the change in plate current for a given change in $\mathcal{I}$ is shown between points A and B of Fig. 7·8. This ratio is taken in the nonionized region and represents a change of 1 μa for a change of 0.06 lumen. A corresponding change in the ionized region is given between points C and D. Note that the change in plate current for the same change in light intensity is now 5 μa. The ratio of the change in the ionized region to the change in the deionized region is the *gas amplification factor* α.

$$\alpha = \frac{i_b \, (\text{ion})}{i_b \, (\text{deion})} \bigg]_{e_b = \text{constant}}$$

For the preceding case, $\alpha = 5$.

Disadvantages. The nonlinearity of a dynamic transfer characteristic for a given gas phototube prohibits its use in high-quality amplification systems. The tube is used in some low-cost sound-reproduction systems. For relay-driving circuits the tube is very desirable because of the increased sensitivity. Linearity in relay circuits is not an excessively important factor.

Because of the slower velocities of the gas ions in the gas phototube, the dynamic response of the tube is slower than that of high-vacuum types. The tubes are usable up to frequencies of about 10 kc.

Most gas phototubes cannot be operated at plate potentials above 100 volts. Analysis of the curves shows a step rise in the plate-current characteristic above 100 volts. At high plate potentials the heavy ionization would exceed the maximum-dissipation rating and result in permanent damage to the tube.

EXAMPLE TWO   Assume the circuit of Fig. 7·9 is to be used in an industrial counting system. The conveyor belt moves at 2 ft per sec and each steel cube is 27 cu in. (3 by 3 by 3 in.) positioned 1 ft apart. If V_1 is a 930 gas phototube, V_2 is a triode-connected 6L6, and the peak 𝔍 of the exciter lamp is 0.08 lumen, draw the output voltage waveshape at the plate of V_2.

SOLUTION   The 8.3-megohm load line for the 930 gas phototube is shown in Fig. 7·8. 𝔍 equals zero when the steel cube is in the path between the exciter lamp and the 930 cathode. In Fig. 7·9 the voltage across R_1 is zero (V_1 plate potential is 100 volts); hence the grid of V_2 is at the E_{cc} potential.

The load line for V_2 is plotted in Fig. 7·10. With the grid of V_2 at -50 volts, the tube is cut off and the full E_{bb} of 300 volts appears at e_o. Since the 3-in. cubes are positioned 1 ft apart and are interrupting the light source at the rate of two cubes per second, the corresponding change in output voltage is shown in Fig. 7·10. When the light source is present, V_1 conducts and a polarity E_x is developed across R_1. This voltage opposes E_{cc} and allows V_2 to conduct. The voltage at E_o drops to 150 volts. A series of counting pulses are developed at the plate of V_2. The signal can be used to drive an electromechanical counter, a relay, or the controls of the conveyor. For example, if the pulse-repetition rate at the plate of V_2 were to decrease to zero (indicating an absence of cubes on the conveyor) the circuit could drive a warning indicator or a switch.

PHOTOVOLTAIC CELLS

The photovoltaic cell converts light energy directly to a change in potential which is proportional to the frequency and intensity of the light. The potential developed by the cell is sufficient to drive a current through a load resistance. No external d-c source is required for its operation.

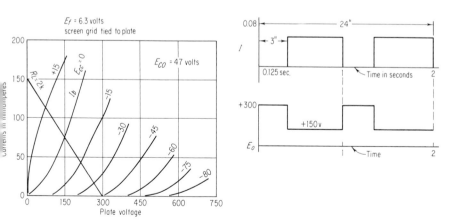

Fig. 7·10   Output characteristics of Fig. 7·9.

Figure 7·11*a* illustrates a basic photovoltaic cell. A semiconductor material such as selenium, germanium, or silicon is bonded to a metal plate. When the semiconductor material is exposed to a light source, valence electrons are liberated from the crystal structure. The liberated electrons flow out of the semiconductor and into the metal. The decreased number of electrons in the semiconductor and the increased number in the metal develop a difference in potential sufficient to cause a current flow through the load resistor. Figure 7·11*b* illustrates a set of output characteristics for a photovoltaic cell used in photographic equipment. When the cell is operating into a 500-ohm load, a change of light intensity from 50 to 150 ft-c produces a change in the load current of 200 µa. The change in load current is proportional to the changes in light intensity. Note that a change in light intensity from 50 to 100 ft-c caused a change of 100 µa. The change from 100 to 150 also caused a change of 100 µa. Increasing the value of load resistance decreases the linear characteristic of the photovoltaic cell.

Modern research has developed photovoltaic cells which incorporate silicon as the semiconductor material. These devices are also known as *solar cells* and are used to generate electric power. They may be connected in parallel to produce large currents or in series to produce large voltages.

APPLICATION OF PHOTOEMISSIVE DEVICES

A typical application of a photosensitive device can be found in the automatic brightness and contrast control of CRTs used in television receivers. The photosensitive device senses any changes in room lighting from total darkness to extreme brightness and adjusts the brightness level of the picture tube.

The theory of intensity modulation was developed in Chap. 6. That

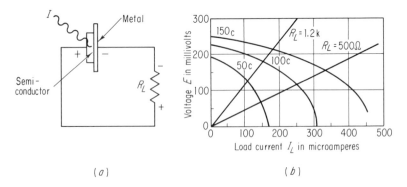

(*a*)   (*b*)

Fig. 7·11   Photovoltaic cell.

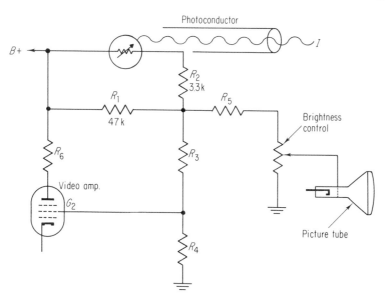

Fig. 7·12   Automatic brightener and contrast control.

is, if the control grid of the CRT is made negative with respect to its cathode the density of the electron stream leaving the gun assembly is decreased. The result is decreased light flux radiated from the screen phosphor. Figure 7·12 illustrates a typical control circuit utilizing the Sylvania 8100 photoconductor. Room light level enters the photoconductor and varies its resistance as shown in Fig. 7·12. The change in resistance of the 8100 photoconductor varies the bias voltage across R_4, thus controlling picture contrast. The current through R_5 and the brightness control are also changed, thereby controlling the brightness as well.

The photoconductor consists of a light-sensitive element of cadmium sulfide pressed to a conductor. The unit is sealed in a glass envelope.

Problems

7·1   What is the r_p of the 925 phototube at a plate potential of 50 volts and light intensity of 0.1 lumen?

7·2   What is the r_p of the 930 gas phototube at the illumination and plate voltage of Prob. 7·1?

7·3   If the 925 phototube has a load resistance of 10 megohms and plate supply of 150 volts, what is the ratio of plate-current change to light intensity if the illumination changes from 0.1 to 0.3 lumen?

7·4   Refer to Prob. 7·3. If the light intensity is held at 0.2 lumen, what is the voltage developed across the load?

7·5   If a 10-megohm load is connected to the plate of the 930 gas photodiode, what is the d-c potential at the plate if the light intensity is constant at 0.06 lumen? Assume a B supply of 90 volts.

7·6   If the load in Prob. 7·5 is decreased to 5 megohms, what is the change in the plate potential?

7·7   Refer to Fig. 7·4. If R_1 is increased to 10 megohms and E_1 is increased to 150 volts, what light intensity at V_1 will cut off V_2?

7·8   Refer to Prob. 7·7. If the value of R_1 is decreased to 500 kilohms, what light intensity at V_1 will cut off V_2?

7·9   If the 8100 photoconductor is driven with a 10 ft-c light source, what is the resistance of the unit? (Fig. 7·13.)

7·10   If the light intensity in Prob. 7·9 is increased to 50 ft-c, what increase or decrease in cell resistance will result?

7·11   In the gas-phototube amplifier of Fig. 7·9, it is necessary to redesign the circuit so that the output voltage of V_2 (8BN8) rises to 375 volts and plate current is limited to 5 ma. Find (a) new E_{bb} value required, (b) R_L, (c) output voltage during conduction of V_2.

7·12   In Fig. 7·9, what change in R_1 is necessary to produce zero volt at the grid of V_2 after the design change in Prob. 7·11 has been completed? Keep lumens at 0.08 and assume $V_1 = 930$.

7·13   What is the new I_p value for the 930 after the change in Prob. 7·12?

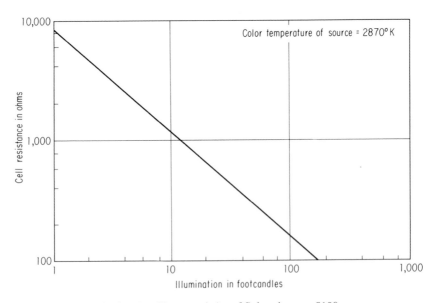

Fig. 7·13   Characteristics of Sylvania type 8100.

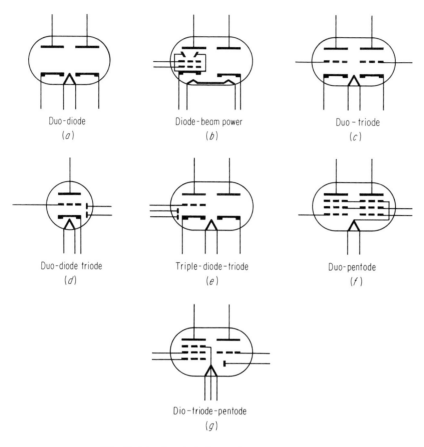

Duo-diode
(a)

Diode-beam power
(b)

Duo – triode
(c)

Duo-diode triode
(d)

Triple-diode-triode
(e)

Duo-pentode
(f)

Dio –triode-pentode
(g)

Fig. 7·14   Symbols for multipurpose tubes.

7·2 MULTIPURPOSE TUBES

A multipurpose tube is one which combines two or more tube structures within one envelope. The result is compactness, economy, and lowered power dissipation. Examples of schematic symbols are shown in Fig. 7·14. The figure illustrates a few of the more common types.

A few precautions should be observed when designing circuits with multipurpose tubes. For example, the duodiode-triode shown as D in Fig. 7·14 utilizes a common cathode for all three tubes. If cathode bias is used for the triode, the same bias will be developed for each of the diode circuits. The following numerical example serves as an illustration.

EXAMPLE THREE   Refer to Fig. 7·15. What value of positive input potential is required at e_{in} to cause the diode to be forward-biased? What polarity pulse at the output will a large positive pulse at e_{in} produce?

SOLUTION   The triode characteristics and the associated load line and bias line are shown in Fig. 7·15b. The potential across the cathode resistor is 0.75 volt. Therefore, the plate of the diode has a reverse bias of 0.75 volt (point Q). Any positive input signal greater than 0.75 volt will forward-bias the diode. The potential at the plate of the triode is approximately 20 volts. A large positive pulse

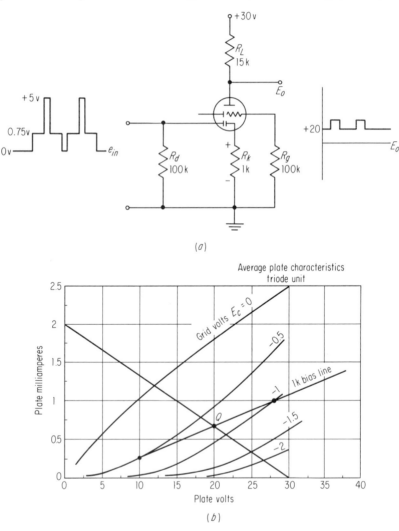

(a)

(b)

Fig. 7·15   Diode–triode circuit.

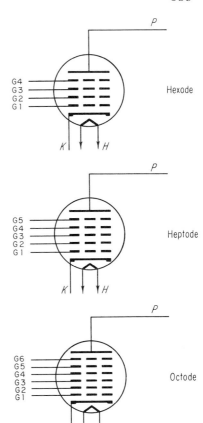

Fig. 7 · 16 Symbols for multigrid tubes.

at the input will cause the diode to conduct a cathode-to-diode plate current. The diode current will cause a greater voltage drop across R_K, thus driving the triode toward cutoff. The potential at the plate will increase, thus creating positive pulses at the output. If a complex pulse, shown in Fig. 7 · 15a, is applied to the circuit, only the upper portion will be reproduced at the output. A number of multipurpose tubes have been designed for specific circuits in radio, television, and f-m. The tube manual should always be consulted before such tubes are used in circuit design.

7·3 MULTIGRID TUBES

Multigrid tubes employ more than three grids between a common cathode and anode. The three most common types are the hexode (four grids), the heptode (five grids), and the octode (six grids). Schematic symbols are shown in Fig. 7·16. The two most common applications of multigrid tubes are (a) conversion circuits and (b) gating circuits. When the tube is used as a converter, its purpose is to mix two r-f signals.

Figure 7·17a illustrates a converter where f_1 is applied to control grid G_1. Control grid G_2 actually acts as an anode for the f_1 circuit. A portion of the space current varying at the f_1 frequency continues on toward the plate. If a second frequency f_2, different from f_1, were applied at the second control grid G_4, the space current would be further influenced. The resultant plate current would vary at the two original frequencies f_1 and f_2 and at their sum and difference frequencies $f_1 + f_2$ and $f_1 - f_2$. Grids G_3 and G_5 act as screen grids.

The converter circuit of Fig. 7·17a is used in superheterodyne receivers for changing the incoming frequency to a fixed intermediate frequency. For example, the signal at f_1 may be a radio-station frequency in the broadcast band, say 1,240 kc. A local oscillator within the receiver will generate a signal at 1,695 kc at f_2. The difference frequency

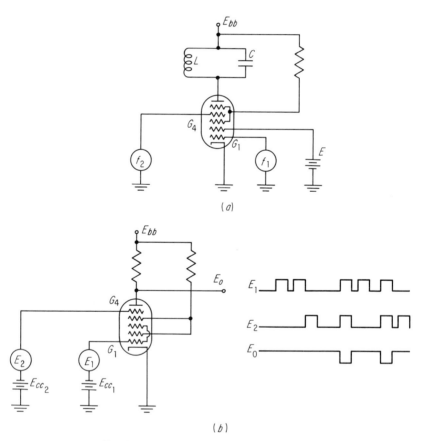

Fig. 7·17 Application of multigrid tubes.

will be 455 kc, which is the standard i-f (intermediate frequency) now used in broadcast-band receivers.

When the tube is used as a gating circuit, the two control grids G_1 and G_4 are used to control the passage of pulses to the plate circuit. For example, with no signals applied at G_1 and G_4 plate current is cut off because of the large bias potentials on the two control grids. When pulse trains are applied simultaneously to both grids, plate current will flow only when there are coincident pulses at G_1 and G_4. Such a circuit is called a *coincidence gate*.

7·4 PHOTOMULTIPLIER TUBES

Refer first to Fig. 7·11*b*. Note that a load resistance of 1.2 kilohms produces an output current of about 100 μa with a 50-candle input. Note also from the characteristics of Fig. 7·8 that point *D* represents an output of only 3 ma at 0.04 lumen. The outputs of most phototubes, gas or vacuum, at these levels of illumination are acceptable and can be fed directly to an amplifier. If, however, the light intensity is in the region of microlumens, the output current from conventional gas vacuum phototubes will be extremely low. Further, if conventional vacuum-tube or transistor amplifiers are used, their noise level may be higher than the signal level developed by these phototubes. The problem can be minimized somewhat by using a photomultiplier tube.

A functional schematic of a simple photomultiplier tube is shown in Fig. 7·18. The device consists of a photocathode which liberates electrons when light strikes its surface. These electrons are attracted to dynode 1 as a result of the 75-volt electrostatic field developed between it and the photocathode. The electrons are also focused because of the electrostatic field between a flat emitting surface and a curve dynode. The electrons bombard dynode 1 and cause secondary emission. A second electrostatic field is developed between dynode 1 and dynode 2. The dislodged electrons (a quantity greater than those initially bombarding the dynode) are attracted toward dynode 2. Again multiplication occurs as a result of secondary emission. The electrons are ultimately attracted to the anode and develop an output voltage across R_L.

The actual number of dynodes present in a practical photomultiplier varies. For example, the RCA 931-A has 9 dynodes while the 6810 has 14. Note the characteristics of the type 931-A photomultiplier shown in Fig. 7·19. Point *A* of Fig. 7·19 shows an output current of 1 ma when 50 microlumens is impinged on the photocathode when 75 volts is applied between the anode and the last dynode. The 931-A has a sensitivity of 2 amp per lumen. This, of course, does not suggest that the tube

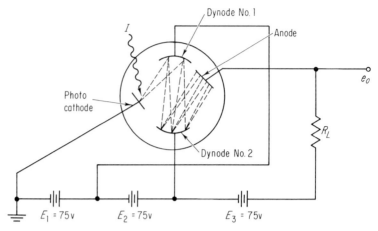

Fig. 7·18   Photomultiplier.

is capable of handling currents of that order. The tube actually works
in the area of microlumens.

EXAMPLE FOUR   If a 931-A photomultiplier is operating with 100 volts between
each dynode what light intensity will cause 2 ma of anode current?

SOLUTION   Refer to Fig. 7·19. Note that point B is on the 100-volt ordinate and
the 2-ma ordinate. Extrapolating graphically, the light flux must be 95 microlumens.

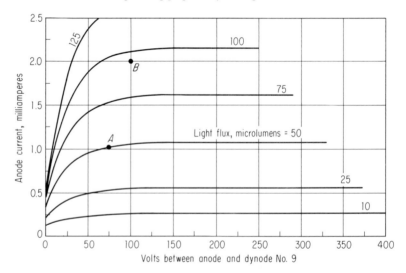

Fig. 7·19   Anode characteristics of 931-A.

Photomultiplier tubes have a practicable limit as to the gain they provide. The number of dynodes cannot be arbitrarily increased. Beyond about 14 dynodes the efficiency begins to decrease as a result of power losses, heat, and power-supply requirements. Large gains are possible. For example, a Dumont type has a sensitivity of 100 amp per lumen or a current amplification of 3,000,000. An RCA 6810 is capable of a gain of 66,000,000!

Problems

7·14   Refer to Fig. 7·15. If the load resistance R_L is increased to 25 kilohms, what positive input voltage is needed at the input to forward-bias the diode?

7·15   If the cathode resistor in Prob. 7·15 is decreased to 500 ohms, what input voltage is needed to forward-bias the diode?

7·16   Refer to the circuit of Fig. 7·17a. If $f_1 = 10$ kc and $f_2 = 800$ kc, what is the maximum frequency produced by heterodyning?

7·17   Refer to the circuit of Fig. 7·17a. If $f_1 = 500$ kc, $L = 235$ microhenry, and $C = 300$ pf, what frequency must be applied at f_2 in order to resonate the tank circuit?

7·18   Refer to Fig. 7·17b. Assume a series of pulses whose duration time is 1 msec and whose frequency is 250 pulses per sec is applied at G_1. Assume also a series of pulses whose duration time is also 1 msec but whose frequency is 200 pulses per sec is applied at G_2. What is the pulse-repetition rate at the plate? (*Hint:* Solve graphically.)

7·19   Refer to Prob. 7·18. If the pulse-repetition frequency of G_2 increases to 500 pulses per sec, what is the pulse-repetition rate at the plate?

7·20   If a photomultiplier is operating with 100 volts between each dynode, how much anode current is produced when 30 microlumens of light flux impinge on the photocathode?

Review Questions

7·1   Explain the difference in the theory of operation of the photoemissive cell compared with the photovoltaic cell.

7·2   What is the fundamental unit of light intensity?

7·3   How do changes in light intensity influence the output current of a high-vacuum phototube?

7·4   What are the advantages of the gas phototube compared with the high-vacuum type?

7·5   What are some of the disadvantages of placing more than one tube under one envelope?

7·6   What is a heptode?

7·7   Give an example of multigrid heterodyning.

7·8   What is the main function of a photomultiplier?

VIII

INTRODUCTION TO SEMICONDUCTORS

This chapter will explore the necessary fundamentals for understanding basic transistor operation. The three types of chemical bonding are discussed with an emphasis on covalent bonding. A detailed analysis of the properties, energy levels, and physical characteristics of those materials used in transistors is included. The chapter ends with a discussion of the intrinsic, N-type, and P-type materials and how these various crystals support current flow.

8·1 REVIEW OF ATOMIC THEORY

In Fig. 8·1 the atom of germanium has its electrons divided into a series of orbits. The various orbits, identified as energy levels, have specific names; however, our interest centers around the outermost shell, the *valence* shell. The first shell closest to the nucleus always contains 2 electrons. The second shell always contains 8 electrons, as shown in Fig. 8·1.

144

The third shell contains 18 electrons, and finally the outermost has 4 electrons. The valence of germanium is 4. In all atoms, regardless of size and number, the number of electrons will align themselves into orbits according to a sequence. One such sequence is 2, 8, 18, 32, 18, and 8. As an example, consider the atom of oxygen, whose atomic number is 8. Oxygen therefore has 8 protons in the nucleus and 8 electrons in orbits. Two electrons in the first orbit leave 6 electrons for the outermost orbit. The valence of oxygen, O, is not 6 but 2, since it requires 2 electrons in the outer shell in order to complete the shell. As another example, consider the atom of sodium (Na), whose atomic number is 11. Two electrons are in the first shell, 8 in the second, and 1 in the outer shell. Here the valence is 1 since it has 1 electron to give up to another atom.

Often, in metals, valence electrons are called *free electrons*. These "free" electrons are loosely bound to their parent atom. Very little change in external energy (a few degrees of room temperature change will suffice) is required to liberate these electrons from their parent atoms. When an electrical potential is placed across a piece of metal, there is a movement of free electrons. Materials such as metals which contain a large amount

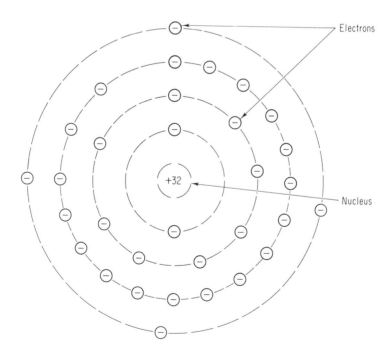

Fig. 8·1   Germanium atom.

of free electrons are identified as *conductors*. Other materials where the valence-shell electrons are tightly bound to their parent atoms will not readily support a movement of electrons. Such materials include rubber and glass and are termed *insulators*. Some materials which are normally termed insulators (or poor conductors) can be treated with impurities. Under such treatment these materials act as moderately good conductors. At room temperature a small piece of germanium will act as an insulator; however, if it is heated, it will conduct a flow of electrons when a voltage is placed across it. As another possibility a controlled amount of impurity is added when the germanium is grown, and the final product acts as a conductor at room temperature; no heating is required. Materials such as silicon and germanium are called *semiconductors*.

8·2 ELECTROSTATIC FORCES

The chief difference between the earth's solar system and that of the atom is that of forces. The electrostatic forces which prevail in the atom can

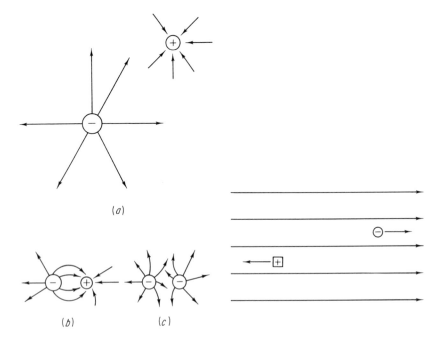

(a)

(b)   (c)

Fig. 8·2 Electrostatic fields.   Fig. 8·3 Charged particles in an electrostatic field.

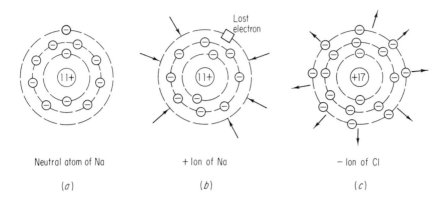

Neutral atom of Na   + Ion of Na   − Ion of Cl

(a)   (b)   (c)

Fig. 8·4   Neutral atom and ions.

be divided and redivided. We are concerned with the force which surrounds the electron particle and the proton. Figure 8·2a is an illustration of an isolated electron and an isolated proton. Note that the
direction of the field (arbitrarily assigned) about the electron extends
from its center outward. The direction of the proton field is opposite.
Figure 8·2b shows the reaction of these fields when two unlike charges
are brought in close proximity. The fields are such as to create an
attracting force upon two particles, hence the rule: *Unlike charges attract.*
Figure 8·2c shows two like particles brought in close proximity. *Like
charges repel.*

If an isolated electron is placed into an electrostatic field as shown in
Fig. 8·3, the electron will move in the direction of the field. Conversely
a positive charge will move in a direction opposite to the direction of the
electrostatic field. In each case the particle will tend to move in the
direction parallel to the lines of force.

An atom that is considered neutral is one which exhibits no external
electrostatic characteristics (or properties). Consider the atom of sodium,
which has an atomic number of 11. The number of electrons in the outer
orbits equals the number of protons in the nucleus. This causes a canceling of the electrostatic fields of each particle. The atom is said to be
electrostatically neutral. Figure 8·4a shows an example of a neutral sodium
atom. If the valence electron were attracted away from the parent atom
as shown in Fig. 8·4b, the atom would be missing one electron. The total
atom would exhibit the electrostatic properties of one proton. The field
surrounding the atom would be similar to the field surrounding an

isolated proton (Fig. 8·2a). Such an atom is called an *ion.* Figure 8·4c represents a negative ion or an atom (such as chlorine) which has acquired an extra valence electron.

8·3 CHEMICAL BONDS

The isolated atoms of the various elements interact with each other or with other atoms to form molecules. The types of bonding of these atoms are important to the study of transistors. These include *covalent* bonding, *ionic* bonding, and *metallic* bonding.

IONIC BONDING

If an atom of chlorine (atomic number 17) is analyzed, it has seven electrons in its valence shell. If an additional electron is added to the valence shell, it becomes an ion with a net electrostatic charge of one electron (Fig. 8·4). At this point it is important to consider two characteristics of atoms. The atom tends to be electrostatically neutral, a condition which places the same number of electrons in orbits as there are protons in the nucleus. The second characteristic causes the atom to complete its outer shell to a specified symmetry. If an atom has six electrons in its outer shell, it will require two more electrons in order to complete the shell. Also, if an atom has three electrons in its outer shell, it will readily give up the three electrons in favor of the next lower, yet complete, shell. This is not a hard-and-fast rule; however, we can apply it here. This second characteristic is what causes one atom to react (or combine) with other atoms.

When atoms of chlorine and sodium are chemically mixed, the sodium atom (one valence electron) will give up its electron to the chlorine (seven valence electrons) atom. Now each of the atoms has a complete shell. The atoms are now oppositely charged ions and are attracted to each other via the electrostatic forces. Such a bonding together of atoms is considered *ionic* bonding. Perhaps the best example of ionic bonding is characterized by cesium fluoride. Here the heavy cesium (atomic number 55) has a low ionization potential and hence is willing to give up its valence electron readily. The electron-grabbing properties of fluoride (atomic number 9) reacting with the cesium produce an ideal ionic bond. Again there are a number of qualifications which should be mentioned. Beryllium chloride is an example of a partial ionic bond. For a more thorough analysis it is necessary to consider the properties of covalent bonding.

COVALENT BONDING

Covalent bonding is sometimes identified as the *sharing* of valence electrons. Consider the atom of silicon as illustrated in Fig. 8·5. There are four valence electrons in the outer shell. The silicon atom would be satisfied or in a stable state if the outer shell had eight electrons in the valence shell. This stability condition occurs when one silicon atom "shares" a valence electron with four other silicon atoms. Figure 8·5*b* indicates the manner in which the atoms combine as a result of covalent forces. Note that each silicon atom is now satisfied and the net electrostatic force of the total molecule is zero.

Another element occurring in the fourth column of the periodic table (shown in Appendix A) which joins in covalent bonding is germanium. Although the possibilities of examples of covalent bonding are unlimited, we shall confine ourselves to the two types involved with the manufacture of transistors: germanium and silicon.

METALLIC BONDING

The binding force present in metals is identified as *metallic* bonding. Metallic bonding is not related to either covalent forces or ionic forces, although it is true that ions are formed. If we examine the properties of such elements as copper or silver, we find that the valence electrons of these metals are loosely bound to their parent atoms. The valence elec-

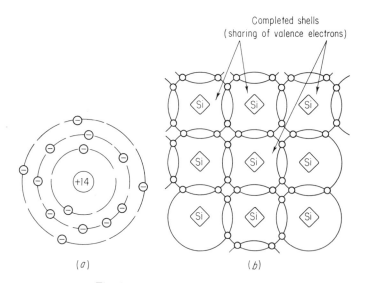

Fig. 8·5 Covalent bond of silicon.

trons are given up when energy is added to the atom. Metallic bonding then consists of positive ions moving about in a heavy cloud of liberated electrons. Ordinary room temperature is sufficient to liberate most of the valence electrons from the parent atoms. These electrons interchange from one ion to another. The bonding force therefore exists in the electrostatic field between the cloud of electrons and the positive ions. The excellent conductive properties of metals stems from the fact that none of the electrons in the cloud is specifically related to any one atom. These electrons move about freely, hence the name "free" electrons.

8·4 ELECTRON-PAIR BONDS

Section 8·3 outlined the basic principles underlying covalent bonding. An extension of some of the properties of covalent bonding is required for understanding the action of transistors. When atoms of silicon or germanium join in a covalent bond, the valence electrons align themselves in *pairs*. One electron from each atom joins in such a manner to produce a force between the electrons. A number of factors, many of which are beyond the scope of this book, contribute to the electron-pair bonds. The two most important, however, are the spins of the electrons and the orbit probability. Figure 8·6a shows the structure, in schematic form, of germanium with the indicated electron pairs.

Each of the electrons in the electron-pair bond is associated with a parent atom. If a source of energy such as heat or light is applied to the structure, one of the electrons may break the pair bond and move about freely in much the same way the free electrons move about in

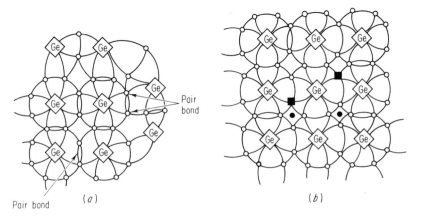

Fig. 8·6   Electron-pair bonds.

metallic bonding. Two distinct levels of free-electron movement actually exist. In one case the electron which broke away from the electron-pair bond moves about between the atoms. In the other case the vacancy left behind in the pair bond may cause electrons from other pair bonds to move from their pair bond and fill the vacancy. If additional energy is added to the structure, other pair bonds will break and more electrons will move into the free-electron category. There is then electron movement on two levels, free electrons moving about through the structure and pair-bond electrons moving between atoms. Figure 8 · 6b illustrates a molecule of germanium which has free electrons and broken electron-pair bonds. Note the broken pair bonds are shown as a square, and the liberated electrons moving freely about in the crystal structure are shown as dark dots.

8·5 CRYSTAL STRUCTURES

The illustration of Fig. 8 · 6 is a schematic representation of the structure of germanium in a two-dimensional plane. The physical characteristics of germanium, and all matter, are three-dimensional. The atoms of germanium align themselves in a definite and orderly manner to form a crystal. All inorganic material in the solid state can be reduced to some orderly processes of crystal structure. The process of identifying the crystal structure is through X rays. When the X rays are passed through a given material, they are diffracted by the particles which make up the crystal. These diffracted rays are then recorded on a photographic plate. From the pattern received on the plate it is possible to determine the three-dimensional crystal structure of a particular substance.

The structural pattern assumed by the atoms is called a *crystal lattice*. Generally the lattice is composed of three different types of crystals: (*a*) atomic crystals, (*b*) ionic crystals, and (*c*) molecular crystals. In the atomic crystals the particles which make up the lattice are atoms. Germanium and silicon, as well as many of the metals, belong to this group. In the case of the ionic crystals, the particles which make up the lattice are generally ions. Figure 8 · 7 is an example of an ionic crystal (sodium chloride). Note that the geometric structure is a series of cubes connected to each other along their respective faces. Correctly identified, the crystal of sodium chloride is a face-centered cubic lattice.

Figure 8 · 8 illustrates the tetrahedral crystal structure of germanium and silicon. The large spheres represent the atom and all electron shells excluding the valence shell. The small spheres represent the electron-pair bonds. Note that the dark sphere has a full complement of electrons in its valence shell.

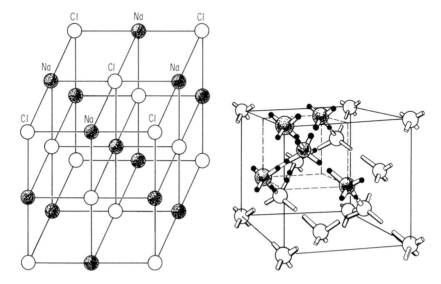

Fig. 8·7   Ionic crystal.   Fig. 8·8   Germanium crystal.

8·6 ENERGY LEVELS

When a flow of electrons is passed through a wire, heat is produced. The amount of heat produced is dependent upon the resistance of the wire. In sequence, the mechanical motion of the electron possesses energy, and the slowing down of the electron causes it to give up energy in the form of heat. *Energy is the ability to do work.*

Energy can be divided into two types, *kinetic* and *potential.* An electron in motion possesses kinetic energy in that when it is brought to rest it gives up energy and hence can do the work. For an electron to be accelerated it would be necessary for it to absorb energy. A body in motion, such as a lead ball falling through space, converts (or gives up) its energy upon impact with the earth's surface.

Potential energy is that energy defined as a result of position. The water contained in a water tower has the ability or potential to do work once it is released. The water held by a dam converts its energy to mechanical energy by driving an alternator, which in turn converts the mechanical energy into electrical energy.

Assume that a zero-velocity electron is suspended in an electrostatic field. The electron begins to move in the direction of the electrostatic field and in doing so absorbs energy from the field. The energy absorbed then becomes kinetic energy. The total energy lost or gained by a quantity charge is defined as

$$W = EQ \qquad (8·1)$$

where W is the energy, E is the voltage or potential difference, and Q is the quantity charge. From Coulomb's law,

$$Q = It \qquad (8 \cdot 2)$$

hence

$$W = EIt = Pt \qquad (8 \cdot 3)$$

where W is the energy in watts per second, or *joules*. If Ohm's law is substituted for E, the energy equation becomes

$$W = I^2Rt \qquad (8 \cdot 4)$$

Energy can be expressed in terms of calories (heat) through the equation

$$W = 4.185 \text{ joules/cal} \qquad (8 \cdot 5)$$

The joule may be expressed in terms of mechanical energy as the work done when 1 newton of force acts through a distance of 1 meter. The mechanical energy may be expressed as heat energy by multiplying by 238×10^{-6}, or

$$H = (238)(10^{-6})(i^2Rt) \qquad \text{kg-cal} \qquad (8 \cdot 6)$$

Unfortunately energy units of one scientific system are not related to another scientific system by a common nomenclature. The result is considerable confusion. As an example, energy may be expressed in ergs, in electron-volts (ev), or in terms of the weight of matter destroyed ($E = mc^2$). In transistor applications it is important to identify energy in terms of electron-volts. As a reference, we may state that 1 electron-volt is approximately equal to 1.6×10^{-19} joule.

$$1 \text{ ev} = 1.6 \times 10^{-19} \text{ joule} \qquad (8 \cdot 7)$$

By definition, the electron-volt (as a unit of energy) is that amount of energy (kinetic) which an electron acquires when accelerated through a potential difference of 1 volt.

EXAMPLE   How much energy is converted to heat when a 60-watt soldering iron is on for 2 min? Give the answer in joules and electron-volts.

SOLUTION   According to Eq. $(8 \cdot 3)$, $W = Pt$ or

$$W = (60)(120) = 7,200 \text{ joules}$$

According to Eq. $(8 \cdot 7)$, 1 joule equals 6.25×10^{18} ev; therefore

$$W = (7,200)(6.25)(10^{18})$$
$$W = 45 \times 10^{21} \text{ ev}$$

The energy represented by 1 ev is the same as the power developed for

1 sec by a 100-megohm resistor when 4 μv are applied! It is necessary now to grasp the concept of how much energy is needed to move an electron from its valence shell.

Assume that an isolated atom of silicon is suspended between the plates of a capacitor contained in a vacuum. Refer to Fig. 8·9. Assume that the voltage E is adjusted to zero volt; hence no electrostatic field exists between the plates of the capacitor. In order to liberate the electrons from the various shells energy must be added to the atom. The orbiting electrons already possess energy by their *position*. The valence-shell electrons are considered the high-energy electrons while the electrons in the first shell are considered the low-energy electrons. A simple analogy which will illustrate this case is demonstrated by two water tanks. If each of the tanks contains an equal amount of water and one of them is twice as high as the other, the water in the higher tank is capable of doing more work. The water in the higher tank has greater potential energy. The same is true of the valence electrons. By their *position* they possess a greater potential energy and hence are capable of doing more work.

If the voltage E of Fig. 8·9 is slowly increased, the energy in the electrostatic field also increases. In the case of the silicon atom, addition of 1.1 ev is sufficient to cause a valence-shell electron to break away from its parent atom. For the case illustrated in Fig. 8·9 the electron, once liberated, would be attracted to the positive plate of the capacitor.

If the crystal of silicon in Fig. 8·9 were replaced with one of carbon (in the diamond form) the energy required to liberate an electron from the valence shell would be 7 ev. Germanium requires about 0.72 ev. It should be remembered that, when sufficient energy has been added, an electron breaks loose and leaves behind a vacancy in the pair bond.

8·7 CONDUCTION BAND

ENERGY LEVELS

In the case of the silicon crystal shown in Fig. 8·9, the action was somewhat simplified for illustrative purposes. It is necessary to consider atoms

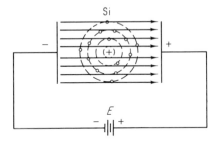

Fig. 8·9 Silicon atom in an electrostatic field.

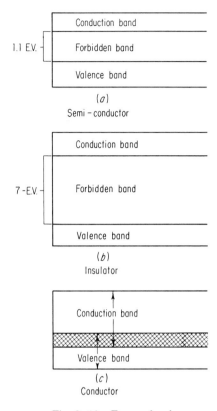

1.1 E.V.

Conduction band

Forbidden band

Valence band

(a)
Semi–conductor

7 –E.V.

Conduction band

Forbidden band

Valence band

(b)
Insulator

Conduction band

Valence band

(c)
Conductor

Fig. 8·10   Energy levels.

in close proximity as in the case of the solid crystal of silicon or germanium. Here *bands* of energy or energy levels determine the position of electrons in relation to the nucleus. In order to move an electron from the valence energy level in the electron-pair bond, it is necessary to add a specific or *discrete* amount of energy to the crystal. The electrons then break the pair bond and move to the next higher energy level. The movement is not a slow continuous transition from one band to the next; instead the action is abrupt. Energy is slowly added and when the amount added reaches a specific amount the electron will shift to the next higher energy level. Once liberated the electron is not bound to its parent atom and is capable of moving about within the crystal structure in the same way free electrons move about in metals. Figure 8·10a shows the energy levels in the crystal structure of silicon. When sufficient energy is applied, the electrons contained in the valence band move to the *conduction band,* the next higher permissible level. Once in the conduction band these electrons will support a current flow with relative ease.

Figure 8·10a is a simplified drawing of the valence band, the vacant or forbidden band, and the conduction band for the crystal of silicon. Note that 1.1 ev of energy is needed for an electron to bridge the gap from the valence to the conduction band.

Figure 8·10b compares the energy bands of the diamond form of carbon (an insulator) with that of the conductor (Fig. 8·10c) and the semiconductor. Note that in the conductor the conduction band extends into the valence-band regions.

CURRENT FLOW

The lack of free electrons in the conduction band of an insulator makes it difficult to support a current flow. If energy is added in the form of heat or an electrostatic field, the crystal will break down before any electrons are moved into the conduction band.

If a crystal of pure germanium or silicon is connected across a d-c supply in series with an ammeter, only a small current will flow. If the section of germanium is heated with a bunsen burner or a soldering iron is held near, the current increases. The heat energy added to the crystal increased the supply of free electrons in the conduction band, hence the increased current.

8·8 CURRENT CARRIERS

According to the electron theory of current flow the electrons are the current carriers. In a conductor the more abundant the supply of free or conduction-band electrons the greater the conductivity of the material. In semiconductor devices there are two basic types of current carriers, electrons and the vacancies left by electrons in the valence shell. These vacancies are also called "holes."

Figure 8·11 is a schematic illustration of a pure crystal of germanium at a temperature slightly above room temperature. Note that some of the electron-pair bonds have been broken. The vacancies in the pair bonds are shown as dark squares. In the portion of the crystal shown, there are seven such vacancies. Since this is a pure crystal, the number of free electrons moving about through the crystal is equal to the number of vacancies. These freed electrons are shown as dark dots.

If a potential were placed across the material, the electrostatic field would be in a direction as shown. The free electrons would move in the direction of the field toward the positive terminal of the battery. The vacancies or holes in the pair bonds have an electrostatic charge equal to that of the electron but opposite in character. The holes begin migrating in a direction opposite to that of the electron, toward the negative terminal.

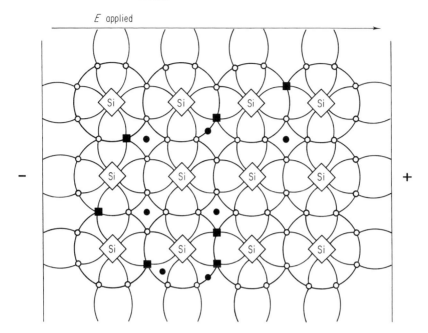

Fig. 8·11 Intrinsic crystal.

The hole therefore becomes a carrier able to support a current flow. This current flow, however, is on a valence energy level rather than on a conduction-band level. If additional heat energy were added to the crystal, more electron-pair bonds would be broken and hence more electron carriers in the conduction band would be available. In addition more hole carriers would be available on the valence energy level as well. The crystal would become increasingly conductive with increased heat. The current flow would be via *electron carriers moving from the negative to positive* and *via holes moving from positive to negative.*

8·9 IMPURITIES

The conductivity of germanium was found to increase as the crystal was heated. In the *intrinsic* or pure crystal, the number of electron carriers produced equaled the number of hole carriers. If the crystal is cooled, holes and free electrons collide (or combine) and both will cease to exist as current carriers. This process of hole-electron collision is known as *recombination*. Theoretically at absolute zero temperature the carriers of a semiconductor are totally recombined and the germanium crystal is nonconductive.

It is possible to increase the conductivity of the crystal by adding impurities to the semiconductor when it is manufactured. Two groups of impurities exhibit important characteristics when joined in the lattice structure of the semiconductor. The impurities of the first group are identified as *donors* and those of the second group as *acceptors*.

DONORS

Some of the atoms listed as donors are arsenic, phosphorus, and antimony. Examination of the periodic table shows that each of these atoms have five valence electrons in its outer shell. When atoms other than germanium combine with germanium atoms, an impure or *extrinsic crystal* is developed. The impurity atom takes the place of a germanium atom in the total crystal structure. Figure 8·12 shows how four of the five valence electrons of the impurity atom join in electron-pair bonds. The fifth electron is contained in the crystal structure but is loosely bound to its parent atom, the impurity. Only a small amount of energy is required to place the impurity electron in the conduction band. Only about 0.05 ev will release the donor atom's electron into the conduction band. This is very low when compared with 0.7 ev required by intrinsic germanium to break an electron-pair bond.

In growing the crystal a controlled amount of impurity is added so that a given ratio of impurity atoms to semiconductor atoms exists. The ratio is about 1 impurity to 10 million germanium atoms. It is important to note that an excess of electron carriers exists in the new extrinsic crystal. When energy is applied to the crystal electron-pair bonds break and additional electrons are placed in the conduction band.

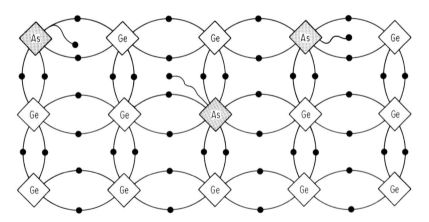

Fig. 8·12 Extrinsic crystal.

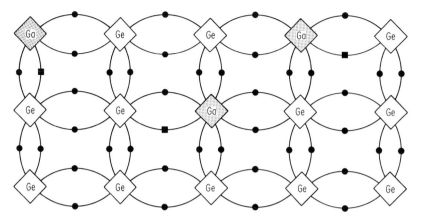

Fig. 8·13   P-type material.

The addition of energy also results in a production of hole carriers. However, as a result of the pentavalent impurity, there are many more electron carriers than hole carriers. In the intrinsic crystal an equal number of hole carriers and electron carriers were developed when energy was added. This new material, with its impurity is known as a *donor material* or an *N-type material*. Since the balance between electron and hole carriers is not the same in an N material, the electron becomes the *majority* carrier and the hole the *minority* carrier.

If a piece of N-type material were connected in series with an ammeter and a battery, current would flow in either direction since ordinary room temperature would be sufficient to provide a large number of carriers in the conduction band of the crystal.

ACCEPTORS

If, in the process of growing the crystal of germanium or silicon, an impurity such as boron, aluminum, gallium, or indium is added, an extrinsic crystal will result. Examination of the periodic table shows that acceptor impurities have three valence electrons. Under these conditions, when an acceptor atom replaces a germanium or silicon atom in the crystal structure, one electron-pair bond is unsatisfied. A hole results. Figure 8·13 is a schematic diagram of a semiconductor with a trivalent impurity added to germanium. Note that this extrinsic material has the hole as the predominant current carrier. Even if energy is added to the crystal and electron-pair bonds are broken, there will be a greater number of hole carriers on the valence level than electron carriers in the conduction-band level. The semiconductor is known as a *P material*. In much the same way that an electron in the conduction band is free to move about, the hole in P material is also free to move about through the crystal. Two things should be noted: (1) In order to move an electron from a pair bond on the valence level to the conduction band, a reasonably large amount of energy is required, between 0.7 and 1.1 ev. (2) In order to move an electron from one valence pair bond to another (should a vacancy exist there) very little energy is required, less than 0.04 ev. The electrons moving and interchanging on the valence energy level give an apparent random movement of holes.

In the P-type material, the majority carrier is the hole and the minority carrier is the electron.

The main source of conduction through extrinsic crystals such as N-type and P-type semiconductors is the result of the movement of electrons or holes. The electrons or holes originate either from an impurity atom in the semiconductor or as a result of incomplete electron-pair bonds.

8·10 SEMICONDUCTOR CHARACTERISTICS

At this point three additional characteristics of semiconductors should be considered, confirmation of the hole theory of current flow, carrier *diffusion,* and *drift.*

DIFFUSION CURRENTS

If an electrostatic field is placed across an N-type semiconductor, the carriers flow in a direction parallel to the direction of the field. However, there is an additional carrier movement within the crystal which is the result of varying carrier densities. A random motion of the carriers tends to equalize the different carrier densities. Carriers move from areas of high density to areas of low density. This action is known as *diffusion,* and the resulting currents are *diffusion currents.*

As an illustration imagine that at a given instant 50 electrons are released at one end of an N-type material. If an electrostatic field is placed across the material, the electrons will be attracted to the other end of the crystal. As a result of diffusion, all 50 electrons will not arrive at the opposite end at the same instant. The action is much like a group of cars bunched together on an expressway. At high speeds they tend to equalize the spacing between them.

DRIFT

When an electrostatic field is placed across a semiconductor crystal, the path of the carriers is not linear. The direction of the carrier is altered as a result of collisions with the crystal-lattice structure, and the result is a scattering effect. The actual path of the carrier follows a zigzag pattern. Drift, therefore, is defined as the movement of a carrier in an electrostatic field as a result of the combined effect of random motion and the electrostatic field.

CURRENT FLOW VIA HOLES

A laboratory experiment illustrated in Fig. 8·14 is generally considered adequate confirmation of the hole theory of current flow. In Fig. 8·14a, note that the piece of P-type semiconductor shows a battery E_1 connected across the crystal. The direction and pattern of the electrostatic field are from the negative terminal to the positive. The ammeter indicates that electrons are leaving the negative terminal of the battery and passing through the semiconductor. However, this is not sufficient proof that the conduction is via holes. Using rigorous laboratory methods, the transition time of the carriers through the semiconductor can be measured.

In Fig. 8·14b, one addition is made to the circuit. An electrostatic

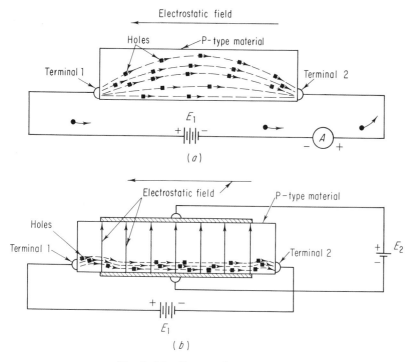

Fig. 8·14 Current flow via holes.

field is placed *across* the semiconductor. The hole carriers in Fig. 8·14*a* followed a large arc in the semiconductor but now are acted upon by the additional field. (The hole is attracted in a direction opposite to the direction of the field.) The transition time of the carrier in Fig. 8·14*b* was less than in Fig. 8·14*a*, the conclusion being that the hole carrier, in fact, does exist. For if the polarity of E_2 were reversed, the transition time is longer.

Problems

8·1   If a theoretical transistor were developed from silicon and an impurity of *gallium* were added, would the crystal be an N, P, or intrinsic material?

8·2   If the impurity of Prob. 8·1 were indium, what type of crystal would result?

8·3   Refer to Prob. 8·1. Is the majority current carrier the electron or the hole?

8·4   An energy level of 1.2 ev represents how many joules?

8·5   An energy level of 0.2×10^{-20} joule represents how many electron-volts?

8·6   If a germanium crystal has antimony added as the impurity, will the minority current carrier be the electron or the hole?

8·7   If a segment of P-type material has an electrostatic field across it, will the majority carriers flow toward the positive or the negative terminal of the battery?

8·8   What kind of energy is represented by the motion of an automobile?

8·9   What change in conductivity occurs when an intrinsic crystal of germanium is heated?

8·10   What kind of energy is represented by an apple hanging from the branch of a tree?

8·11   What three different types of crystals generally form a crystal-lattice structure?

8·12   What quantity of charge is held by a substance receiving 300 μa in 0.02 sec?

8·13   If 0.3 volt was necessary to produce the quantity of charge in Prob. 8·12, how much energy was stored?

8·14   What are the three separate bands of energy level in a crystal structure?

Review Questions

8·1   What is meant by the term valence electron? What is its energy level?

8·2   Compare the atomic structure of conductors, insulators, and semiconductors.

8·3   What electrostatic charge is represented by a "hole"?

8·4   What are the main differences between ionic bonding, covalent bonding, and metallic bonding?

8·5   Give an example of kinetic energy. Of potential energy.

8·6   List some sources of energy which can be used to move an electron from the valence band into the conduction band.

8·7 What is an intrinsic crystal?

8·8 What current carriers are associated with a "donor" material? With an acceptor material?

8·9 What is meant by diffusion current?

8·10 Define the term "drift" as it applies to semiconductors.

IX
SEMICONDUCTOR DIODES

9·1 PN JUNCTIONS

The most popular method of producing semiconductor diodes consisting of a junction of P and N material is in the process of growing the crystal. If a germanium crystal "seed" is touched to the surface of liquid germanium additional crystals will grow from the seed if it is removed at a very slow rate. Very rigid environmental conditions are also required. If the liquid germanium is doped with a trivalent or pentavalent impurity, the crystal grown will be a P- or an N-type material. A PN junction is produced by growing part of a crystal with one type of doping, then changing the doping at a given time to the other type. The resulting slug will be half P material and half N material.

DEPLETION REGION

The net electrostatic charge of a section of N material is zero. That is, every atom of the semiconductor and every atom of the impurity have an equal number of electrons and protons. There is no net electrostatic charge resulting from a loss or gain of electrons. Such is the case even though there is an abundance of electron carriers in the material. These excess electrons exist by virtue of the impurity. If some of the electrons are removed from the N material the impurity atoms as well as many of the germanium atoms will have fewer electrons in their valence shells. The N-type material will be *ionized* and exhibit the properties of a positive electrostatic charge, depending upon how many electrons were removed.

The same conditions prevail for P-type material. The P material is electrostatically neutral even though the impurity atoms have one electron missing in the pair bonds. If electrons are added to the material, filling up the holes, there will be many more electrons than protons in the nuclei of the individual atoms. The ionized P material exhibits a negative electrostatic charge.

When a PN junction is produced, electrons from the N material cross over the junction and fill the holes of the P material. This process is called *diffusion* and *recombination*. When this occurs, the electrons leave the N material, thus leaving a section of N material which is no longer electrostatically neutral. The same would be true of the P material where the electrons have filled the vacant electron-pair bonds. The result is an ionized layer on each side of the junction. The combined depth of the two ionized layers is shown in Fig. 9·1 and is known as the *depletion region*. It is so termed because the region is devoid of free electrons in the N material and of holes in the P material.

BARRIER POTENTIAL

The ionized layer in the P material has an excess of electrons in the crystal structure. The resultant electrostatic charge is negative. The opposite is the case for the N material (Fig. 9·1). This difference in the density of electrons can be represented by an electrostatic field whose

Fig. 9·1   Depletion region.

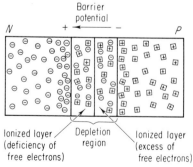

Ionized layer (deficiency of free electrons)   Depletion region   Ionized layer (excess of free electrons)

direction is from negative to positive. The case is similar to a charged capacitor where an electrostatic field exists across the dielectric.

The entire diode does not become ionized because the negative carriers in the N material and the holes of the P material are repelled by the barrier potential. The depth of the ionized layer, and hence the barrier potential, depends upon the type of semiconductor, the type of impurities, and the ratio of impurity atoms to semiconductor atoms.

9·2 FORWARD BIAS

A PN junction is forward-biased when an electrostatic field is present across the entire diode as shown in Fig. 9·2a. This is achieved by connecting the negative terminal at the voltage source to the N material and the positive to the P material. The electrostatic field E overcomes the field of the barrier potential E'. Electrons in the N material previously repelled by the barrier potential can now travel toward the junction. The same would be true of the holes in the P material. Without forward bias they are repelled from the junction as a result of the barrier potential. However, when the external bias is such as to oppose the barrier potential, holes can once again flow toward the junction. Recombination occurs, and the crystal supports a flow of electrons in the direction of E. A current flows in the external circuit as shown in Fig. 9·2a. The schematic circuit and symbol are shown in Fig. 9·2b. The series resistor R has been added to the circuit to limit the current. The resistance of the forward-biased diode is low and excessive currents would destroy the crystal structure. The actual voltage needed to overcome the barrier potential is only a few tenths of a volt.

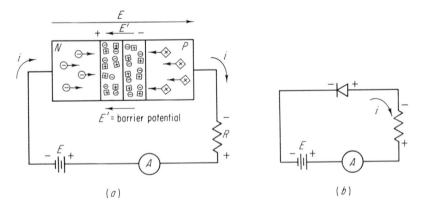

(a)

(b)

Fig. 9·2   Forward bias.

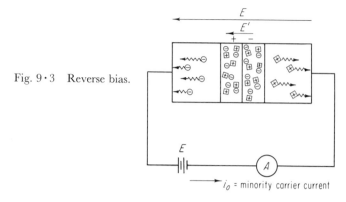

Fig. 9·3   Reverse bias.

i_0 = minority carrier current

9·3 REVERSE BIAS

Changing the polarity of the battery in Fig. 9·2a results in a reversed electrostatic field across the crystal. The reverse-bias field E (Fig. 9·3) is now in the same direction as the barrier-potential field. The carriers in the N and P materials are drawn away from the junction and recombinations are not possible. The crystal exhibits a high resistance in the reverse-biased direction. The reverse bias does not permit recombinations to occur; hence the crystal will not support a current flow.

MINORITY-CARRIER CURRENT FLOW

Section 8·7 developed the theory of minority-carrier current flow. The minority carrier in the N material is the hole. The minority carrier in the P material is the electron. Since the reverse-biased field extends from the P material to the N material, minority carriers in both materials will migrate to the junction and recombinations will occur. The resultant current in the external circuit is only a few microamperes at low reverse potentials. If the temperature of the diode is increased, more electron-pair bonds are broken and more minority carriers are available in both the materials. The result is an increased reverse-bias current i_0.

AVALANCHE BREAKDOWN

When the reverse bias across the diode is increased, the minority carriers are injected into the barrier region with increased velocity. At a given reverse-bias potential the minority carriers reach a critical velocity. The electrons bombard valence-band electrons with sufficient force to free additional electrons into the conduction band. The result is a chain-type reaction which produces an avalanche of electrons moving in the direction of the electrostatic field. A sharp rise in the reverse current results. If this reverse current is not limited, damage to the crystal will result.

The reverse potential across the diode which produces the avalanche is known as the zener potential. Many diodes are designed to operate in the zener region. Switching circuits and control circuits utilize zener diodes because of their faster switching time and their constant-voltage variable-current characteristic.

JUNCTION CAPACITY

A reverse-biased diode exhibits a capacity whose value depends upon the magnitude of the reverse bias. Capacity is defined as charge concentration on a given applied voltage ($C = Q/e$). As an example refer to Fig. 9·4a. The diode shown is unbiased. A given charge concentration exists in the N and the P material along the ionized layer of the barrier-potential region. The gap between the two concentrations can be likened to the parallel plates of a capacitor. If a reverse-bias field is applied, the charge concentration is drawn farther away from the junction (Fig. 9·4b). The effect is that of a capacitor whose plates have been moved farther apart. Hence, from the relationship $C = Q/e$ and Eq. (4·1), the junction capacity decreases as the reverse-bias potential is increased. The junction capacity is influenced by the reverse potential, the type of material used (silicon or germanium), and the amount of impurity doping. A good approximation of junction capacity is

$$C = C_o/\sqrt{E} \qquad (9·1)$$

where C_o is the zero bias junction capacity and E is the reverse bias.

EXAMPLE ONE   A sampling diode has a zero bias junction capacity of 0.8 pf. What increase or decrease in this capacity occurs when a reverse bias of 8 volts is applied?

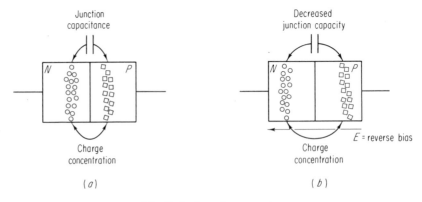

Fig. 9·4   Junction capacity.

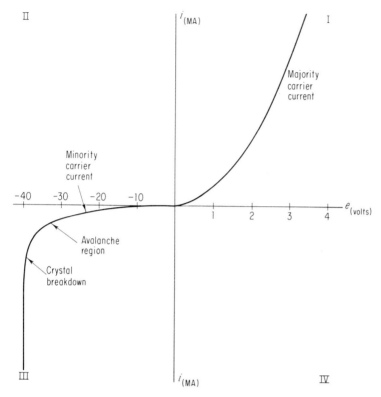

Fig. 9·5   Diode characteristics.

SOLUTION

$$C_o = 0.8 \text{ pf}$$
$$C = C_o/\sqrt{E} = (0.8)(10^{-12})/\sqrt{8} = (0.8)(10^{-12})/2.83 = 0.283 \text{ pf}$$

The capacity *decreased* 0.517 pf.

9·4 CHARACTERISTIC CURVE

The forward-biased characteristics of the diode are similar to the forward-biased vacuum-diode characteristic. A typical characteristic is illustrated in Fig. 9·5. The response curve shown in the first quadrant represents forward-bias characteristics and the curve in the third quadrant represents reverse-bias characteristics. Note that the increments of current for forward bias are in milliamperes while the increments of current for reverse bias are in microamperes. The gradual rise in reverse current is the result of minority carriers. The current change between

−20 and −40 volts represents the avalanche region. The zener potential for the diode illustrated is −40 volts.

The semiconductor diode, like the vacuum diode, has both a d-c and an a-c resistance. In addition, however, the semiconductor diode has a reverse resistance. (In the vacuum tube this reverse resistance was infinitely large or ideal.) These resistances can be determined graphically.

Refer to Fig. 9·6a. The characteristic curve is for a 1N63 diode. Notice that a forward-bias voltage of 0.2 volt does not produce any forward current. The 0.2 volt has not overcome the barrier potential. The characteristic curves show that about 0.4 volt is required to overcome the barrier potential.

FORWARD RESISTANCE

Refer to point A of Fig. 9·6a. A voltage of 2 volts across the diode will produce a forward current of 23.5 ma. According to Ohm's law the forward or ON resistance of the diode is R_s.

$$R_s = E_f/I_f$$
$$R_s = 2/(23.5)(10^{-3}) = 85 \text{ ohms} \tag{9·2}$$

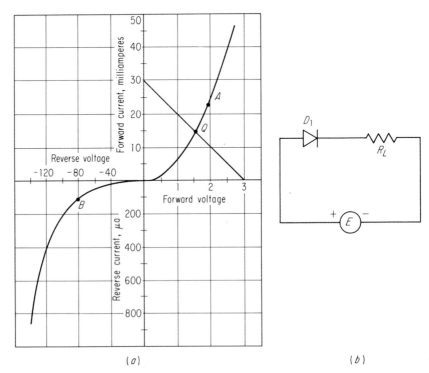

(a)   (b)

Fig. 9·6   (a) 1N63 diode characteristics. (b) Diode circuit.

As the forward voltage across the diode is increased, the on resistance decreases. For example, when the forward voltage across the diode is 2.5 volts, the current is 37.5 ma. The resultant on resistance $R_s = 66.5$ ohms.

REVERSE RESISTANCE

The reverse resistance is a finite value and is identified as R_o. It is sometimes called the OFF resistance.

$$R_o = E_r/I_r \qquad (9 \cdot 3)$$

Refer to point B of Fig. $9 \cdot 6a$. Note that a reverse voltage of 80 volts produces a minority-carrier current of 120 μa. According to Eq. $(9 \cdot 3)$ the off resistance $R_o = 80/(125)(10^{-6}) = 640$ kilohms.

EXAMPLE TWO   If the R_L of Fig. $9 \cdot 6b$ is 100 ohms, $E = 3$ volts and D1 is a 1N63, what is (a) the voltage across D1; (b) the current in the circuit; (c) the voltage across the load R_L? (d) What is the on resistance?

SOLUTION   A load line must extend from $E = 3$ volts to $E/R_L = 30$ ma. The voltage at point Q is 1.55 volts; hence the voltage across the diode is 1.55 volts. The current corresponding to point Q is 14 ma. The voltage across R_L is 1.45 volts $(E_{R_L} = E - E_{D_1})$. According to Eq. $(9 \cdot 2)$ the on resistance is 111 ohms.

$9 \cdot 5$ POINT-CONTACT DIODE

The PN junction diode is by far the most popularly used type of diode. It suffers, however, from relatively high junction capacitances and thus is impractical for high-frequency a-c operation. The large capacitance provides a low-impedance path and r-f currents are attenuated. Point-contact diodes are generally used in communication and high-frequency rectifying circuits.

A point-contact diode consists of a stiff metal (generally phosphor bronze) whose point is pressed against a piece of N material (Fig. $9 \cdot 7$). The junction is created by passing a large current pulse through the metal "catwhisker" and the N material. Atoms from the tip of the wire diffuse into the N material to produce a P region. The depletion region resulting from this process is quite small; thus there is a small junction capacitance. A typical value of junction capacitance for the point-contact diode is about 1 pf.

Though the point-contact diode operates well at high frequencies there are a number of limitations. Because of the small junction area the diode is limited to very small forward-bias currents. In addition the reverse current characteristics increase rapidly at relatively low reverse potentials.

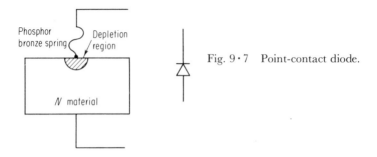

Fig. 9·7   Point-contact diode.

Because of the poor reverse-bias response characteristic, the point-contact diode is limited in its application to small-signal rectification. The following numerical example illustrates how the choice of load influences the response of the rectified output.

EXAMPLE THREE   Assume a 1N58A is to be used as a detector. What is the rectified output waveshape if the load connected to the circuit of Fig. 9·8 is 200 ohms? The peak-to-peak input signal is 24 volts.

A 200-ohm load line is constructed on the 1N58A characteristic in Fig. 9·9. Note that the load line is plotted on the reverse and the forward characteristic. During the positive half of the input signal the diode is forward-biased and the voltage across the load reaches a maximum of 9 volts at the output (Fig. 9·9,

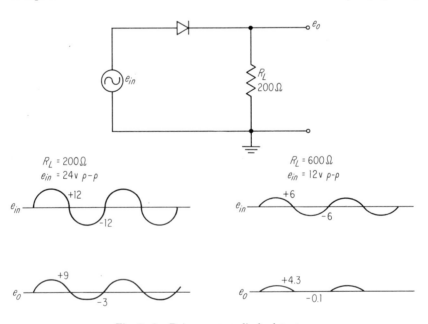

Fig. 9·8   Point-contact diode detector.

point A). During the negative half of the input signal the voltage across the load resistor reaches a peak of about 3 volts. (The slope method of plotting the load line is necessary.) At a large input signal of 24 volts peak-to-peak the rectification is unusable. Note in Fig. 9·8 that the resultant is not a rectified output but another sine wave with the negative halves distorted.

If the load resistance is increased and the amplitude of the input sine wave is decreased, the rectification characteristic improves. A 600-ohm load line and a peak input potential are plotted in Fig. 9·9. Note that the positive output response is now 4.3 volts and the negative 0.1 volt.

In actual circuits the input peak potential is held to maximum values of about 1 volt and the load resistances are maintained above 5,000 ohms. Under these conditions the circuit is almost an ideal switch. The student should prove this to himself by plotting a 5,000-ohm load line when the maximum applied voltage is 6 volts.

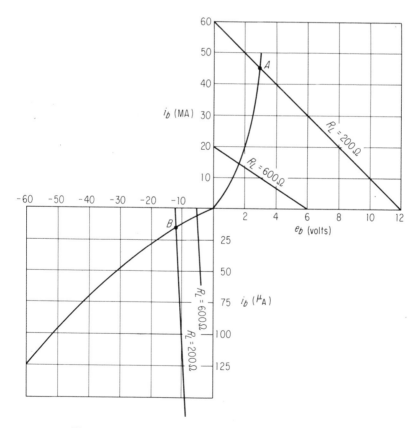

Fig. 9·9   Current-voltage characteristic for a IN58A.

9·6 TUNNEL DIODE

The tunnel diode is a device which exhibits a negative resistance characteristic in the forward-bias region. As a result the diode can be used as an amplifier, as an oscillator, and as a switching element in computer circuits. The current-voltage characteristics of the device are shown in Fig. 9·10.

A qualitative analysis can be developed by first considering a conventional PN junction diode. If in the growing of a PN junction a high ratio of impurity to semiconductor material is maintained, the result will be a heavily doped crystal. As a consequence, the barrier potential will be higher than with conventional diodes. In addition the depletion region will be extremely narrow (about 10^{-6} in.). The reverse breakdown potential will be decreased to a value very near zero. Hence large currents flow when a tunnel diode is reversed-biased (Fig. 9·10, third quadrant).

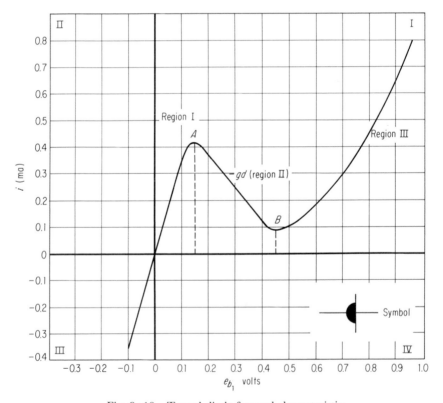

Fig. 9·10   Tunnel-diode forward characteristic.

When the tunnel diode is forward-biased, it would be assumed that large forward potentials would be required to overcome the high barrier potential. However, at very low forward-bias potentials the electron carriers react in a manner explained by quantum mechanics. Even though the electron has not received enough energy to overcome the barrier potential it is injected through the narrow depletion region at a very high velocity. The force which causes the electrons to "tunnel" through the barrier is the result of two different charge concentrations and energy levels present in the P and the N material when a small forward bias is applied. When the bias is increased, the tunneling current decreases and circuit current returns to a low value. With further increases of forward bias the tunnel diode reacts like a conventional diode.

NOMENCLATURE

The current and voltage at point A are called the peak current I_p and the peak voltage V_p, respectively. For the diode of Fig. 9·10, $I_p = 0.42$ ma and $V_p = 0.16$ volt. The current and voltage at point B are called the valley current I_v and valley voltage V_v. $I_v = 0.08$ ma and $V_v = 0.43$ volts. The portion of curve between points A and B is called the negative-resistance region and is defined as a conductance

$$-g_d = 2(I_p - I_v)/(E_v - E_p) \qquad (9·4)$$

where g_d is the negative conductance. The g_d for the diode illustrated is $-2,330$ μmho. The schematic symbol used to illustrate the tunnel diode is shown in Fig. 9·10.

AMPLIFICATION

Amplification of low-frequency signals using a tunnel diode is difficult. The construction of the circuit is generally such that large circuit components give rise to distributed capacitances which cause the circuit to oscillate at high frequencies. Because of these limitations the diode is generally used at uhf and vhf frequencies.

The equivalent circuit for a 1N2939 tunnel diode is shown in Fig. 9·11a. The circuit is typical of most tunnel diodes. L_s represents lead inductance, R_s the resistance of the device, and C the input capacitance.

Figure 9·11b illustrates a low-frequency circuit which will produce an approximate small-signal power gain $A_p = p_o/p_{in} = 1,000$. The amplifier equivalent circuit is shown in Fig. 9·11c. It must be first assumed that a positive conductance which represents a positive resistance dissipates energy while a negative conductance generates energy. Consider the functional schematic of Fig. 9·12a. The circuit illustrates, anecdot-

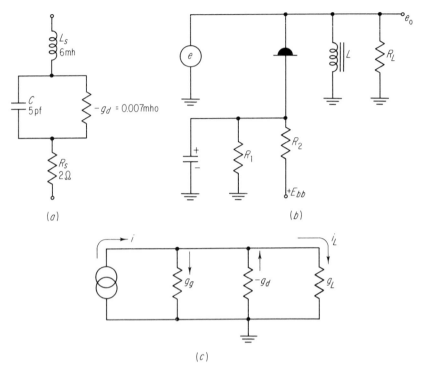

Fig. 9·11   Tunnel-diode amplifier.

ally, how a negative-resistance branch of a parallel circuit increases the current in a given load. The current flowing into the two parallel resistors R_1 and R_2 is 1 amp since the parallel combination is 12 ohms. The current flowing into the 6-ohm resistor is 2 amp; hence the power developed at R_L is 24 watts. If the 20-ohm resistor is replaced with a negative resistance of 20 ohms, the absolute value of the parallel equiva-

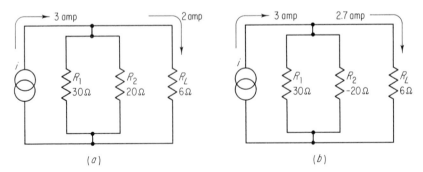

Fig. 9·12   Functional schematic showing negative resistance.

lent resistance is now 60 ohms and the current to the load has increased to 2.7 amp. The following example illustrates the parallel equivalent resistance of 60 ohms, and therefore increased load current:

$$(30)(-20)/[30 + (-20)] = -600/10 = -60 = |-60| = 60 \text{ ohms}$$

The power output at R_L is also increased. The power delivered to the load is very near the power delivered to the circuit. For the equivalent circuit of Fig. 9·11c assume that the power at the load is

$$P_L = i_L^2/g_L \qquad (9\cdot5)$$

and the ratio current into the load is

$$i_L = g_L i/(g_g + g_L - g_d) \qquad (9\cdot6)$$

The average power available from the generator is given as

$$p_g = i^2/4g_g \qquad (9\cdot7)$$

The available power gain for the stage is given as

$$A_p = P_L/P_g \qquad (9\cdot8)$$

Substituting Eq. (9·6) into Eq. (9·5) and then Eq. (9·7) and Eq. (9·5) into Eq. (9·8) yields the available power gain for a stage of tunnel-diode amplification.

$$A_p = 4g_g g_L/(g_g + g_L - g_d)^2 \qquad (9\cdot9)$$

As the combined values of $g_g + g_L$ approach the value of g_d the denominator approaches zero, thus producing a power gain. The range of values of g_g and g_L, where a power gain greater than 1 would result, is limited for a given tunnel diode. However, the power-gain equation (9·9) illustrates that tunnel diodes are feasible devices for oscillators.

SWITCHING CHARACTERISTICS

The tunnel-diode characteristic can be divided into three regions. Refer to Fig. 9·10. Regions I and III are stable regions and II is considered unstable. Assume the voltage across the diode is 0.1 volt. The resultant current is 0.33 ma. If the voltage remains constant, the current will remain at that level. However, when the voltage across the diode is moved into the unstable region, say 0.3 volt, the voltage across the device will drift toward either region I or region III. This condition can be seen more clearly when a load line is plotted on the tunnel-diode characteristic.

Refer to Fig. 9·13. Assume that a 5-kilohm load resistor is connected to the device. If the d-c supply voltage is 4 volts, a load line may be plotted. The point along the current ordinate is $E/R_L = 4/(5)(10^3) = 0.8$ ma (shown as point x in Fig. 9·13). The 4-volt point along the ordinate is off the graph; hence the slope technique of load-line plotting is necessary.

$$\text{Slope} = -\frac{1}{R_L} = -\frac{1}{\Delta E/\Delta i}$$

$$R_L = -\frac{\Delta E}{\Delta i}$$

$$-\Delta i = \frac{\Delta E}{R_L}$$

Assume a 0.4-volt (from 0 to 0.4 volt) increment is chosen.

$$\Delta i = 0.4/(5)(10^3) = 0.08 \text{ ma}$$

The current decreases to 0.72 ma when the voltage is 0.4 volt. This is point y in Fig. 9·13.

Points A and B represent the switch points. In stable region I the current through the device is about 0.8 ma with 0.2 volt across the diode. If the voltage across the diode is increased momentarily, say with a pulse, the device switches and stabilizes in region III. This point is represented at B and is $E = 0.38$ volt at 0.72 ma. If the voltage across the device is decreased (it must be decreased into the unstable region) the voltage switches to point A.

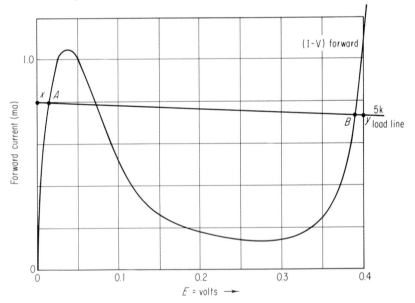

Fig. 9·13   Current-voltage characteristic of a tunnel diode.

Problems

9·1 Assume the 1N63 diode (Fig. 9·6a) is operated with 1 volt across it, what is the forward resistance of the device?

9·2 Refer to Prob. 9·1. If the voltage is increased to 2.5, what is the new forward resistance R_s?

9·3 What is the value of the reverse (or off) resistance of the 1N63 at 60 volts? What is it at 100 volts?

9·4 At what reverse current is R_o equal to the ON resistance of Prob. 9·1?

9·5 Assume a 1N63 is connected in series with a load resistance and a forward-bias d-c voltage. If the current through the diode is 20 ma when the voltage across the diode is 1.75 volts and the forward bias is 5 volts, (a) What is the value of load resistance? (b) Does the power developed across the diode exceed the maximum rating of 150 mw?

9·6 If the load resistance of Prob. 9·5 is decreased in half, (a) Will the voltage across the load increase or decrease? (b) Will power developed across the diode increase or decrease?

9·7 What is the on resistance of a 1N58A (Fig. 9·9) at (a) a bias of 2 volts; (b) a bias of 3 volts?

9·8 What is the a-c resistance of the 1N58A at (a) a forward bias of 2 volts; (b) a reverse bias of 30 volts?

9·9 Assume a 1N58A is to be used where the load resistance is 300 ohms and the applied voltage is 8 volts rms. (a) What is the peak amplitude of the positive output wave? (b) What is the peak amplitude of the negative output?

9·10 Refer to Prob. 9·9. If the load is doubled, will the peak-to-peak amplitude of the output increase, decrease, or remain unchanged?

9·11 Refer to the tunnel diode of Fig. 9·13. What is the negative conductance $-g_d$ of the device?

9·12 If the tunnel diode of Fig. 9·13 has a load of 2.5 kilohms and a forward bias of 1 volt d-c, (a) what are the two stable voltage points? (b) What are the ON current and the OFF current?

9·13 Assume the tunnel diode of Fig. 9·13 is to operate as an amplifier. If the applied forward bias E is 0.125 volt and the load is 75 ohms, (a) plot a load line (use the slope method). (b) At what current point does the load line pass through region II?

9·14 Draw the schematic symbol for (a) a semiconductor diode, (b) a tunnel diode.

9·15 Draw the schematic of a semiconductor diode in a series circuit including a load and a bias supply. Indicate the polarities for forward bias.

Review Questions

9·1 How does increasing the number of impurities influence the width of the depletion region?

9·2 Explain the effect of reverse bias on the depletion region and barrier potential.

9·3   Give an example of minority-carrier current flow. What factors would tend to increase it?

9·4   What is the relation of zener potential to avalanche breakdown? What remains constant at the point of avalanche breakdown?

9·5   How does junction capacity vary with the width of the depletion region? What type of bias would decrease junction capacity?

9·6   Draw the circuit necessary to bias the diode in Fig. 9·5 at the 30-volt avalanche point.

9·7   How does the doping of a tunnel diode differ from that for an ordinary PN junction diode?

9·8   Explain why the forward characteristic in a tunnel diode contains a negative resistance.

9·9   Identify the tunnel-diode forward characteristic of peak current and valley current.

9·10   Explain how a tunnel diode can produce a power gain. Use a circuit example.

X

TRANSISTORS

10·1 INTRODUCTION

The transistor is a three-element device which exhibits many of the amplifying characteristics common to vacuum tubes. In Chap. 2 the vacuum tube was shown to be a triode capable of amplifying changes in voltage. A change in the grid-bias potential caused a change in the plate potential. The transistor is a triode capable of amplifying a change in current. A changing current at the input produces a changing current at the output which results in a signal power gain.

The transistor amplifier provides a number of advantages, among which are lower cost and in some cases improved efficiency. It should not be assumed, however, that transistors will replace vacuum tubes. In many applications they cannot be used because of their inherent disadvantages. Among these are unreliability over a wide temperature range, high noise factor, lack of performance reliability (except in expensive types), and their sensitivity to nuclear radiation (thus limiting their application in space and missile circuits).

This chapter develops the parameters required for applying the triode transistor as a circuit element. No attempt is made to explore manufacturing techniques. Chapter 11 develops *circuit* parameters.

10·2 PHYSICAL AND SCHEMATIC REPRESENTATION

The junction transistor can be viewed as two junction diodes placed back to back and sharing a common impurity material. Figure 10·1a illustrates the physical construction of a PNP junction transistor. The three elements of the transistor are labeled *emitter, base,* and *collector.* The schematic symbol for the PNP transistor is shown in Fig. 10·1b. The schematic symbol for the triode vacuum tube is shown in Fig. 10·1c. The emitter can be compared with the cathode since it is the source of carriers. The base performs a function in the transistor similar to that of the grid in a vacuum tube. The grid controls space current while the base controls the flow of carriers. The plate of a vacuum tube can be thought of as "collecting" electrons. Figure 10·1d illustrates the NPN transistor as a physical device. The schematic symbol is shown in Fig. 10·1c. The operation of both types of transistors, NPN or PNP, is the same. Different schematic symbols are necessary since methods of circuit biasing differ for the two types.

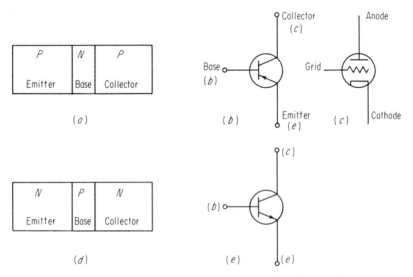

Fig. 10·1   Physical and schematic representations of a transistor.

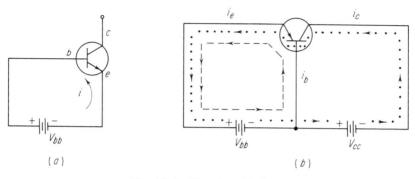

Fig. 10·2 Transistor biasing.

10·3 TRANSISTOR BIASING

One of the most important factors in understanding the operation of a transistor is an understanding of proper biasing and current flow. Four basic guideposts, which apply to all transistor circuits regardless of their connection in the circuits, should be committed to memory.

ELECTRONS ALWAYS FLOW AGAINST THE ARROW

This point is the same as in the rule for semiconductor diodes. In the diode, the *electron flow* was in a direction against the arrow. It applies to transistors as well.

BASE-EMITTER JUNCTION MUST ALWAYS BE FORWARD-BIASED

In order to obtain transistor action, and hence amplification, the base-emitter junction must be forward-biased. Figure 10·2a is an example of the bias for an NPN transistor. Note that the battery connected into the circuit has its negative terminal connected to the emitter. Electrons will leave the negative terminal of the battery and flow *against the arrow* through the transistor base-emitter junction to the positive terminal of the battery V_{bb}.

BASE-COLLECTOR JUNCTION MUST BE REVERSE-BIASED

If the transistor is to operate as an amplifier, reverse bias of the base-collector junction is necessary. There are some exceptions such as switching circuits where the bias requirements can be varied, depending upon the circuit. Note in Fig. 10·2b that the negative terminal of V_{cc} is connected to the P-type material of the collector (a PNP type transistor) and the positive terminal of V_{cc} is connected to the N-type material of the base. This is reverse bias.

BASE AND COLLECTOR CURRENT ALWAYS EQUAL THE
EMITTER CURRENT

Stated as an equation,

$$i_e = i_c + i_b \qquad (10 \cdot 1)$$

Figure $10 \cdot 2b$ is an example of the application of all four of the basic guideposts for remembering transistor circuit operation. The input loop, shown as the base-emitter circuit, shows the current as a dashed line. The output loop, the emitter collector circuit, shows the path of current as a dotted line. Both the currents flow through the emitter terminal. Electrons are flowing against the arrow and the base-emitter junction is forward-biased.

$10 \cdot 4$ PHYSICAL CIRCUIT OPERATION (NPN)

TRANSISTOR ACTION

Analysis of the transistor operation is performed using electrostatic lines of force. As has already been shown, electrons, when subjected to the force of an electrostatic field, are impelled *in the direction of the electrostatic field.* Refer to Fig. $10 \cdot 3$. Battery V_{bb} acts as the forward bias in the base-emitter circuit. The circuit conducts since the electrons of the N material are impelled toward the junction. The majority carriers of the base material (holes) are also impelled toward the junction, and recombina-

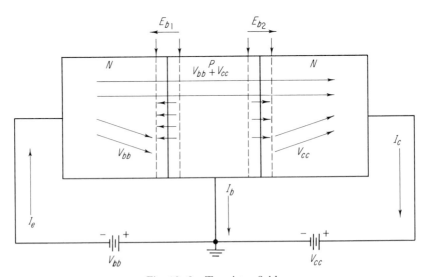

Fig. $10 \cdot 3$ Transistor fields.

tions occur. The result is a current flow across the junction. Electrons *leaving* the base material generate holes and these holes in turn migrate to the junction for recombination with electrons. An electron source is available to the emitter from the negative terminal of the battery. The current i_e flows in the external circuit.

When battery V_{cc} is inserted as reverse bias between the base and collector, an electrostatic field is developed in the direction shown in the figure. Here the majority carriers of the N material in the collector are electrons, and they are impelled away from the base-collector junction. The majority carriers of the base, holes, are also impelled away from the junction and hence no recombinations occur. A third field $V_{bb} + V_{cc}$ exists across the entire structure.

The barrier potentials between the junctions are shown as E_{b1} and E_{b2}. The two fields V_{bb} and $V_{bb} + V_{cc}$ oppose the barrier E_{b1}; hence negative charges are emitted into the base region. The fields V_{cc} and $V_{bb} + V_{cc}$ are in the same direction as E_{b2} and hence any holes in the base are repelled away from the barrier E_{b2}.

If we reexamine the forward-biased emitter-base junction, electrons are migrating from the emitter into the base region where recombinations occur (an electron combining with a hole thus eliminating both carriers). However, the number of holes available in the base region is fewer than the number of electrons migrating through the junction. This condition is achieved by either making the base physically smaller or by controlling the number of impurity atoms in the crystal at the time of manufacture. The result then is a large number of electrons in the base which cannot recombine with holes. It should also be remembered that electrons in a P material are the minority carrier. Minority carriers migrate toward the junction under reverse-bias conditions. These electrons are therefore impelled by the fields of V_{cc} and ($V_{bb} + V_{cc}$) through the collector and into the associated circuitry.

The ratio of the number of electrons which are recombined and flow in the base circuit to the electrons which are not recombined and flow in the collector circuit is predetermined in the manufacture of the transistor (i.e., the width of the base region). It is this ratio which determines the transistor's ability to amplify.

CURRENT GAIN

If the value of V_{bb} in Fig. 10·3 is varied the result is a changing current in the emitter circuit. Assume this change is identified as Δi_e. Since varying values of V_{bb} causes varying amounts of carriers to be dumped into the base region, it follows that the collector current will vary as well. Assume this change to be identified as Δi_c.

The ratio of the change in i_c to the change in i_e is termed the alpha (α), or current-gain parameter to the transistor.

$$\alpha = \left. \frac{\Delta i_c}{\Delta i_e} \right]_{V_c = k} \tag{10 \cdot 2}$$

where Δi_c = change in collector current
Δi_e = change in emitter current
V_c = collector voltage held constant

Since one of the basic premises of transistor operation states that the emitter current is always equal to the sum of the base current and the collector current the denominator of Eq. (10·2) will always be larger than the numerator and hence alpha can never be greater than 1.

POWER GAIN

It would appear that a transistor with a gain of less than 1 is not actually an amplifying device. Though an actual current gain is not produced by this circuit configuration of the transistor, it is considered an amplifier because a power gain is realized. The current flowing in the collector flows through a higher impedance than does the current at the emitter. This relationship is best illustrated with a numerical example.

EXAMPLE ONE   Assume the transistor of Fig. 10·3 has an alpha (α) equal to 0.9. Since the base-emitter junction is forward-biased, the resistance at the input is low. Assume this resistance to be 1 kilohm. The base-collector junction is reverse-biased; hence it represents a high resistance; assume it to be 10 kilohm.

If a change of 2 ma flows in the emitter circuit, the power developed at the input (base to emitter) is

$$P_i = i^2 R$$
$$P_i = [(2)(10^{-3})]^2(10^3)$$
$$P_i = 4 \times 10^{-3} = 4 \text{ mw}$$

Since the alpha is 0.9, the current through the collector is

$$i_c = (\alpha)i_e = (0.9)(2)(10^{-3}) = 1.8 \text{ ma}$$
$$P_o = i^2 R$$
$$P_o = [(1.8)(10^{-3})]^2(10^4)$$
$$P_o = 2.24 \times 10^{-2} \text{ or } 22.4 \text{ mw}$$

The power gain is therefore

$$A_p = P_o/P_i = 22.4/4 = 5.6 \tag{10 \cdot 3}$$

where A_p is the power gain.

h PARAMETER

In the vacuum tube the characteristics of the *device* were given as μ, r_p, and g_m. These identifications are standard throughout the field. This degree of uniformity does not yet exist with transistors. Manufacturers differ as to the identification of the *device* parameters. The *h parameters*, from the word hybrid, is used by most manufacturers.

The current gain of a transistor is identified as the *forward current transfer ratio* α. The circuit shown in Fig. 10·3 has the base terminal grounded. It is important to note that the forward current transfer ratio known as α applies only to circuits where the base is operated at ground potential. Alpha can be indicated as an h parameter h_{fb}, where the f stands for forward current transfer ratio. The subscript b means the circuit has the base terminal at ground. One additional symbol, h_{21}, is used to indicate current-gain grounded-base conditions. Since manufacturers do not agree as to which notation should be used in the data sheets and transistor manuals, the student should know that all three terms mean the same thing.

$$\alpha = h_{21} = h_{fb} = \text{forward current transfer ratio}$$

10·5 PHYSICAL CIRCUIT OPERATION (PNP)

The action of PNP transistors is the same as that of NPN transistors. Current directions of the external circuit are different and current carriers are holes instead of the electrons. The resultant circuit parameters are also the same. Examine the circuit of Fig. 10·4a and note that the bias across the base emitter V_{bb} is in the forward direction. V_{cc} biases the collector-base junction in the reverse direction. The combined voltages of V_{bb} and V_{cc} produce an electrostatic field across the emitter-collector terminals.

The holes in the P material of the emitter are the majority carriers. These carriers flow to the junction in a direction opposite to the direction of the electrostatic field of V_{bb}. Electrons in the base are the majority carriers and also flow to the junction in the direction of the electrostatic field. Recombination occurs and a resultant current flows in the base-emitter circuit.

The collector-base junction is reverse-biased. Large numbers of hole carriers are present in the base region since only a limited number of recombinations occur. These carriers are collected as a result of the electrostatic field produced by V_{cc} and ($V_{bb} + V_{cc}$). The result is a current flow in the external collector-emitter circuit. Figure 10·4b is the

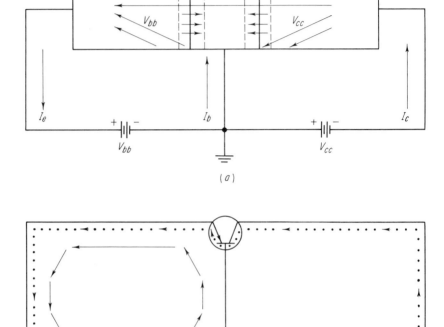

Fig. 10·4 PNP transistor.

equivalent schematic representation. The base-emitter current is shown as a dashed line and the collector-emitter current is shown as a dotted line.

The alpha for the PNP is the same ratio of currents as for the NPN.

10·6 FORWARD CURRENT TRANSFER RATIO

In the grounded-base circuit of Fig. 10·4, the current-gain parameter was identified as the ratio of the change in collector current to the change in emitter current. The base grounded was at ground potential. In the circuit of Fig. 10·5 the emitter is grounded; hence a different current-gain parameter β must be identified. The emitter-base current is shown as a dashed line and the collector-emitter current path is a dotted line. When the potential V_{bb} in Fig. 10·5 is varied, the current in the base and the collector circuits will vary. The ratio of the change in current at the collector to the change in current at the base is termed the *forward current transfer ratio*. The ratio is indicated as h_{fe} but is most frequently identified as beta (β).

$$\beta = h_{fe} = \frac{\Delta i_c}{\Delta i_b}\bigg]_{V_c = k} \qquad (10 \cdot 4)$$

If the h_{fe} parameter is compared with the h_{fb} parameter, it becomes apparent that the current gain is greater than 1 for the grounded-emitter case. This principle can best be illustrated through an example.

EXAMPLE TWO   Assume that potentials of V_{bb} and V_{cc} in Fig. 10·5 are adjusted such that when V_{bb} is varied a change in base current of 75 μa produces a change in collector current of from 15 to 21 ma. What is the forward current transfer ratio of the transistor?

$$h_{fe} = \Delta i_c / \Delta i_b$$
$$h_{fe} = (6)(10^{-3})/(75)(10^{-6}) = 80$$

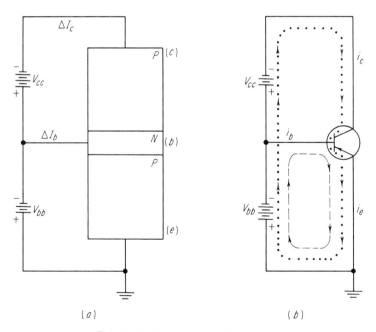

Fig. 10·5   Grounded-emitter circuit.

The static characteristics of transistors, as in the case of vacuum tubes, are used in predicting quiescent conditions in circuits as well as some operating conditions. In Fig. 10·5 if the values of V_{bb} and V_{cc} are adjusted to a fixed operating potential, a direct current will flow in the collector circuit as well as the base circuit. The ratio of the d-c collector current to the d-c base current is identified as the *d-c forward current transfer ratio*. The symbol for this d-c transfer current ratio is h_{FE}. For the d-c parameter the subscripts are capital letters.

$$h_{FE} = I_c/I_b \qquad (10·5)$$

Refer to the circuit of Fig. 10·5. Assume that 50 μa direct current flows at the base and 18 ma flows in at the collector.

$$h_{FE} = I_c/I_b = (18)(10^{-3})/(50)(10^{-6}) = 360$$

It has been shown that a transistor exhibits one of two a-c forward current transfer ratios depending upon how it is connected into the circuit. Either it is a grounded base, and hence α or h_{fb}, or it is a grounded emitter, and hence β or h_{fe}. Since it is the same transistor connected differently in a circuit, the two relationships are not completely independent of each other.

The emitter current must always be the sum of the base current and the collector current [Eq. (10·1)] regardless of how the transistor is connected into the circuit. A series of substitutions shows the relationship between h_{fe} and h_{fb}.

If Eqs. (10·4) and (10·2) are substituted into Eq. (10·1), the result is (the deltas Δ have been omitted for mathematical ease)

$$i_e = i_c/h_{fe} + (i_e)h_{fb}$$
$$i_e - (i_e h_{fb}) = i_c/h_{fe}$$
$$i_e(1 - h_{fb}) = i_e/h_{fe}$$
$$h_{fe}(1 - h_{fb}) = i_c/i_e$$

However, $i_c/i_e = h_{fb}$; therefore,

$$h_{fe}(1 - h_{fb}) = h_{fb}$$
$$h_{fe} = h_{fb}/(1 - h_{fb}) \qquad (10·6)$$
$$\beta = \alpha/(1 - \alpha) \qquad (10·6a)$$

EXAMPLE THREE   Assume that in the circuit of Fig. 10·5 the bias potential V_{bb} is varied. The resultant change in collector current is 8 ma when the base current varies from 50 to 200 μa. What is the forward current transfer ratio h_{fb} for this transistor? Before determining h_{fb} it is necessary to determine h_{fe}.

$$h_{fe} = \Delta i_c/\Delta i_b = (8)(10^{-3})/(150)(10^{-6}) = 53.3$$
$$h_{fb} = h_{fe}/(1 + h_{fe}) = 53.3/54.3 = 0.982$$

Problems

10·1   What type (NPN or PNP) of transistor is shown in Fig. 10·6? Which element is at ground potential?

10·2   In the circuit of Fig. 10·6, (*a*) What is the d-c voltage developed across R_L if I_1 is 0.01 ma and I_2 is 0.25 ma? (*b*) What is the voltage across the transistor T_1?

10·3   In Prob. 10·2 what is the d-c voltage between base and emitter if $V_{bb} = 1$ volt?

10·4   What is the direction of the electron current flow through the meter shown as I_2 in Fig. 10·6? What is the polarity across R_L?

10·5   In Fig. 10·6 is the electron current flow *into* or *away from* the base connection?

10·6   Draw the schematic of an NPN transistor in a grounded-base configuration with the two bias batteries connected for proper transistor action.

10·7   If a 2N244 transistor has a rated forward current transfer ratio α of $h_{fb} = 0.97$, (*a*) theoretically what current should flow in the collector circuit if 3 ma flows in the emitter circuit? (*b*) What is the h_{fe} of this transistor?

10·8   The d-c forward current transfer ratio h_{FE} for a 2N377 germanium NPN transistor is listed as 20. The characteristic is measured with 1 volt d-c at the collector and 30 ma flowing in the collector circuit. What current must flow at the base?

10·9   The current-gain rating for a 2N414 is listed as 60. If the circuit is connected in a grounded-base configuration, what theoretical a-c collector current will flow when a change of 2 ma flows through the emitter? (Assume the collector potential is constant.)

10·10 In Prob. 10·9 if the transistor is connected as a grounded emitter and a change of 50 μa is measured at the base, what change in collector current is observed?

10·11 A given transistor has an α of 0.97. If the device is connected with its emitter grounded, what change in collector current will flow if the change in base current is 2.8 ma?

Fig. 10·6   Circuit for Probs. 10·1 through 10·5.

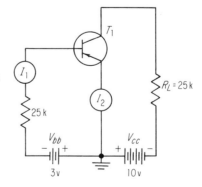

10·7 OUTPUT CHARACTERISTICS

Transistors circuits are divided into two basic groups, small-signal amplifiers and power amplifiers. Parameters such as h_{fe} and h_{fb} provide accurate transistor constants for predicting circuit operation of small-signal amplifiers. Power-amplifier circuit problems, however, must be solved using the graphical representations of the parameters. All circuits, small-signal, power-amplifier, and switching, may be analyzed using characteristic curves.

COMMON EMITTER

The grounded emitter is also identified as the common emitter. The circuit of Fig. 10·5 is a common-emitter configuration.

Assume that the potential V_{bb} is adjusted to provide a bias current of 20 μa. If the potential V_{cc} is varied from zero to 10 volts, the resultant increase in collector current is shown in Fig. 10·7. If the value of V_{bb} is increased in increments to produce 20-μa increases in bias, a family of curves representing the *output characteristics* of the transistor results. The family of curves shown in Fig. 10·7 represents the output characteristics of a 2N207. A number of additional factors are available from the collector characteristics. Note that the collector voltage V_{ce} is shown as a

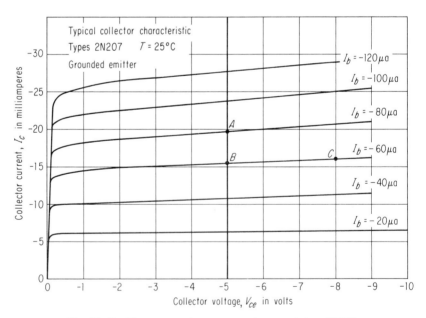

Fig. 10·7   Common-emitter output characteristics: 2N207.

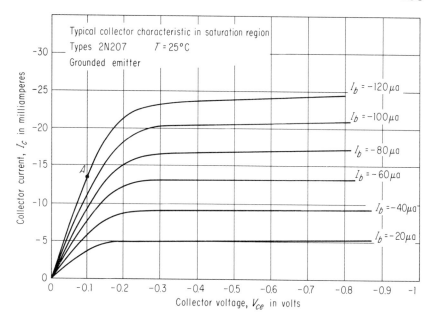

Fig. 10·8 Collector output characteristics: 2N207.

negative quantity. The collector supply V_{cc} should have its negative terminal connected to the collector. It also signifies that the device is a PNP type. Some manufacturers show this same set of characteristics upside down, signifying the PNP type. Note that the output characteristics of the 2N207 look similar to pentode characteristics. The output current rises rapidly to a "knee" and then rises gradually as the collector voltage is increased.

Often it is necessary to analyze a circuit at very low collector potentials. With the curves shown in Fig. 10·7 this becomes quite difficult. For example, if the collector voltage is −0.1 volt and the bias at the base is $I_b = -120$ μa, what is the collector current? The answer appears somewhere along the saturation curve; however, the exact answer is not available. The expanded output characteristics of 2N207 are shown in Fig. 10·8. Note that point A in the figure represents a collector voltage V_{ce} of −0.1 volt at a bias of −120 μa. The collector current is −13.2 ma.

FORWARD CURRENT TRANSFER RATIO

The forward current transfer ratio for the common emitter was given as

$$\beta = h_{fe} = \frac{\Delta i_c}{\Delta i_b}\bigg]_{V_c=k}$$

The graphical solution for this ratio is found in the output characteristics. Figure 10·7 illustrates the process of solving for h_{fe} of a 2N207. A constant collector potential is selected at 5 volts. The perpendicular passes through all the base-bias curves. Two of these curves are selected, points A and B, for the increment of base current. Point A represents a bias of 80 μa and a collector current of 19.6 ma. Point B represents a base bias of 60 μa and a collector current of 15.5 ma. Since

$$h_{fe} = \Delta i_c / \Delta i_b = (4.0)(10^{-3})/(20)(10^{-6}) = 200$$

Graphical solution for h_{fb}, the current-gain parameter for the common-base configuration, is somewhat more difficult because of the errors inherent in small graphical measurements. However, the h_{fb} can be found using the equation

$$h_{fb} = h_{fe}/(1 + h_{fe})$$
$$h_{fb} = 200/(1 + 200) = 0.995$$

OUTPUT CONDUCTANCE

The plate family of curves for a vacuum tube yields two of the basic tube parameters, μ and r_p. The amplification factor was represented as μ and the plate resistance as r_p. The output characteristics of the transistor yield two of the basic transistor parameters as well, the *forward current transfer ratio* h_{fe} and the output conductance h_{oe}.

$$h_{oe} = \frac{\Delta i_{ce}}{\Delta e_{ce}}\bigg]_{i_{be}=k} \tag{10·7}$$

where Δi_{ce} = change in collector current
Δe_{ce} = change in collector voltage
i_{be} = base current held constant

Refer to Fig. 10·7. Assume a constant base bias of 60 μa. Point B represents a collector potential of 5 volts and a collector current of 15.5 ma. Point C represents a collector voltage of 8 volts and a collector current of 15.9 ma.

$$h_{oe} = \Delta i_{ce} / \Delta e_{ce} = (0.4)(10^{-3})/3 = 133 \text{ μmhos}$$

10·8 INPUT CHARACTERISTICS

A second set of characteristic curves representing transistor parameters is given as *input characteristics*. Not all manufacturers supply these curves with their data sheets. The use of the curves in circuit analysis is limited to only a few applications. They do, however, show the graphical representation of the parameters and aid in the development of understanding circuits.

DEVELOPMENT OF THE CURVES

Figure 10·5 is a schematic of a common-emitter configuration. If the value of the collector bias V_{cc} is maintained at zero volts and the base current is varied from 0 to 3 ma, an input curve for $V_{ce} = 0$ results. Note, for example, in Fig. 10·9 that when the base current is -0.5 ma the base voltage is -0.24 volt, assuming the constant collector voltage of zero volts. If the collector voltage is changed to 0.1 volt and a sweep of base voltage and current is effected, a second input characteristic results. The resulting family of input characteristics is shown in Fig. 10·9. Note that the curves for the $V_{ce} = -0.3$ volt and $V_{ce} = -1$ volt are very close to each other. If additional curves at $V_{ce} = -2$ or -3

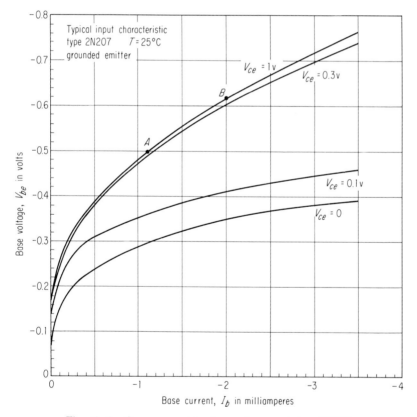

Fig. 10·9   Common-emitter input characteristics: 2N207.

or even -5 volts were also drawn on the characteristic, they would be very nearly on top of the $V_{ce} = -1$ volt curve. The reason is that the base-emitter voltage is virtually independent of increases in collector emitter voltages in excess of about 1 volt. Two additional parameters may be developed from these characteristics.

INPUT IMPEDANCE

The input resistance of a vacuum tube was not given as a parameter since the grid is generally maintained at a negative potential, and hence the input resistance would be an infinite impedance. For the transistor, however, feedback between the output and the input circuit is inherent in the physical structure of the device. Any changes in the output circuit result in changes at the input. The equation for the input impedance parameter assumes a constant collector bias and is given as

$$h_{ie} = \frac{\Delta e_{be}}{\Delta i_{be}}\bigg]_{V_{ce}=k} \qquad (10\cdot8)$$

In order to determine the h_{ie} parameter graphically, a constant collector bias of 1 volt is chosen. Point B of Fig. $10\cdot9$ represents a base voltage of 0.62 volt and a current of 2 ma. Point A represents a base voltage of 0.5 volt and a base current of 1.1 ma.

$$h_{ie} = \Delta V_{be}/\Delta i_{be} = (0.12)/(0.9)(10^{-3}) = 132 \text{ ohms}$$

The fact that the input resistance of a transistor device is only 132 ohms is important. Compare this with the vacuum tube's infinite input resistance at low frequencies. It should be apparent now why the vacuum tube must be driven with a changing voltage while the transistor must be driven by a changing current.

REVERSE VOLTAGE TRANSFER RATIO

The *reverse voltage transfer ratio* parameter identifies the voltage characteristic of a transistor. It is similar to the voltage parameter of a vacuum tube in that it measures the ratio of changes in output voltage to changes in input voltage. It is given as

$$h_{re} = \frac{\Delta V_{be}}{\Delta V_{ee}}\bigg]_{i_{be}=k} \qquad (10\cdot9)$$

and can be calculated graphically from the input characteristics. However, because of the small increments involved, graphical solutions become quite unreliable. This parameter as well as the input impedance parameter are generally supplied by transistor manufacturers in their published transistor manuals and should be used in preference to the graphical representations.

10·9 GROUNDED-BASE CHARACTERISTICS

In the discussions of α and β, the two forward current transfer ratios, it was found that an interrelationship existed: $\alpha = \beta/(1 + \beta)$. The graphical solution for β (h_{fe}) was outlined in Fig. 10·7. Manufacturers sometimes provide two sets of output characteristics for a given transistor, one set for common-emitter connection and another for common-base connection.

Figure 10·10 shows the output characteristics for a 2N34. The manufacturer lists the α for this transistor as 0.975. There is a considerable loss of accuracy when this parameter is derived from the characteristics. For example,

$$\alpha = h_{fb} = \Delta i_c/\Delta i_e$$

If points A and B of Fig. 10·10 are chosen as the increments, they represent $\Delta i_c = 5.8\,\text{ma} - 3.9\,\text{ma} = 1.9 \times 10^{-3}$ and $\Delta i_b = 6 - 4\,\text{ma} = 2\,\text{ma}$.

$$\alpha = (1.9)(10^{-3})/(2)(10^{-3}) = 0.95$$

The error is large enough to give incorrect circuit calculations. It is for this reason that most manufacturers supply α in specification sheets.

A number of other factors concerning the difference between the common-emitter and the common-base curves can be seen in comparing Fig. 10·10 with Fig. 10·11. Both characteristics represent the 2N34; Fig. 10·11 is the common-emitter characteristic. Note the nonuniform

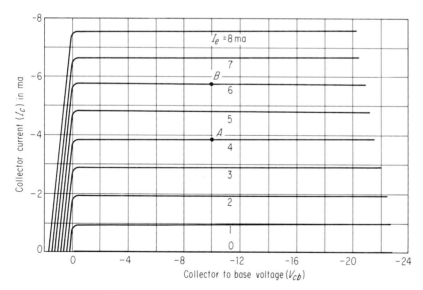

Fig. 10·10   Output characteristics: 2N34.

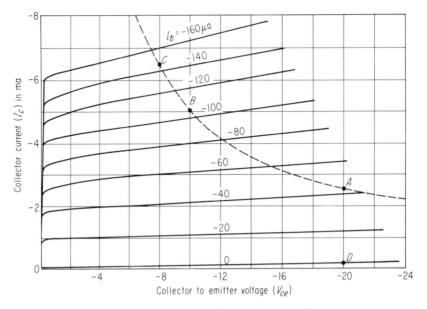

Fig. 10·11   Output characteristics: 2N34.

spacing and the changing slope of the emitter characteristics. The common-emitter circuit introduces more distortion than the common-base configuration. This subject however is beyond the scope of this book.

10·10 MAXIMUM RATINGS

MAXIMUM POWER DISSIPATION

The maximum power dissipation rating for a transistor defines the maximum amount of energy which can be dissipated at the collector in the form of heat. In circuit design it is necessary that circuit components be of a value such as not to exceed this dissipation. The selection of operating biases and load resistance must be made in the framework of the maximum-dissipation curve.

The dotted curve of Fig. 10·11 shows a plot of a maximum-dissipation curve. The manufacturer lists 50 mw as the maximum collector dissipation. This 50-mw point is shown as a series of IE points along the curve. For example, point A represents 50 mw because according to $P = IE$, $(50)(10^{-3}) = (20)(2.5)(10^{-3})$. Point B represents 50 mw since the product of 10 volts and 5 ma is 50 mw. Point C is 50 mw = (8 volts)(6.25 ma).

The selection of load resistance and collector supply voltage must be in the region below the maximum-dissipation curve.

COLLECTOR VOLTAGE AND CURRENT

Specification sheets and transistor manuals list a maximum d-c collector current for every transistor. For example, the 2N34 collector current should not exceed 50 ma. The maximum voltage ratings are divided into two parts, collector-to-emitter and collector-to-base. Not all data sheets give both ratings. If only one is given, it is understood to be the maximum forward voltage between collector and emitter.

10·11 LEAKAGE CURRENTS

Note that in Fig. 10·11 a collector current flows even though the base is biased at 0 ma. Point D shows that with 20 volts between collector and emitter there is a leakage current of about 0.02 ma. Refer to Fig. 10·12. When the collector-base junction is reverse-biased and the emitter connection is left open a small current flows because of minority carriers. At room temperature it is usually a few microamperes but increases rapidly with temperature. For germanium, I_{co} doubles for each 10°C increase in temperature. For silicon, I_{co} triples for each 10° increase in temperature; however, the value is smaller to start with than that for germanium. For example, at 20°C, I_{co} for silicon is only about 1/1,000 that of germanium. A silicon transistor at a given temperature usually has a much smaller value of I_{co} than does a germanium.

If the transistor of Fig. 10·12a is connected as shown in Fig. 10·12b, the minority-carrier collector current is called I_{ceo}. This is called the common-emitter leakage current and is much higher than I_{co}.

Figure 10·13 is a normally biased, grounded-emitter circuit. Several currents are flowing. The emitter current i_e splits up into the base current i_b and the collector current i_c according to Eq. (10·1). Besides these currents the reverse current I_{co} is still present at the collector-base

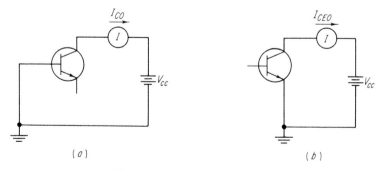

(a)   (b)

Fig. 10·12   Leakage currents.

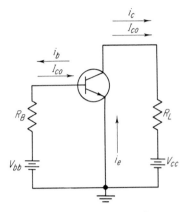

Fig. 10·13   Common-emitter circuit: leakage currents.

junction. This current is in the same direction as i_c and opposite to i_b. The net base and collector currents are

$$I_b = i_b - I_{co} \qquad (10\cdot10)$$
$$I_c = i_c + I_{co} \qquad (10\cdot11)$$
$$i_b = I_b + I_{co} \qquad (10\cdot10a)$$
$$i_c = I_c - I_{co} \qquad (10\cdot11b)$$

Substituting into Eq. (10·1)

$$i_e = (I_b + I_{co}) + (I_c - I_{co}) \qquad (10\cdot12)$$

which means that the emitter current will equal the sum of the base and collector currents, whether the leakage current is considered or not.

Since the definition of the emitter to collector current-gain alpha is

$$\alpha = i_c/i_e \qquad (10\cdot13)$$

the i_c becomes $i_c = \alpha i_e$, which is substituted into Eq. (10·11),

$$I_c = \alpha I_e + I_{co} \qquad (10\cdot14)$$

From Eq. (10·12), $i_e = I_c$ when $I_b = 0$, and substituting this into Eq. (10·14), $I_c = I_c + I_{co}$. Solving for I_c, $I_c = I_{co}/(1 - \alpha)$. This value of collector current with zero base bias is the I_{ceo} mentioned above and measured with the circuit shown in Fig. 10·12b. Therefore,

$$I_{ceo} = I_{co}/(1 - \alpha) \qquad (10\cdot15)$$

Since $\alpha = \beta/(\beta + 1)$ the leakage-current equation becomes

$$I_{ceo} = (\beta + 1)I_{co} \qquad (10\cdot16)$$

EXAMPLE THREE   If the 2N34 at 25°C has an α of 0.975 and $I_{co} = 200$ μa at a collector voltage of 30 volts, what is the I_{ceo} at 25°C and at 35°C?

SOLUTION   According to Eq. (10·15),

$I_{ceo} = (200)(10^{-6})/(1 - 0.975) = 8$ ma
At 35°C the $I_{co} = (200)(10^{-6})(2) = 400$ μa
$I_{ceo} = (400)(10^{-6})/0.025 = 16$ ma

Note that at 55°C the leakage current in the preceding example becomes prohibitively high, 64 ma!

10·12 CIRCUIT CONFIGURATION

Two of the basic circuit configurations have already been mentioned. The third configuration is the grounded collector or common collector. These configurations have their counterparts in vacuum-tube circuits. This section will explore how the transistor configurations compare with their vacuum-tube counterparts and the advantages and disadvantages of using the various configurations.

COMMON EMITTER

Figure 10·14 illustrates the similar circuit arrangement between the common-emitter amplifier and the grounded-cathode amplifier in vacuum-tube circuits. The tube circuit was characterized as the most popular circuit because it provided a large voltage gain. In transistor

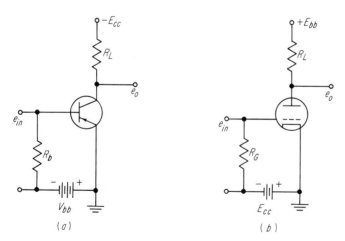

Fig. 10·14   Common-emitter and common-cathode amplifiers.

circuitry, the common emitter is also the most popular configuration. The reasons for its popularity will be explored in Chapter 11. The common-emitter configuration is characterized by

1. High current gain
2. High voltage gain
3. High power gain

In addition to the three points mentioned, the circuit is very adaptable in coupling amplifiers one to another in cascade. The input and output impedances of the device are such as to enable a reasonable transfer of energy with only a moderate loss in the coupling networks. A detailed analysis of circuit parameters is presented in Chap. 11.

COMMON BASE

Figure 10·15 illustrates the comparison of the common-base amplifier to the grounded-grid amplifier. The grounded-grid amplifier provided a voltage gain with a low noise factor. In the transistor circuit the grounded-base circuit provides better fidelity than the grounded-emitter amplifier. The circuit is also characterized by

1. Low current gain (less than 1)
2. High voltage gain
3. Moderate power gain

In addition, the low input impedance and the high output impedance of the device prevent the common-base amplifier from being connected in cascade. Matching impedances of such a wide difference requires a large energy loss in the coupling network.

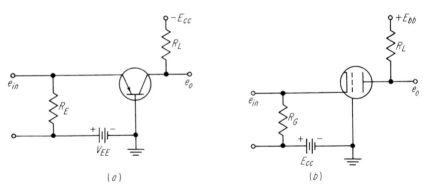

(a)   (b)

Fig. 10·15   Common-base and common-grid amplifiers.

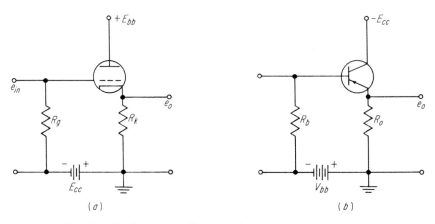

Fig. 10·16   Common-collector and common-plate amplifiers.

COMMON COLLECTOR

The common collector (grounded collector) illustrated in Fig. 10·16 can be compared with the grounded-plate (cathode follower) amplifier. The cathode follower is primarily used as a matching device in tube circuits. It is especially useful in matching a high impedance to a low impedance. The function of the common collector, also called the emitter follower, is the same in transistor circuitry, e.g., impedance matching. The circuit is characterized by

1. High current gain
2. Low voltage gain (less than 1)
3. Medium power gain
4. High input impedance
5. Low output impedance

The forward current transfer ratio h_{fc} for the common-collector circuit is given as the ratio of the emitter-current to the base-current change.

$$h_{fc} = \frac{\Delta i_e}{\Delta i_b}\bigg]_{E_c=k} \tag{10·17}$$

The current gain will generally be similar to that of the common emitter. If the equations for h_{fe} and h_{fb} are equated to the general equation for I_e [Eq. (10·1)],

$$i_e = i_b + i_c$$

and since

$$h_{fc} = \Delta I_{ec}/\Delta I_{bc}$$

(deltas will be omitted)

$$i_c/h_{fb} \approx i_b + h_{fe}i_b$$
$$i_c \approx i_b(1 + h_{fe})h_{fb}$$
$$i_c/i_b \approx (1+h_{fe})(h_{fe})/(1+h_{fe})$$
$$h_{fc} \approx h_{fe} \qquad\qquad (10 \cdot 18)$$

10·13 SUMMING UP

BIASING

The four basic guideposts used in biasing all transistor circuits are

1. Electrons flow against the arrow.
2. Base-emitter junction must be forward-biased.
3. Base-collector junction must be reverse-biased.
4. $i_c = i_b + i_c$

CIRCUIT CONFIGURATIONS

Transistor circuits divide into three basic configurations. The elements connected to the signal ground establish the reference point.

1. Common emitter
2. Common base
3. Common collector

PARAMETERS

Each of the three circuit configurations results in a basic set of *transistor* parameters. (Circuit parameters will be discussed in the next chapter.)

TABLE 10·1

	Common emitter	Common base	Common collector
Forward current transfer ratio	h_{fe}	h_{fb}	h_{fc}
Reverse voltage transfer ratio	h_{re}	h_{rb}	h_{rc}
Input impedance	h_{ie}	h_{ib}	h_{ic}
Output conductance	h_{oe}	h_{eb}	h_{oc}

Problems

10·12   Draw the schematic of a grounded-emitter NPN transistor showing the correct base and collector potentials. Identify the current directions.

10·13   The 2N119 silicon transistor parameter for the forward current transfer ratio is given as $h_{fb} = 0.98$. What is the forward current transfer ratio for the grounded-collector configuration?

10·14   If graphical analysis is used, determine the h_{fe} and the h_{oe} for the 2N224 transistor (see Appendix B).

10·15   From the information derived from Prob. 10·14, what is the forward current transfer ratio for the 2N224 connected as a common-base circuit?

10·16   Assume that the 2N224 has the following static (d-c) references: base-current bias, 1.5 ma; collector-supply bias, 15 volts. Determine the h_{FE}.

10·17   If the collector supply of Prob. 10·16 is reduced to 5 volts, what is h_{FE}?

10·18   Using graphical analysis determine the h_{ie} and the h_{re} for the 2N224 germanium transistor (see Appendix B).

10·19   If the 2N224 transistor has a collector supply of −10 volts and a base bias of 2.5 ma, determine the h_{oe}.

10·20   Draw a schematic of a common-collector NPN transistor showing correct bias potentials. Identify current directions.

10·21   Determine the a-c output conductance parameter for the 2N207 transistor at a base bias of 120 μa and a collector bias of 3 volts.

10·22   If the base bias in Prob. 10·21 is decreased to 50 μa, what increase or decrease in the output conductance is recorded?

10·23   Is the transistor shown in Fig. 10·16 an NPN or a PNP?

10·24   If the maximum collector dissipation of the 2N224 is 500 mw, draw a maximum collector dissipation curve. Can the device operate with (a) a base bias of 2.5 ma and a collector bias of 20 volts, (b) a base bias of 3 ma and a collector voltage of 5 volts?

10·25   If the d-c forward current transfer ratio h_{FE} for the 2N408 is 75, what fixed base bias is flowing if the collector current is 50 ma? What current flows in the emitter?

10·26   If the I_{co} for a 2N584 is given as 5 μa and the β is 40, what is the I_{ceo}?

10·27   If the collector cutoff current I_{co} for a 2N104 is 10 μa and the I_{ceo} is 0.45 ma, (a) what is the α of the device, (b) what is β?

10·28   If the transistor of Prob. 10·27 is connected in a common-base configuration, what change in current will flow at the collector if the change in emitter current is 6 ma?

10·29   If the vacuum tube is compared with the transistor, what vacuum-tube element corresponds to (a) the base, (b) the collector, (c) the emitter?

Review Questions

10·1   What are the four requirements of biasing and current flow needed to produce proper transistor action?

10·2   What are the majority carriers in an NPN transistor? In a PNP transistor?

10·3   What are the three symbols representing forward current transfer ratio?

10·4 Describe the difference between parameters h_{fc} and h_{fe}. Give an example of how each is used.

10·5 What relationship exists between α and β?

10·6 What is the carrier of the leakage current in an NPN transistor?

10·7 Compare the three circuit configurations of the transistor device with those of the vacuum tube.

10·8 The emitter follower is represented by which transistor circuit configuration?

XI

TRANSISTOR
AMPLIFIERS

11·1 INTRODUCTION

Chapter 2 developed the three basic *tube* parameters. The resistance of the device r_p, the voltage-amplification factor μ, and the transconductance g_m were derived from their graphical representation, the output characteristics of the tube. Chapter 3 developed the basic *circuit* parameters, that is, the parameters of the device when operated into a load. These were defined as the circuit's voltage gain

$$A_{vc} = -\mu R_L/(r_p + R_L)$$

given as Eq. $(3 \cdot 11)$ and the circuit's output impedance

$$Z_o = r_p R_L/(r_p + R_L)$$

illustrated in Figs. $3 \cdot 19$ and $3 \cdot 20$.

Chapter 10 developed the four basic transistor parameters by graphical methods. These were input resistance h_{ie}, output conductance h_{oe}, reverse voltage transfer ratio h_{re}, and forward current transfer ratio h_{fe}; the only additional parameter for the transistor device compared to the vacuum tube device was the input resistance. This parameter was neglected in the vacuum-tube case since this value at low frequencies is infinitely large so long as the grid is maintained at a negative bias.

This chapter develops the basic *circuit* parameters for a transistor operating into a resistive load. These circuit parameters apply when the devices are operated as small-signal amplifiers.

The circuit of Fig. 11·1 is a stage of transistor amplification. The transistor and its associated load exhibit five circuit parameters. These are

A_{ve} = voltage gain
A_{ie} = current gain
A_{pe} = power gain
R_{ie} = input resistance
R_{oe} = output resistance

These five parameters are used in evaluating the operation of one stage or many stages operating in cascade (one after another). Note that all the basic requirements for transistor action have been met. V_{bb} forward-biases the input and V_{cc} reverse-biases the output. The *voltage gain* of the stage is the ratio of the output voltage to the input voltage.

$$A_{ve} = e_o/e_{in} \qquad (11 \cdot 1)$$

The *current gain* is the ratio of the current through the load and the base current.

$$A_{ie} = i_c/i_b \qquad (11 \cdot 2)$$

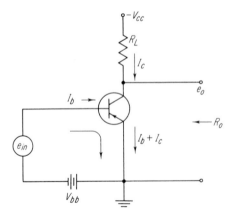

Fig. 11·1   Basic transistor circuit.

Similarly the *power gain* is the *IE* product of the voltage and current gain.

$$A_{pe} = (A_{ie})(A_{ve}) \qquad (11 \cdot 3)$$

As in the case of the vacuum-tube amplifier, it is useful to identify these gains without wiring the circuit. For example, in order to determine the voltage gain of a stage using Eq. $(11 \cdot 1)$ it would be necessary to build a prototype, apply a signal, make the measurements, and thus determine the gain. This is a perfectly valid method; however, it would be easier and faster if the gain could be determined in advance.

The *circuit* parameter equations do just that. By analyzing the circuit of Fig. $11 \cdot 1$ in terms of the *device* parameters and the constant R_L plus any other constants, the five circuit parameters will be developed.

11·2 CURRENT GAIN

The circuit of Fig. $11 \cdot 2$ is an equivalent circuit of Fig. $11 \cdot 1$. Note that the directions of the currents in Fig. $11 \cdot 1$ correlate to the currents in the equivalent circuit. That is, $i_e = i_c + i_b$. The current gain of the stage is given as the ratio of the output current to the input current [Eq. $(11 \cdot 2)$].

Since the current flowing through the load is the collector current,

$$e_o = i_{ce}R_L \qquad (11 \cdot 4)$$

However, e_o is also equal to the voltage across the output conductance (h_{oe}, which is effectively in parallel with R_L). Therefore,

$$e_o = I_x/h_{oe} \qquad (11 \cdot 5)$$

I_x can be evaluated from Kirchhoff's law since the three currents at junction A must equal zero.

$$I_x = h_{fe}i_{be} - i_{ce} \qquad (11 \cdot 6)$$

Substituting Eq. $(11 \cdot 6)$ into $(11 \cdot 5)$ and equating the resultant into Eq. $(11 \cdot 4)$,

$$i_{ce}R_L = (h_{fe}i_{be} - i_{ce})/h_{oe}$$

Multiplying through by h_{oe},

$$i_{ce}R_L h_{oe} = h_{fe}i_{be} - i_{ce}$$

Solving of i_{ce}/i_{be},

$$i_{ce}/i_{be} = h_{fe}/(h_{oe}R_L + 1) \qquad (11 \cdot 7)$$

Equating Eq. (11·2) with (11·7) the resultant equation gives the circuit's current-gain parameter for any value of load resistance.

$$A_{ie} = h_{fe}/(h_{oe}R_L + 1) \qquad (11 \cdot 8)$$

11·3 VOLTAGE GAIN

The voltage gain of the circuit of Fig. 11·1 can be determined from the equivalent circuit of Fig. 11·2. The voltage gain is given as

$$A_{ve} = e_o/e_{in}$$

Refer to the circuit of Fig. 11·2. The input voltage according to Kirchhoff's law is the sum of the voltage drops around the input loop.

$$e_{in} = i_{be}h_{ie} + h_{re}e_o \qquad (11 \cdot 9)$$

Substituting Eq. (11·4) into (11·9) the input voltage becomes

$$e_{in} = i_{be}h_{ie} + h_{re}i_{ce}R_L \qquad (11 \cdot 10)$$

Substituting Eqs. (11·10) and (11·4) into (11·1) results in

$$A_{ve} = i_{ce}R_L/(i_{be}h_{ie} + h_{re}i_{ce}R_L)$$

Dividing the numerator and the denominator by i_{ce} results in

$$A_{ve} = R_L/[(i_{be}/i_{ce})(h_{ie}) + h_{re}R_L]$$

However, i_{be}/i_{ce} is the reciprocal of Eq. (11·8); hence a substitution results in the voltage-gain equation

$$A_{ve} = h_{fe}/[(h_{ie}/R_L) + \Delta h_e] \qquad (11 \cdot 11)$$
where $$\Delta h_e = h_{oe}h_{ie} + h_{re}h_{fe} \qquad (11 \cdot 12)$$

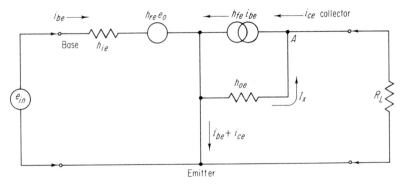

Fig. 11·2   Equivalent circuit.

EXAMPLE ONE   In a transistor whose parameters are $h_{ie} = 2$ kilohms, $h_{oe} = (25)(10^{-6})$, $h_{fe} = 40$, and $h_{re} = (5)(10^{-4})$, what are the current and voltage gain of the stage when a 5-kilohm load is used?

$$A_{ie} = h_{fe}/(h_{oe}R_L + 1)$$
$$A_{ie} = 40/[(25)(10^{-6})(5)(10^{+3}) + 1]$$
$$A_{ie} = 40/1.125 = 35.5$$
$$A_{ve} = h_{fe}/[(h_{ie}/R_L) + \Delta^{he}]$$
$$\Delta^{he} = h_{oe}h_{ie} + h_{re}h_{fe}$$
$$\Delta h_e = (25)(10^{-6})(2)(10^{+3}) + (5)(10^{-4})(40) = 0.07$$
$$A_{ve} = 40/[(2{,}000/5{,}000) + 0.07]$$
$$A_{ve} = 40/0.47 = 85.1$$

11·4 POWER GAIN

The power gain for small-signal amplifiers is given as the product of the voltage gain and the current gain since $p = ie$.

$$A_{pe} = A_{ie}A_{re}$$

$$A_{pe} = \frac{(h_{fe})^2}{h_{oe}h_{ie} + h_{ie}/R_L + h_{oe}R_L\Delta h_e + \Delta h_e} \qquad (11 \cdot 13)$$

EXAMPLE TWO   The circuit of the example in Sec. 11·3 has what power gain?

SOLUTION   The voltage gain was given as 85.1 and the current gain as 35.5.

$$A_{pe} = A_{ve}A_{ie} = (85.1)(35.5) = 3{,}020$$

If the load resistance in the circuit of the above example is increased to twice its value, the current gain of the circuit decreases to 32 and the voltage gain increases to 148. The resultant is an increase in the power gain to 4,736. This represents an increase of almost 1,700. If, however, the load resistance is increased to 1 megohm, the current gain decreases to $A_{ie} = 1.5$ and the voltage gain increases to $A_{ve} = 555$. The resultant power gain is now $A_{pe} = 832$.

The following listing shows how the power gain varies for increasing values of load resistance:

$R_L = 5$ kilohms	$A_{pe} = 3{,}020$
$= 10$ kilohms	$= 4{,}736$
$= 33$ kilohms	$= 6{,}820$
$= 50$ kilohms	$= 6{,}420$
$= 1$ megohm	$= 832$

It would appear that a given transistor has a maximum possible power gain at some specific value of load resistance. If the power gain equation $(11 \cdot 13)$ is solved for the maximum point of where A_{pe} varies with respect to R_L, the resultant is an equation defining the R_L for a *maximum possible power gain* for a given transistor.

$$R_L = \sqrt{h_{ie}/h_{oe}\Delta h_e} \qquad (11 \cdot 14)$$

EXAMPLE THREE   What value of load resistance should be connected to the transistor used in Example One for maximum possible power gain?

SOLUTION   Since $h_{ie} = 2$ kilohms, $h_{oe} = (25)(10^{-6})$, and $\Delta h_e = 0.07$, then R_L according to Eq. $(11 \cdot 14)$ is

$$R_L = \sqrt{\frac{(2)(10^3)}{(25)(10^{-6})(0.07)}} = 33 \text{ kilohms}$$

(Note that in the listing of load resistance versus power gain, $A_{pe} = 6,820$ when $R_L = 33$ kilohms.)

Problems

11·1   A transistor amplifier produces an output-current change of 30 ma when a 300-μa change is developed at the input. What is the current gain of the stage?

11·2   A transistor amplifier has a voltage gain of 310. What change in input voltage is needed to produce a 10-mv peak-to-peak output?

11·3   Assume that the following transistor, $h_{ie} = 1,200$ ohms, $h_{oe} = (20)(10^{-6})$ mhos, $h_{re} = (4)(10^{-4})$, and $h_{fe} = 45$, has a 3-kilohm load connected to it. What are (a) the current gain of the stage, (b) the voltage gain of the stage, (c) the power gain?

11·4   If the load resistor of Prob. 11·3 were reduced to 1 kilohm, what are the new (a) current gain, (b) voltage gain, and (c) power gain?

11·5   A 2N465 has the following device parameters: $h_{oe} = 18$ μmhos, $h_{re} = (4.3)(10^{-3})$, $h_{fe} = 45$, and $h_{ie} = 1,400$. If a 1,500-ohm load is connected to the circuit what is the current gain?

11·6   If the load in Prob. 11·5 is increased from 1,500 ohms toward 4 kilohms, will the power gain increase, decrease, or remain unchanged?

11·7   If the transistor of Prob. 11·3 is to provide the maximum possible power gain, what value of load resistance should be connected in the load?

11·8   If the transistor of Prob. 11·5 is to provide the maximum possible power gain, what value of load resistance should be used?

11·9   Assume the transistor of Prob. 11·3 is to be connected as a common-emitter amplifier. The device is to raise a 200-μv signal to a level of 10 mv. What value of load resistance should be used? What is the power gain of the stage?

11·10   Refer to Prob. 11·9. What value of load resistance would be needed if the transistor of Prob. 11·5 were used? Which of the two circuits provides more power gain (Prob. 11·9 or 11·10)?

11·11   If the load resistance on a common-emitter amplifier is increased, does the current gain increase, decrease, or remain unchanged?

11·12   If the load resistance on a common-emitter amplifier is increased, does the voltage gain increase, decrease, or remain unchanged?

11·5 INPUT RESISTANCE

Section 11·2 developed *circuit* current-gain parameter. The circuit current gain of Fig. 11·3 shows that the current gain of the stage is 35.5 if the h_{fe} of the transistor is 40 and the h_{oe} is 25×10^{-6}. Assume that 50 μa is leaving the generator i_g of Fig. 11·3. The current divides and a portion flows through R_a and the remainder flows into the base junction of the transistor. In order to evaluate what current flows into the base, the *input resistance* R_{ie} of the *circuit* must be evaluated. This input resistance R_{ie} should not be confused with the input resistance parameter h_{ie}. One is a circuit parameter—the other a device.

In order to determine the equation for the input resistance of the stage with a given R_L, refer to the equivalent circuit of Fig. 11·2. The input resistance R_{ie} according to Ohm's law becomes the input voltage divided by the current leaving the generator e_{in}.

$$R_{ie} = e_{in}/i_{be} \qquad (11 \cdot 15)$$

According to Kirchhoff's law, the voltage drop around the input loop must equal the applied voltage; hence

$$e_{in} = h_{ie}i_{be} + h_{re}e_o \qquad (11 \cdot 16)$$

However, the output voltage is equal to the input voltage times the voltage gain of the stage, $e_o = e_{in}A_{ve}$. Substituting this value into Eq. (11·16),

$$e_{in} = h_{ie}i_{be} + h_{re}e_{in}A_{ve}$$

Solving for e_{in}/i_{be},

$$e_{in} - h_{re}e_{in}A_{ve} = h_{ie}i_{be}$$
$$e_{in}(1 - h_{re}A_{ve}) = h_{ie}i_{be}$$
$$e_{in}/i_{be} = h_{ie}/(1 - h_{re}A_{ve}) \qquad (11 \cdot 17)$$

Substituting Eqs. (11·11) and (11·12) into Eq. (11·17) and simplifying, the equation for the input resistance of the stage becomes

$$R_{ie} = h_{ie} + \frac{h_{fe}h_{re}R_L}{h_{oe}R_L + 1} \qquad (11 \cdot 18)$$

If the parameters of the transistor in the circuit of Fig. 11·3 are $h_{ie} = 2$ kilohms, $h_{re} = 5 \times 10^{-4}$, $h_{oe} = 25 \times 10^{-6}$, and $h_{fe} = 40$, the input resistance to the stage becomes

$$R_{ie} = (2)(10^3) + (40)(5)(10^{-4})(5)(10^3)/[(25)(10^{-6})(5)(10^3) + 1]$$
$$R_{ie} = (2)(10^3) + (0.09)(10^3) = 2.09 \text{ kilohms}$$

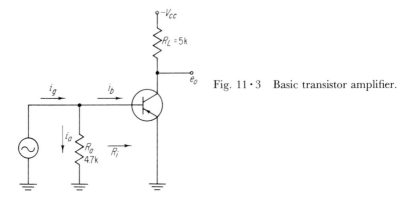

Fig. 11·3   Basic transistor amplifier.

If the current leaving the generator is 50 μa, the current flowing into the base can now be evaluated. The current leaving the generator divides between the two resistances R_a and R_{ie} according to the ratio of their sizes. According to the current ratio, the current flowing into the 2.09-kilohm resistance will be

$$i_{be} = R_a i_g / (R_a + R_{ie})$$
$$i_{be} = (4.7)(10^3)(50)(10^{-6})/(4.7)(10^3) + (2.09)(10^3) = 34.6 \ \mu a$$

If this 34.6 μa is a signal (changing) current, then the current through the load resistor will be 35.5 times larger than the current flowing into the base terminal of the transistor. The current through R_L becomes 1.21 ma.

EXAMPLE FOUR   Assume a 2N332 transistor has the following device parameters: $h_{fe} = 15, h_{re} = (32)(10^{-6}), h_{ie} = 694$, and $h_{oe} = (4)(10^{-6})$. How does the input resistance vary with different values of load resistance?

SOLUTION   Successive substitutions into Eq. (11·18) result in the following listing of input resistance R_{ie}:

$R_L = 1$ kilohm	$R_{ie} = 694 + 0.47 = 694.47$
$= 10$ kilohms	$= 694 + 4.6 \ = 698.6$
$= 100$ kilohms	$= 694 + 34.3 = 728.3$
$= 1$ megohm*	$= 694 + 96 \ \ = 790$
$= 10$ megohms*	$= 694 + 117 = 811$
$= 100$ megohms*	$= 694 + 120 = 814$
$= 1,000$ megohms*	$= 694 + 120 = 814$

  * Large values of load resistance are not very practical; however, the listing does show that the input resistance to the stage reaches an upper limit of about 800 ohms regardless of the load resistance. This value is reached when the load is about 100 kilohms.

Note that the input resistance of a common-emitter amplifier can never be any lower than the input resistance of the device itself h_{ie}.

11·6 OUTPUT RESISTANCE

The selection of the load resistor in Fig. 11·3 depends upon a number of factors. It has been shown that the load-resistance value determines the current gain of the stage, the voltage gain, the power gain, and the input resistance. Often a specific amount of voltage gain is desired; hence the value of the load becomes a fixed value. Assume that the main function of the stage is to transfer the maximum amount of energy from the input to the output. Under these conditions it is desirable to select a value of load resistance equal to the output resistance of the transistor. The first impulse is to assume that this output resistance of the device is the reciprocal of the output conductance h_{oe}. This, however, is not the case. The value of output resistance *of the stage* must be evaluated in terms of transistor parameters and the base resistor R_a. Refer to Fig. 11·4.

The output resistance, according to Ohm's law, becomes $R_{oe} = e_o/i_{ce}$. According to Kirchhoff's law, the current $i_{ce} = h_{fe}i_{be} - i_x$; however, i_x can be defined as e_oh_{oe}. Therefore,

$$i_{ce} = h_{fe}i_{be} - e_oh_{oe} \qquad (11·19)$$

The input circuit can be used to evaluate i_{be}.

$$i_{be} = h_{re}e_o/(h_{ie} + R_a) \qquad (11·20)$$

Substituting Eq. (11·20) into Eq. (11·19),

$$i_{ce} = h_{fe}h_{re}e_o/(h_{ie} + R_a) - h_{oe}e_o$$

and solving for the absolute value of e_o/i_{ce},

$$e_o/i_{ce} = (h_{ie} + R_a)/(- h_{fe}h_{re} + h_{oe}h_{ie} + h_{ie}R_a)$$

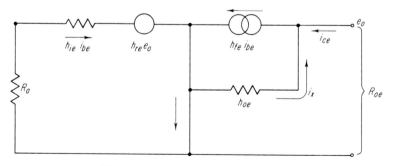

Fig. 11·4   Equivalent circuit for R_{oe}.

The output resistance for a given stage with a given R_a becomes

$$R_{oe} = \frac{1}{h_{oe} - h_{fe}h_{re}/(h_{ie} + R_a)} \qquad (11 \cdot 20a)$$

EXAMPLE FIVE   What value of load resistance should be connected to the transistor of Fig. $11 \cdot 3$ in order to produce a maximum transfer of energy to the load? Assume that R_a is equal to 4.7 kilohms. Substituting the transistor parameters and the value of R_a into Eq. $(11 \cdot 20)$ yields

$$R_{oe} = \frac{1}{(25)(10^{-6}) - \dfrac{(40)(5)(10^{-6})}{(2)(10^3) + (4.7)(10^3)}}$$

$$= \frac{1}{(25)(10^{-6}) - (.03)(10^{-6})}$$

$$= 40 \text{ kilohms}$$

Hence the load resistor R_L should equal about 40 kilohms in order to produce a maximum transfer of energy.

$11 \cdot 7$ PARAMETER CONVERSIONS

The preceding sections developed the five basic circuit parameters for the common-emitter configuration. Chapter 10 developed the device parameters and showed that there are four basic device parameters for each transistor when applied to a given configuration. As an example, the device parameters for a given transistor operated in a common-emitter configuration are $h_{ie} = 500$ ohms, $h_{re} = 2.5 \times 10^{-4}$, $h_{fe} = 11.5$, and $h_{oe} = 12.5 \times 10^{-6}$. These device parameters are used in the calculation of circuit parameters such as voltage gain and input resistance. *If the transistor is to be operated as a common-base amplifier, the circuit equations do not change.* The device parameters do change, however, and these device parameters are not the same values as for the common emitter. As an example, the common-base device parameters for the transistor mentioned above are

$$h_{ib} = 40 \text{ ohms}, \ h_{rb} = 2.5 \times 10^{-4}, \ h_{fb} = 0.92, \text{ and } h_{ob} = 10^{-6} \text{ ohm}.$$

EXAMPLE SIX   What is the current gain of a stage of amplification when a 4-kilohm load resistor is connected with a 2N332, (a) when it is connected as a common emitter, (b) when it is connected as a common base? [Assume $h_{fe} = 15$, $h_{oe} = (4)(10^{-6})$, $h_{re} = 32$, $h_{ie} = 694$, and $h_{ib} = 43$, $h_{ob} = 0.25 \times 10^{-6}$, $h_{rb} = 1.5 \times 10^{-4}$, $h_{fb} = 0.938$.]

SOLUTION   The equation for the current gain of a common-emitter amplifier is

$$A_{ie} = \frac{h_{fe}}{1 + h_{oe}R_L} = \frac{15}{1 + (4)(10^{-6})(4)(10^3)} = 14.75$$

The equation for the current gain of a common-base amplifier is the same as the common emitter; however, common-base parameters are used.

$$A_{ib} = \frac{h_{fb}}{1 + h_{ob}R_L} = \frac{0.938}{1 + (0.25)(10^{-6})(4)(10^3)} = \frac{0.938}{1.001} = 0.937$$

Frequently transistor manuals list only one set of parameters and sometimes a combination of some common-emitter and common-base device parameters. As a result, any additional parameters must be calculated from those given.

Chapter 10 pointed out the interrelationship which exists between device parameters. If the common-emitter current-gain parameter is known, the common-base current-gain parameter can be determined from the equation

$$h_{fe} = \frac{h_{fb}}{1 - h_{fb}} = \frac{\alpha}{1 - \alpha} = \beta$$

A similar relationship between all parameters is given in Table 11·1. Note that some of the parameters are the same for different configurations, while some conversions are given as close approximations.

EXAMPLE SEVEN   What is the common-collector input resistance h_{ic} for a 2N332 transistor?

TABLE 11·1   *Parameter Conversions*

Common emitter to common collector	Common base to common emitter	Common base to common collector	Common emitter to common base
$h_{ic} = h_{ie}$	$h_{ie} = \dfrac{h_{ib}}{1 - h_{fb}}$	$h_{ic} = \dfrac{h_{ib}}{1 - h_{fb}}$	$h_{ib} = \dfrac{h_{ie}}{1 + h_{fe}}$
$h_{rc} \approx 1$	$h_{re} = \dfrac{h_{ib}h_{ob}}{1 - h_{fb}} - h_{rb}$	$h_{rc} = \dfrac{1}{1 - h_{fb}} + h_{rb}$	$h_{rb} = \dfrac{h_{ie}h_{oe}}{1 + h_{fe}} - h_{re}$
$h_{fc} = 1 + h_{fe}$	$h_{fe} = \dfrac{h_{fb}}{1 - h_{fb}}$	$h_{fc} = \dfrac{1}{1 - h_{fb}}$	$h_{fb} = \dfrac{h_{fe}}{1 + h_{fe}}$
$h_{oc} = h_{oe}$	$h_{oe} = \dfrac{h_{ob}}{1 - h_{fb}}$	$h_{oc} = \dfrac{h_{ob}}{1 - h_{fb}}$	$h_{ob} = \dfrac{h_{oe}}{1 + h_{oe}}$

SOLUTION According to Table 11·1, the conversion equation is

$$h_{ic} = h_{ib}/(1 + h_{fb}) = (43)/(1 - 0.938)$$
$$= 694 \text{ ohms}$$

Problems

11·13 If a given transistor has the following parameters, $h_{ie} = (2.2)(10^3)$ ohms, $h_{re} = (5)(10^{-4})$, $h_{oe} = (24)(10^{-6})$, and $h_{fe} = 44$, what is the input resistance to the stage when a 1-kilohm load is connected to the device?

11·14 If the load in Prob. 11·13 is increased to 5 kilohms what are (a) the input resistance to the stage, (b) the current gain, (c) the voltage gain, and (d) the power gain?

11·15 What is the output resistance of the transistor of Prob. 11·13 if the input resistor connected between base and emitter is 4 kilohms?

11·16 If the resistor of Prob. 11·15 is doubled, will the output resistance increase, decrease, or remain unchanged?

11·17 The 2N223 transistor has the following device parameters: $h_{ob} = (10^{-6})$ mhos, $h_{rb} = (2.5)(10^{-4})$, $h_{ib} = 35$ ohms, and $h_{fb} = 0.991$. If the circuit is to be connected as a common-base amplifier with a load of 5 kilohms, what are (a) the current gain, (b) the voltage gain, (c) the power gain, (d) the input resistance of the stage?

11·18 What value of load resistance connected to the 2N223 will produce an input circuit resistance of 40 ohms?

11·19 What are the common-emitter h parameters for the 2N223 transistor?

11·20 What are the common-base h parameters for the 2N332 transistor?

11·21 What are the circuit current gains of the 2N223 working into a 3-kilohm load, when the device is connected as (a) a common-base amplifier, (b) a common-emitter amplifier, (c) a common-collector (emitter follower) amplifier?

11·22 What are the input circuit resistances for the 2N223 working into a 3-kilohm load resistance for the (a) common-emitter configuration, (b) common-base configuration, (c) common-collector configuration?

11·23 Assume a 2N223 transistor has a 3-kilohm load connected to it and a 5-kilohm resistor between base and emitter. The circuit is connected in a common-emitter configuration as shown in Fig. 11·3. If 1 ma is leaving the generator, what current is flowing into the base? What is the collector current?

11·8 TRANSISTOR BIAS CIRCUITS

The circuit of Fig. 11·1 and the equivalent circuits of Figs. 11·2 and 11·4 illustrate a stage of transistor amplification showing the pertinent circuit components influencing signal conditions. The correct collector supply and bias supply voltages have been assumed. In vacuum-tube circuits, the equivalent circuits did not involve the B+ supply and the grid-bias supply since these voltages were assumed to be proper for active-region operation.

SEPARATE BIAS SUPPLY

Figure 11·5a and b illustrates a medium-power 2N1154 in a common-emitter and common-base configuration. Each of the circuits operates into an 800-ohm load. The input bias supplies are shown as V_{bb} and V_{ee}, respectively.

The output characteristics for the common-emitter configuration are shown in Fig. 11·5c. Note that the active region extends from point A (base bias of 0 ma) to the saturation point B (base bias of 4.5 ma). The allowable input-signal swing must not exceed an increment of 4.5 ma. The center of this increment is about 2.25 ma (point C). A proper value of V_{bb} must now be chosen in order to establish a quiescent base current of 2.25 ma. Figure 11·5e illustrates the equivalent input circuit. Note that the base bias supply is in series with the base resistor R_a and the input resistance of the circuit R_{ie}. According to Ohm's law, the current flowing in the circuit is

$$i_{be} = V_{bb}/(R_a + R_{ie})$$

The R_{ie} can be neglected since it is small compared with the 5-kilohm R_a.

$$V_{bb} = (i_{be})(R_a)$$
$$V_{bb} = (2.25)(10^{-3})(5)(10^3) = 11.25 \text{ volts}$$

It can be concluded that the value of the bias resistor R_a and the bias supply V_{bb} determine the input current when the value of R_a is large compared with the input resistance of the stage. A similar analysis can be conducted on the common-emitter stage; however, the equation becomes even more accurate since the input resistance of the common-base amplifier is much lower than that of the common-emitter.

In the common-base circuit the operating point is chosen at Q (Fig. 11·5d). Note that the emitter bias current is 20 ma. The value of R_a must be reduced in order to hold the value of bias supply V_{ee} within reasonable limits. When the circuit is converted from a common-emitter to a common-base configuration, R_a is reduced to 2 kilohms.

$$V_{ee} = (i_{eb})(R_a) = (20)(10^{-3})(2)(10^3) = 40 \text{ volts}$$

SINGLE BIAS SUPPLY

There are two basic disadvantages of the bias arrangement shown in Fig. 11·5: (a) Two sources of direct current are required for each circuit.

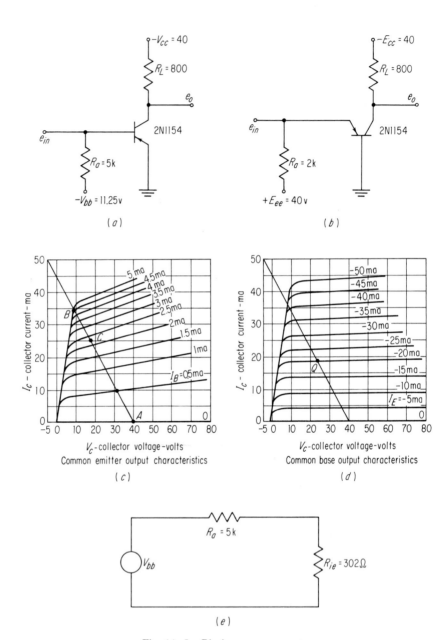

Fig. 11·5   Biasing arrangements.

220

(*b*) The bias current remains fixed though the bias requirements of the circuit may vary with changes in temperature and transistor specifications. The first item is difficult to eliminate in the common-base configuration because the two bias supplies require voltage sources of opposite polarity. In the common-emitter configuration, the two bias sources (collector and base) can be taken from the same d-c source. This accounts for the greater popularity of the common-emitter configuration compared with the common-base. Refer to the circuit of Fig. 11·6. The bias current is shown as a dotted line. The output characteristics of Fig. 11·5 showed the quiescent bias current to be 2.25 ma. With a collector supply of 40 volts, the values of R_1 and R_2 can be determined from Ohm's law.

$$R_1 + R_2 = E_{cc}/i_{be}$$
$$R_1 + R_2 = 40/(2.25)(10^{-3}) = 18 \text{ kilohms}$$

The selection of a method of dividing the 18 kilohms between the two resistors is frequently determined by the input-impedance requirements of the stage. For example, if the input resistor should be a value similar to the one shown in Fig. 11·5*a*, then $R_2 = 5$ kilohms and $R_1 = 13$ kilohms. Capacitor C_1 decouples the input circuit from the collector supply E_{cc}. If capacitor C_1 is large, of the order of 50 μf, the equivalent input signal circuit is the same as shown in Fig. 11·5*a*. If, however, for impedance-matching purposes, the value of R_2 must be selected such that it exceeds the total of R_1 and R_2 (18 kilohms) the bias arrangements shown cannot be used. Assume that resistor R_2 must be 25 kilohms. The value of R_1 must be zero. However, a 25-kilohm resistor limits the bias down to 1.6 ma (a value much lower than the quiescent operating point).

An alternate arrangement of bias incorporates a voltage-divider net-

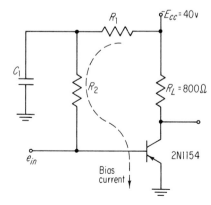

Fig. 11·6   Common-emitter bias arrangement.

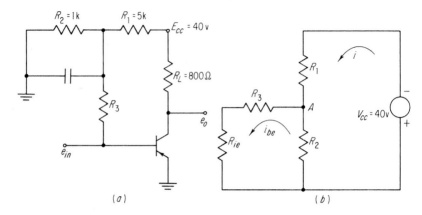

Fig. 11·7   Bias network.

work (refer to Fig. 11·7a). The voltage-divider type of bias is less efficient since it dissipates more power than the two previously described methods. The selection of R_1, R_2, and R_3 can be determined from the equivalent circuit shown in Fig. 11·7b. Assume that the bias current through R_{ie} must be 2.25 ma. Assume that R_1 and R_2 are arbitrarily selected to be 5 and 1 kilohms, respectively. What value of R_3 is required in order to ensure proper bias? In order to solve for R_3, two current loops are assumed in the equivalent circuit, i_{be} and i. The two simultaneous equations representing these loops are

$$E_{cc} = (R_1 + R_2)i - (R_2)i_{be}$$
$$0 = -(R_2)i + (R_2 + R_3)i_{be}$$
$$R_3 = (E_{cc}/i_{be} - R_L)(2)/(R_1 + R_2)$$
$$R_3 = 2.11 \text{ kilohms}$$

If the value of R_3 must be fixed at a higher resistance, then the problem can be solved for either R_1 or R_2.

11·9 BIAS STABILIZATION

Bias-stabilization circuitry attempts to reduce the problems of changing circuit conditions resulting from changes in ambient temperature and the variation of transistor parameters from one unit to the next. Chapter 8 showed that the generation of carriers in a transistor required the addition of energy to the device. Since an increasing temperature is a form of adding energy to the crystal structure, transistors become temperature-dependent. Figure 11·8 shows two curves from a family of output characteristics. The solid lines indicate the characteristics at 25°C. The dashed lines indicate the characteristics at 65°C. Note that at 25°C a collector current of 6 ma flows when the base bias is 100 μa. When the temperature is increased the same bias causes an increased collector current to 8 ma. Large changes in temperature can cause the transistor to change its operating region into the saturation region, causing serious distortion.

Note that a change of 2 ma of collector current in Fig. 11·8 resulted in a quiescent change of collector voltage of from 10 to 7 volts.

The temperature dependence of I_{co} (leakage current) and hence I_{ceo} [Eq. (10·15)] could cause a condition known as *thermal runaway*. The increased collector current causes an increased temperature at the crystal. This further increases the leakage current, which further increases the temperature, etc. Eventually the crystal breaks down.

Refer to Fig. 11·8. The change in temperature caused the $I_b = 100$ μa curve to change position. The positional change of the characteristic curve is actually the change in leakage current I_{co}. In this case $I_{co} = 80$ μa. If the change in collector current (2 ma) could have been held to about 80 μa, this change would not have represented any serious change in quiescent-point position.

Assume that *stability factor* is established as the ratio

$$S = \Delta I_c / \Delta I_{co}$$

For the transistor illustrated in Fig. 11·8 the stability factor is

$$S = (2)(10^{-3})/(80)(10^{-6}) = 25$$

For an ideal case the stability factor should be unity (1). With this condition the small change in ΔI_{co} would result in a similarly small change ΔI_c.

Fig. 11·8   Temperature effects on I_c.

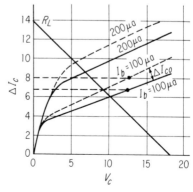

A number of circuit arrangements can be used to hold S within tolerable limits. Values between 3 and 12 can be considered acceptable. Refer to the circuit of Fig. 11·9a. Resistor R_s in the emitter circuit helps to reduce the stability factor. It is often called a *swamping resistor*.

Figure 11·9b is an equivalent circuit. There are two currents through R_s, the collector circuit (1) and the base circuit (2). According to Kirchhoff's law the voltage drops around 2 are

$$V_{bb} = (R_b + R_s)I_b + (R_s)I_c \qquad (11·21)$$

If Eq. (10·14) is solved for I_{co} and I_e is replaced with $I_e = I_b + I_c$ the equation becomes

$$I_c = \alpha(I_b + I_c) + I_{co}$$
$$I_{co} = (-\alpha)I_b + (1 - \alpha)I_c \qquad (11·22)$$

If Eqs. (11·21) and (11·22) are solved simultaneously for I_c the resultant is

$$V_{bb} = (R_b + R_s)I_b + (R_s)I_c$$
$$I_{co} = (-\alpha)I_b + (1 - \alpha)I_c$$
$$I_c = \frac{(R_b + R_s)(I_{co}) + V_{bb}\alpha}{(R_b + R_s)(1 - \alpha) + R_s}$$
$$I_c = \frac{(R_b + R_s)I_{co}}{R_b + R_s - R_b\alpha} + \frac{V_{bb}\alpha}{R_b + R_s - R_b\alpha} \qquad (11·23)$$

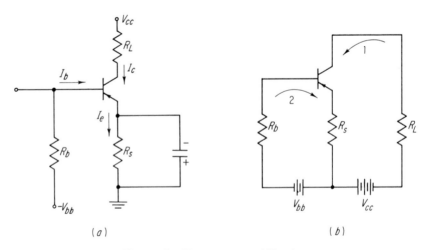

(a)   (b)

Fig. 11·9   Temperature stabilization.

Since I_{co} is contained only in the first term, the circuit conditions of the second term do not influence the stability factor.

Solving the first term of Eq. (11·23) for $\Delta I_c / \Delta I_{co}$ results in

$$S = \frac{\Delta I_c}{\Delta I_{co}} = \frac{R_s + R_b}{R_s + (1 - \alpha)R_b} \qquad (11 \cdot 24)$$

EXAMPLE EIGHT   What is the stability factor for the circuit of Fig. 11·9 if $\alpha = 0.98$, $R_b = 5$ kilohms, and $R_s = 1$ kilohm? What is the S if R_s is decreased to zero?

SOLUTION   According to Eq. (11·24),

$$S = \frac{(10^3 + (5)(10^3)}{10^3 + (1 - 0.98)(5)(10^3)} = \frac{(6)(10^3)}{(1.1)(10^3)} = 5.45$$

If R_s is replaced with a short circuit the stability-factor equation becomes

$$S = \frac{R_b}{(1 - \alpha)R_b} = \frac{1}{1 - \alpha} = \frac{1}{0.02} = 50$$

The stability factor of a circuit can be improved by making R_s large and R_b small. There are, of course, practical limitations to how much resistance can be introduced in the emitter circuit. If the value of R_s approaches more than one-tenth the value of R_L, the R_s must be considered in d-c load-line calculations.

Once the stability factor of a given circuit is known, the influence of temperature changes can be predicted.

EXAMPLE NINE   The 2N139 lists a collector-cutoff current of 6 μa at 25°C. Assume this germanium transistor has an α of 0.978 and is connected in a circuit whose stability factor is 10. What is the change in quiescent collector current if the ambient temperature increases to 45°C? What would the stability factor be without a stabilization resistor R_s?

SOLUTION   The leakage current for a germanium transistor doubles for every 10°C increase. Hence the change in leakage current is

$$\Delta I_{co} = 24\mu a$$

Since

$$S = \Delta I_c / \Delta I_{co}$$
$$\Delta I_c = (S)(\Delta I_{co}) = (10)(24)(10^{-6}) = 0.24 \text{ ma}$$

If the circuit did not include any stabilization, the factor would be

$$S = \frac{1}{1 - \alpha} = \frac{1}{1 - 0.978} = 45.45$$

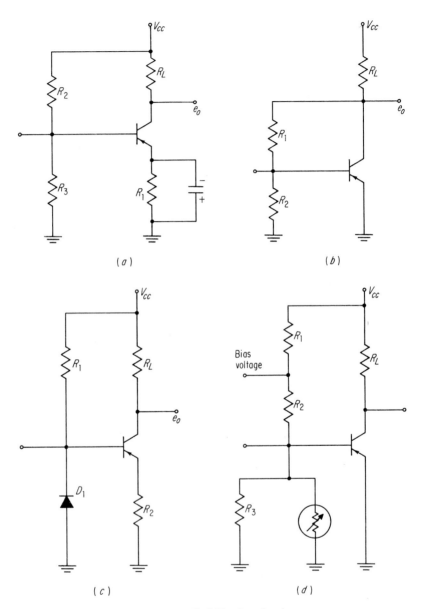

Fig. 11·10   Stabilization circuits.

226

Many forms of compensation are used to improve the stability factor. More complicated circuit arrangements provide good stabilization but also provide poorer circuit efficiency. Diodes and temperature-sensitive elements are also used in compensation circuits. Figure 11·10 illustrates four typical stabilization circuits.

The circuit of Fig. 11·10a represents a very popular stabilization circuit. Resistors R_1, R_2, and R_3 make up the principal stabilization network.

$$S = \frac{\Delta I_c}{\Delta I_{co}} = 1 + \frac{R_2 R_3}{R_1(R_2 + R_3)} \qquad (11·25)$$

A second circuit which provides good stabilization is shown in Fig. 11·10b and is called *voltage-feedback stabilization*. The stability factor is given as

$$S = \Delta I_c/\Delta I_{co} = 1 + R_1/R_L \qquad (11·26)$$

where the value of R_1 is the quiescent collector voltage divided by the quiescent base-bias current.

The circuit of Fig. 11·10c employs a junction diode as stabilization. The diode's changing resistance (it is forward-biased) with temperature changes alters the bias point on the transistor output characteristics. The stability factor for such a circuit must be determined experimentally.

The stabilization circuit of Fig. 11·10d employs a *thermistor*. Since the thermistor's resistance decreases with increases in temperature, the bias current is controlled. The resultant is a fairly constant I_c within a wide range of temperature changes.

11·10 PHASE RELATIONSHIPS AND CIRCUIT CONFIGURATIONS

Section 3·4 of Chapter 3 outlined the voltage phase relationships for the three circuit configurations. A common-cathode vacuum-tube amplifier inverts the phase of the incoming wave by 180° (see Fig. 3·9). The other two circuit configurations, common grid and common plate, produce no voltage phase shift (Fig. 3·11).

In transistor amplifier circuits the phase considerations are exactly the same as those of the vacuum tube counterpart. That is, the common-emitter amplifier (equivalent of common cathode) inverts the input voltage by 180°. The other two circuit configurations provide no phase shift of voltage. The output voltage in the common-collector configuration is taken across the emitter resistor; hence it is in phase with the input voltage.

For the common-emitter circuit refer to Fig. 11 · 5a. Note that the voltage across the 2N1154 is 18 volts (Fig. 11 · 5c). When e_{in} goes negative the transistor current bias increases (more current flows into the base); hence more current flows in the collector. The movement along the load line is from point C toward point B. Note that the voltage across the resistor R_L is increasing with increasing current i_c. The result is a less negative (or positive-going) voltage at e_o. The output has a 180° phase reversal.

For the common-base circuit of Fig. 11 · 5b, if the voltage at e_{in} goes negative, the forward bias between emitter and base is decreasing; hence less input current flow. In Fig. 11 · 5d the point on the load line is moving down from point Q. Collector current is decreasing; hence the voltage across R_L is decreasing. The result is that the voltage at e_o is becoming more negative. The output voltage is in phase with the input voltage.

The student need not confuse himself by trying to remember current phase relationships. None of the three circuit configurations introduces a phase shift. That is for all circuits, the output current is in phase with the input driving current.

Some of the literature introduces a great deal of confusion by using negative signs in the circuit equations. Often the student will be told that the current gain parameter of the device has a negative sign ($h_{fb} = -0.98$). Such signs should be disregarded since they serve only to confuse. Remember that all device parameters are positive quantities. Only one circuit parameter, A_{ve}, should carry with it a negative sign ($-A_{ve}$) where this sign merely denotes a 180° phase shift.

Problems

11 · 24   Assume a transistor in a common-emitter configuration is to develop 30 ma of base bias. This bias is to be developed by connecting a resistor from the base to a 24-volt collector supply. What value of resistance is needed?

11 · 25   Assume that a 2N1154 is to be connected as shown in Fig. 11·5a. If the load resistor $R_L = 1.2$ kilohms, $V_{cc} = 55$ volts, and $R_a = 2$ kilohms, what value of base bias V_{bb} is needed to bias the device in the center of the peak-to-peak collector-current swing?

11 · 26   If the circuit of Prob. 11 · 25 were changed to a common-base configuration, what value of bias supply voltage is needed?

11 · 27   If the transistor of Prob. 11 · 13 were used in an unstabilized common-emitter amplifier, what would be the stability factor?

11 · 28   Refer to Prob. 11 · 27. If the transistor were replaced with one having a

large β, would the unstabilized stability factor increase, decrease, or remain unchanged?

11·29 A 2N223 is connected as shown in Fig. 11·9a. $R_L = 3$ kilohms, $R_b = 5$ kilohms, $V_{cc} = 30$ volts, $V_{bb} = 4$ volts, and $R_s = 800$ ohms. What are (a) the current gain of the stage, (b) the stability factor of the stage?

11·30 If the value of R_s in Prob. 11·29 is increased to 1,200 ohms, what are (a) the new stability factor, (b) the new current gain?

11·31 Refer to the circuit of Prob. 11·29. What value of R_s should be connected into the circuit to produce a stability factor of 15?

11·32 Assume a given germanium transistor is connected in a circuit as shown in Fig. 11·10a. If the leakage current at 25°C is given as 10 μa and the circuit's stability factor is 8, what is the change in collector current if the temperature increases to 55°C?

11·33 Refer to the circuit of Fig. 11·10a. If $V_{ec} = 20$ volts, $R_L = 2$ kilohms, $R_1 = 1$ kilohm, $R_2 = 5$ kilohms, $R_3 = 2$ kilohms, and the transistor is a 2N175, what is the stability factor of the circuit?

11·34 Refer to Prob. 11·33. If the value of R_2 is doubled, what is the new stability factor?

11·35 Refer to Prob. 11·33. If the value of R_3 is decreased to half, will the new stability factor increase, decrease, or remain unchanged?

Review Questions

11·1 What are the five basic transistor circuit parameters?

11·2 How do changes in resistive load on a transistor amplifier influence (a) the current gain, (b) the voltage gain, (c) the power gain?

11·3 How do changes in the resistive load on a transistor amplifier influence (a) the quiescent voltage at the collector, (b) the input resistance to the stage?

11·4 Increasing the bias current into the base of a common-emitter amplifier has what influence on the collector current?

11·5 Why is it more practical to use a common-emitter configuration compared with common-base?

11·6 What is the maximum possible voltage gain available from a common-collector amplifier?

11·7 Why is a swamping resistor used in the emitter lead of a common-emitter amplifier?

11·8 What are the disadvantages of using a thermistor in a stabilization circuit?

XII

GAS-FILLED TUBES

12·1 INTRODUCTION

Because vacuum tubes which contain residual gases cause tube operation to be erratic, as much gas as possible is removed through the use of magnesium or metallic barium getters. Though gas causes erratic operation in ordinary vacuum tubes, specially designed gas-filled tubes are capable of carrying larger currents, functioning with higher efficiency, performing high-speed switching operations, and operating as voltage regulators. For an understanding of how these functions are possible, a discussion of electrical conduction in gas is presented.

12·2 IONIZATION

Ionization is the process by which atoms of gas lose or gain electrons through their exchange of energy from either cosmic radiation (ever-present high-energy waves from the atmosphere), heat, light photons, or a voltage potential. An atom of gas that loses an electron is said to be positively ionized, one that has gained an electron negatively ionized. Since the word *ion* is not so definitive as an electron, proton, or neutron in terms of polarity of electrical charge, it will be assumed to be positive because of the predominance of positive ions in electric-gas phenomena. Consider Fig. 12·1. Atom 1 is a positive ion; atom 2 is a negative ion. The arrows indicate the path of travel for each atom in accordance with the laws of electricity. Ions react similarly to electrons and holes in an electrostatic field. They are, of course, many thousands of times heavier than electrons. A gas tube has several billion of such atoms traveling about within the envelope. Initially, ions are formed by the effect of light photons and cosmic rays forcing the atom to give up an electron (atom 1 in Fig. 12·1). The potential *E* in millivolts is large enough to create an attractive force, and current flows. Such a condition will require more atoms between the plates of Fig. 12·1. This current is called *dark current*. The dark current will remain in the microampere region at low levels of applied voltage. No noticeable light or glow will be given off since energy transfer is at a low level.

Note that thermionic emission has no part in the ionization of the atoms shown in Fig. 12·1. All movement is created by external forces (light photons, cosmic rays) and sustained by potential *E*. A definite concentration of ions is reached, however, and a process called *recombination* begins. In recombination, ions recombine to become neutral atoms. Recombination occurs as ions and electrons chance to drift toward one another. As voltage potential *E* is increased, however, there is less chance of recombination because of increased direct travel and less random electron-ion movement. Two other factors controlling recombination are gas pressure and electrode spacing.

The foregoing can be summed up by referring to Paschen's law. Paschen, a nineteenth century physicist, found a relationship between ignition potential, electrode spacing, and gas density. If the length of the

Fig. 12·1   Ion travel.

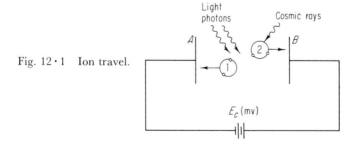

gas tube is doubled and gas pressure is reduced to one-half, the ignition voltage does not change. If the length of the tube is tripled and the pressure remains the same, the ignition potential must be raised to three times its former value to keep discharge constant. An equation expresses this relationship:

$$L = i/g \qquad\qquad (12\cdot1)$$

where L = length of tube
i = ignition potential
g = gas pressure

Thus recombination can be postponed if gas pressure is reduced and ignition potential increased.

12·3 CHARACTERISTICS OF COLD-CATHODE GAS DIODES

In diodes ionization occurs in two ways, one by means of thermionically emitting electrons which bombard the gas atoms and second by applying an electrostatic potential to the tube elements large enough to force electrons and gas atoms to collide. This second method applies to cold-cathode diodes since the cathode is not thermionically heated.

Gas atoms have a neutral electrical charge and are not affected by electrostatic fields. In order for a gas atom to become an ion and support a current flow, the electrons must receive enough energy to leave the parent atom. This energy comes from cosmic rays, radioactive air particles, and light photons.

Figure 12·2 shows a circuit used to measure current in a cold-cathode tube. Resistance R is necessary to limit current in the tube following complete ignition. I_b is the current and V is the voltage measured between plate and cathode. As E_{bb} is increased slowly, ions formed by natural sources such as cosmic rays produce a low current on the order of a few microamperes. This current is called *dark current* or *threshold current*.

Figure 12·3 plots the conduction stages of a cold-cathode diode. Current rises and remains steady from point 1 to point 2 in the region

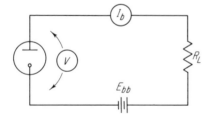

Fig. 12·2   Circuit for measuring cold-cathode emission.

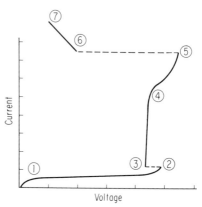

Fig. 12·3 Cold-cathode-emission characteristic.

of *dark* current. At point 1 dark current begins to saturate. Saturation at this low current is possible because the ionization rate from natural sources is relatively low and few electrons are drawn to the plate and equally few positive ions return to the cathode. Available electrons are quickly used, and further increase in voltage does not increase current.

As voltage is further increased toward point 2, current will gradually increase because the higher plate voltage increases the velocity of the few electrons available by natural ionization. The current up to point 2 is a non-self-maintained ionization. At point 2 not only does the voltage accelerate the gas electrons, but also the positive gas ions receive enough energy to move toward the cathode at a greater velocity. The positive ion bombardment dislodges electrons from the cathode through second-ary emission. The heat produced from the bombarding positive ions in-creases the cathode temperature to primary emission levels. More electrons are emitted. At this point the tube acquires a self-maintaining glow discharge. This condition is shown as point 3 to point 4 in Fig. 12·3. This is the normal glow-discharge region for most cold-cathode tubes. Note that the voltage necessary to maintain normal discharge has decreased. This is due to more complete ionization. There is less of a potential difference between cathode and plate because of relatively equal numbers of electrons, positive ions, and their recombinations. Current is limited only by resistance external to the tube. As voltage is raised beyond point 4, saturation again occurs because of the limited number of free electrons. At point 5 voltage has increased enough to cause an increased number of positive ions to bombard the cathode, rais-ing the cathode temperature, emitting more electrons, and resulting in increased current. The current pattern from points 4 to 5 is referred to as the *abnormal*. From points 5 to 6, a sharp reduction in voltage precedes the *arc-discharge* region from points 6 to 7. The arc discharge exhibits intense glow and increases in current until one or more circuit components fail.

Tubes of this type are usually used as voltage regulators, references, or rectifiers. One common cold-cathode tube found in millions of auto radios and used as a rectifier is the 0Z4. Voltage regulation, however, is a more popular application. The 0A2, 0B2, and 0D2 family of cold-cathode tubes serve as voltage regulators.

12·4 VOLTAGE REGULATORS

Refer to Fig. 12·3. The area from points 3 to 4 is the normal ionization region. Note that voltage remains almost constant from points 3 to 4 while current increases. This is the principal requirement for a voltage regulator.

If the 0B2 characteristics were analyzed, it would be seen that the 0B2 is a cold-cathode glow-discharge tube capable of maintaining a constant d-c output of 107 volts independent of load and line variations. Refer to Fig. 12·4. Note the following characteristics in the curves of Fig. 12·4:

Maximum d-c cathode current   30 ma
Minimum d-c cathode current   5 ma

The 30 ma is comparable with point 4 in Fig. 12·3. The 5-ma point compares with point 3 in the same figure. The *maximum inverse voltage* rating is the peak voltage on the cathode with respect to the plate before breakdown. For the 0B2, this value is −50 volts. The tube requires 130 volts to start a self-sustaining discharge comparable with the voltage at point 2 in Fig. 12·3.

Figure 12·5 illustrates a typical circuit for a voltage regulator. Proper operation of a voltage regulator requires a supply voltage E_{in} greater than the starting voltage for the tube. Resistor R_s must be within proper range to limit the current I to the given maximum and minimum current ratings for the tube. Refer to Fig. 12·5. Consider the three conditions under which tube current I_t will be maximum:

1. When E_{in} is maximum
2. When I_L is minimum
3. When E_L is minimum

The value of R_s must be within the following boundaries:

$$R_s > \frac{E_{in}(\text{max}) - E_L(\text{min})}{I_T(\text{max}) + I_L(\text{min})} \qquad (12 \cdot 2)$$

$$R_s < \frac{E_{in}(\text{min}) - E_L(\text{max})}{I_T(\text{min}) + I_L(\text{max})} \qquad (12 \cdot 3)$$

Once the value of R_s is determined, a double check is necessary to determine if the starting potential for the tube is high enough. If the starting voltage is given as E_x then

$$E_x \leqq \frac{R_L E_{in}}{R_s + R_L} \qquad (12 \cdot 4)$$

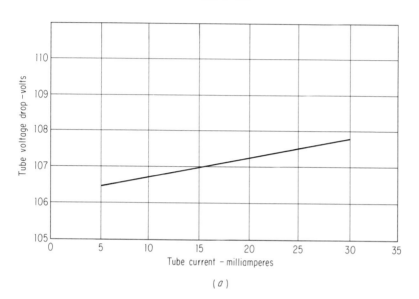

(a)

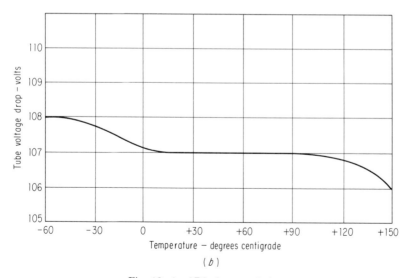

(b)

Fig. 12·4   0B2 characteristics.

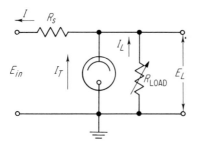

Fig. 12·5   Voltage regulator.

EXAMPLE ONE   If a 5651 voltage regulator is used in Fig. 12·5. Given a constant load current of 2 ma and 5651 ratings; tube operating voltage = 85 volts. Minimum tube current = 1.5 ma. Maximum tube current = 3.5 ma. Starting voltage = 115 volts. Maximum E_{in} = 300 volts. Find the necessary series resistance and minimum input voltage to operate the circuit.

$$R_L = \frac{E_L}{I_L} = \frac{85}{(2)(10^{-3})} = 43 \text{ kilohms}$$

$$R_s = \frac{E_{in}(\text{max}) - E_L}{I_T(\text{max}) + I_L} = \frac{300 - 85}{(3.5)(10^{-3}) - (2)(10^{-3})} = 39 \text{ kilohms}$$

$$E_{in}(\text{min}) = \frac{(E_{\text{start}})(R_s + R_L)}{R_L} = \frac{(115)(39 + 43)(10^3)}{(43)(10^3)} = 220 \text{ volts}$$

Note that *load current* was constant and input voltage varied, producing tube-current changes. What is the minimum tube current, and is it within the limits of the tube rating?

$$I_T(\text{min}) = \frac{E_{in}(\text{min}) - E_L}{R_s} - I_L$$

$$= \frac{220 - 85}{(39)(10^3)} - 0.002 = 1.5 \text{ ma}$$

which is equal to the tube minimum of 1.5 ma and could be expected to fall within the operating range.

12·5 THERMIONIC GAS DIODES

CHARACTERISTICS

Thermionic gas diodes function efficiently as rectifiers with less tube-voltage drop for the same reasons as do cold-cathode tubes. The advantage of heated-cathode operation is that less starting voltage is required, as illustrated in Fig. 12·6. In addition, note the area ABC; the gas diode reaches ionization potential more quickly than the plate voltage on the vacuum diode. A typical circuit used to develop gas-diode characteristics is shown in Fig. 12·7a with the characteristic in Fig. 12·7b. Before applying plate voltage to the tube, it is important to allow a minute or

Fig. 12·6   Vacuum- and gas-diode comparison.

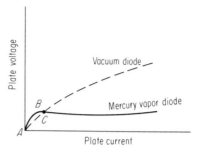

two for the cathode to attain operating temperature. If plate voltage were applied immediately, cold-cathode operation would follow, resulting in cathode damage. Thermionic gas diodes have oxide-coated cathodes and hence cannot operate effectively as cold-cathode emitters. Note the constant-voltage variable-current characteristic similar to points 3 to 4 of Fig. 12·3.

POTENTIAL DISTRIBUTION

Figure 12·8 reveals typical tube potential voltage distribution. Current rises almost immediately as voltage is increased because of the ready supply of electrons from the heated cathode. This characteristic is followed by a linear plasma region and a slight voltage rise or drop as electrons approach the plate. Plasma means a combination of electrons, ions, and neutral gas atoms. As an electron emitted from the cathode approaches and bombards a neutral gas atom it dislodges an electron

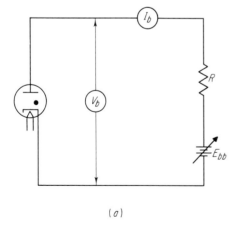

(a)

Fig. 12·7a   Thermionic-gas-diode test circuit.

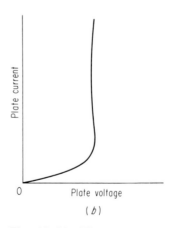

(b)

Fig. 12·7b   Thermionic-gas-diode characteristic.

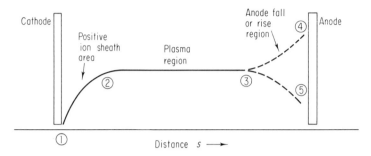

Fig. 12·8   Voltage distribution.

from the atom. The gas atom is now a positive ion and is attracted to the negative cathode. There are now two electrons to bombard two more gas atoms, thus producing more available electrons. The gas ions form a positive ion *sheath* around the cathode, waiting their turn to be neutralized (pick up an electron). The ion sheath creates a positive potential from points 1 to 2 in Fig. 12·8. The plasma region is constant because a balance is established between the number of electrons, ions, and gas atoms between the plate and cathode. As electrons approach the plate a rise in potential results because of the increased physical area and external voltage potential. The rise or dip is called the *anode* or *dip space*.

12·6 THYRATRONS

Thyratrons are three- or four-element gas tubes. Figure 12·9a shows a typical thyratron symbol. The 6D4 shown in Fig. 12·9b and c is an argon-filled triode with negative control-grid characteristics. The 6D4 is used as a relay control-tube sawtooth oscillator or as an R_L noise generator in compact and portable equipment. Figure 12·9d illustrates a circuit for developing control-grid characteristics.

CONTROL-GRID ACTION

The thyratron acts as a triode below the ionization voltage. Plate current increases as plate voltage increases and is dependent upon the negative value of grid bias. Below ionization the grid voltage can be varied to control plate current. When ionization occurs, positive gas ions neutralize the triode space charge, increasing the current and reducing the voltage drop of the tube. Positive ions are simultaneously attracted to the control grid, canceling its negative effect. Once ionization occurs, the control grid can no longer function as a control of plate current. The control-grid function is to determine what plate voltage is necessary to ionize the tube.

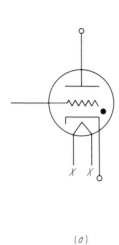

(a)

Fig. 12·9a   Thyratron symbol.

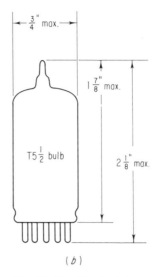

(b)

Fig. 12·9b   Physical characteristics, 6D4 thyratron.

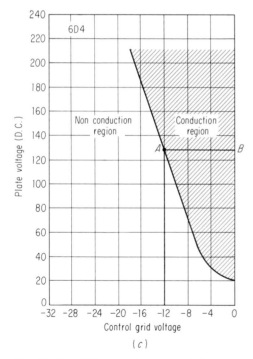

(c)

Fig. 12·9c   6D4 control characteristics.

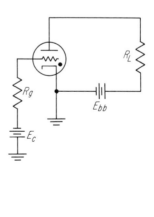

(d)

Fig. 12·9d   Test circuit for thyratron characteristic.

239

Refer to Fig. 12·9c. Point A represents a grid voltage of -12 volts. The tube will ionize when the plate potential is at approximately 127 volts (point B). Similarly at 180 volts on the plate the 6D4 will ionize when the grid voltage is -16 volts or less. The shaded area represents the conduction region.

To regain grid control once the tube has ionized, plate voltage must be reduced below the ionization potential by one of three ways:

1. Opening the plate circuit
2. Lowering the plate voltage
3. Reversing the plate voltage by applying an alternating current between plate and cathode

As the tube ages, the ambient operating temperature rating varies, the heater voltage fluctuates, and gas pressure will be affected. The operating curve of Fig. 12·9c will be affected and the ionization voltage may vary. Because of aging and because of the general unreliability of working with ionization the characteristic curves for gas tubes are only good approximations. A wide variation is possible even within the same classification. Note the characteristics for tubes of the same type as illustrated by Fig. 12·10.

Consider the circuit of Fig. 12·11a. When an a-c voltage is applied to the primary of the transformer the secondary will see a stepped-up alternating current. E_c is the grid-bias voltage for the tube and is used to control the firing point of the tube. R_g is a grid-current-limiting resistor. It

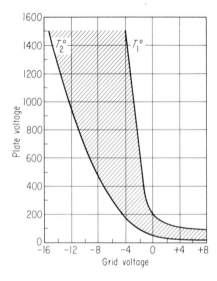

Fig. 12·10   Thyratron comparison.

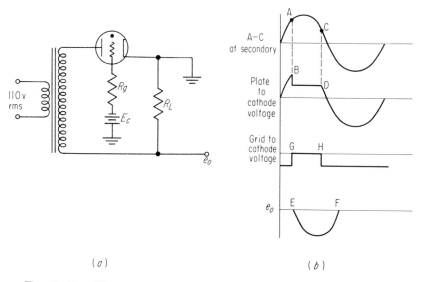

(*a*)

Fig. 12·11*a*   Thyratron rectifier.

(*b*)

Fig. 12·11*b*   Voltage waveshapes.

is mostly a protection device. Assume that E_c has been set at a suitable negative voltage to cause the tube to ionize at point B (Fig. 12·11*b*) when the secondary voltage reaches point A. The output voltage will go negative because of current in the counterclockwise direction for the period of time from E to F. At point C the secondary voltage is low enough to deionize the tube, causing current to cease through the load resistance. Note that from G to H in Fig. 12·11*b* the grid-to-cathode voltage goes positive during tube conduction. The amount of voltage from 0 volt to point D is the deionization voltage of the tube.

EXAMPLE TWO   (Refer to Fig. 12·11*a*)   An 884 thyratron is to be used as a rectifier with a load resistance of 10 kilohms. E_c is set to -14 volts and R_g is 500 kilohms. The peak secondary voltage is 200 volts. The 884 deionizes at approximately 16 volts. What will be the peak voltage across R_L? What is the peak load current?

SOLUTION   Refer to Fig. 12·12 for the 884 characteristics. It can be seen from the curve that with -14 volts on the grid, the 884 will fire (ionize) at 140 volts. Therefore, when the secondary voltage reaches 140 volts on its positive swing, the tube will ionize, dropping the tube voltage to 16 volts and dropping 140 − 16 volts, or 124 volts, across R_L. As the secondary voltage reaches 200 volts, the R_L voltage increases negatively to 184 *volts peak* (as shown in Fig. 12·11*b*). The peak load current thus becomes

$$184/(10^4) = 18.4 \text{ ma}$$

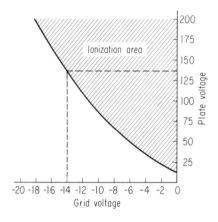

Fig. 12·12   Grid voltage, ionization characteristic.

TYPES OF CONTROL-GRID VOLTAGES

There are three types of voltages which may be used on the thyratron control grid:

1. D-C bias
2. A-C voltage (sinusoidal varying at the same frequency as the plate potential)
3. Pulse voltages

Refer to Fig. 12·12. Ionization can be predicted from the characteristic curve. For example, if the control grid were held at −8 volts, the plate potential necessary for ionization would be approximately 65 volts. Conversely, if the plate voltage were held at 50 volts, −6 volts on the control grid would be necessary to fire the tube. The graph of Fig. 12·12 is adequate to show the relationship of d-c potentials, but not for a-c voltages.

CRITICAL CONTROL-GRID CHARACTERISTICS

Figure 12·13 shows the development of the *critical control-grid characteristic* for a thyratron with an a-c plate voltage. The purpose is to show the relationship between the a-c plate voltage and grid voltage to produce the required ionization. Initially, points *A* through *D* taken from the d-c grid- and plate-voltage curve such as Fig. 12·12 were transferred to points *A'* through *D'* on the positive a-c plate-voltage wave. Dropping each point down until it intersects it with the predrawn vertical grid-voltage scale produces points *E* through *H*, creating the critical grid-voltage curve. Point *B*, which represents 65 volts at the plate, requires a grid voltage of −6 volts to fire the tube. Of course, anything less negative will cause ionization to occur.

USING THE CONTROL-GRID CHARACTERISTIC

Consider the circuit of Fig. 12·11a. E_c is set at 16 volts; however, the grid will be approximately − 8 volts when the secondary voltage (a-c plate-voltage supply) has a peak of 130 volts. Through use of the critical control-grid characteristic curve, selection of the proper grid voltage can be made depending upon how much rectification of the secondary voltage is needed. For example, refer to Fig. 12·14. With the grid-to-cathode voltage at − 8 volts, the tube fires when the plate voltage reaches slightly above 50 volts positive. The tube then conducts until the plate voltage drops to zero.

Note that the grid-to-cathode voltage of 16 volts is too negative to affect the firing potential to the tube. In fact, − 10 volts between grid and cathode would be needed to fire the tube at 130 volts.

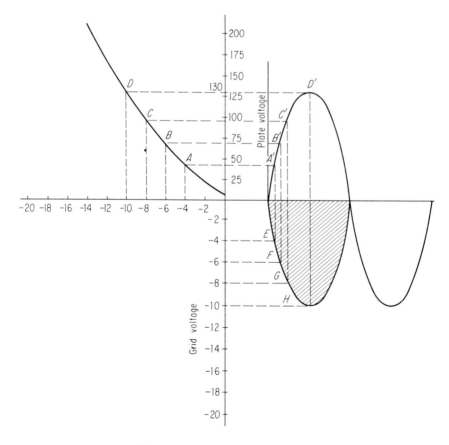

Fig. 12·13   Grid-control transfer.

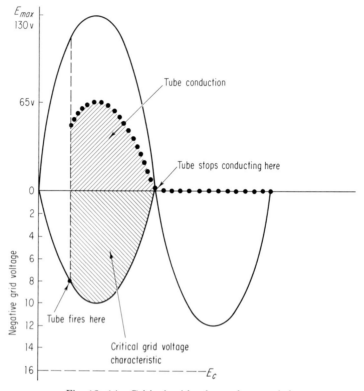

Fig. 12·14   Critical grid-voltage characteristic.

SHIELDED-GRID THYRATRONS

A four-element thyratron is referred to as a shielded-grid thyratron. By addition of the shielded-grid interelectrode capacitance between the control grid and cathode is reduced since less control-grid current will flow. Figure 12·15a illustrates shielded-grid thyratron construction and its symbol. The shielded grid can be either positive or negative in relation to the cathode. Figure 12·15b shows the characteristic curve for the Tung-Sol 5643 subminiature shielded-grid thyratron often used as a switching tube, counter, or grid-controlled rectifier. Because of its shielded-grid construction and resultant high input impedance, it requires no preceding isolation stage and will work directly from a vacuum phototube or cadmium sulfide photocell. With no resistance in the shielded-grid circuit R_{G2} and 100 kilohms in the control-grid circuit, the 5643 will fire at a shielded-grid voltage of -4 volts, a control-grid voltage of 4 volts, and an anode voltage of approximately 50 volts. If the characteristics of Fig. 12·15b are compared with control characteristics for a three-element thyratron, it can be seen that a great deal more versatility of operation is possible for the shielded-grid thyratron. Less grid current flows because of hollow-cylinder construction, reducing thermionic emission and interelectrode capacitance and enabling the shielded-grid thyratron to produce more exact control characteristics.

APPLICATIONS

From the previous discussion the following facts concerning thyratrons should be apparent:

1. The grid potential controls the firing point of the tube.
2. Grid bias may be either a-c or d-c.

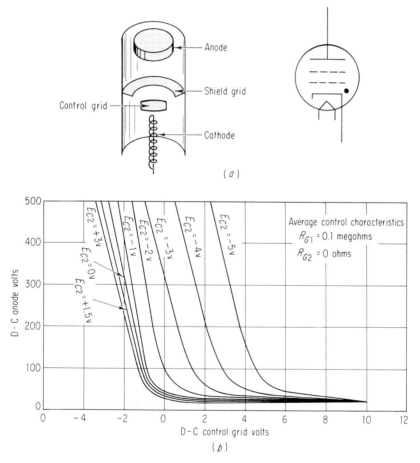

Fig. 12·15   (a) Shielded-grid thyratron; (b) characteristic for Tung-Sol 5643.

3. The grid acts as a starter, and once the tube fires it has no more control.
4. The thyratron can be fired at any predetermined plate potential by selection of proper bias from the critical control-grid characteristic curve.

Because of these versatile characteristics, many practical circuits use thyratrons. The circuit of Fig. 12·16 is called a holding circuit. Its function is to connect a load through a relay in the plate circuit upon reception of light from the phototube. With no-light conditions the thyratron remains deionized because of the negative potential of E_c. The relay contacts in the plate circuit are open. When a proper level of light impinges upon the cathode of the phototube, a current flow develops a voltage drop across R, with the polarity as indicated. The voltage drop across R is large enough to overcome E_c, causing the control grid to go positive, firing the tube, closing the relay, and thus connecting the load. Such a device could be used, for instance, at a supermarket cashier stand to drive the rotating platform moving grocery items during checkout. As long as the light path is unbroken, the rotating-platform motor (the load) continues to drive the platform. However, when any grocery item blocks the light path from the light source to the phototube, current closes in the phototube circuit, eliminating the voltage drop across R and cutting off current through the thyratron.

Figure 12·17 shows another circuit used in response indication such as that used on TV quiz shows or in physiological testing devices. Assuming that switch S_1 opens first, a high negative bias from E_c is removed from the grid of V_1. Immediately V_1 conducts, closing relay 1. As V_1 conducts a voltage is developed across R_1 of sufficient amplitude to hold V_2 off. R is a common-cathode resistor to V_1 and V_2. If S_2 were

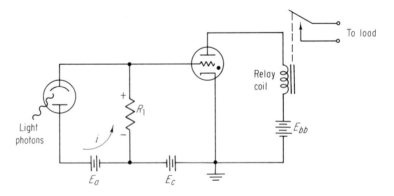

Fig. 12·16   Relay control.

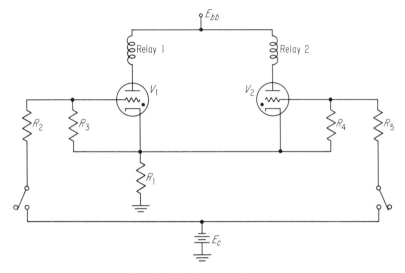

Fig. 12·17   Reaction circuit.

opened after S_1 was opened, it could not ionize V_2 and close relay 2 because of voltage drop across R_1. The circuit is used to indicate which
switch was opened first.

Problems

12·1   If the ON voltage of a gas diode is 70 volts and the circuit is in series with
a 3-kilohm resistor, what is the current through the diode if 150 volts d-c
is applied to the circuit?

12·2   If the resistor in the circuit of Prob. 12·1 is doubled, is the voltage across
the diode increased, decreased, or unchanged?

12·3   A 6542 voltage regulator has the following ratings:

Anode operating voltage   147 volts
Minimum tube current   5 ma
Maximum tube current   25 ma
Starting ionization voltage   185 volts

If a maximum supply voltage of 350 volts is to be used in the circuit of
Fig. 12·7, find (*a*) the load resistance, (*b*) the minimum supply voltage
for circuit operation.

12·4   If the maximum voltage of Prob. 12·3 is reduced from 350 to 300 volts,
what is the new value for (*a*) load resistance, (*b*) minimum supply voltage
for circuit operation?

12·5   A 5651 is to be used in the circuit of Fig. 12·18 so that it will draw 2.5 ma
of current. If the supply voltage E_{in} is 250 volts and R_1 is 620 kilohms, what
is the value of R_2? Refer to the 5651 characteristics (Fig. 12·19).

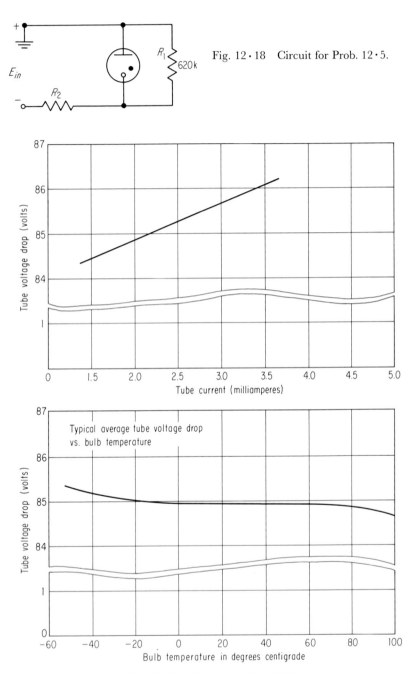

Fig. 12·18 Circuit for Prob. 12·5.

Fig. 12·19 Characteristics (5651).

248

12·6   If the load resistance R_1 in Prob. 12·5 is decreased to 400 kilohms, what new value of R_2 will be required?

12·7   An 884 thyratron is to be used in the circuit of Fig. 12·16. The relay in the plate circuit has a resistance of 2 kilohms and operates with a current of 17 ma. If the phototube has an anode current of 1 ma during illumination and $E_c = -10$ volts, (a) what value of R_1 is necessary to fire the tube at 50 volts? (*Note:* The 884 normally ionizes at 50 volts with a grid-to-cathode voltage of 6 volts.) (b) What supply voltage is necessary for the 884?

12·8   Refer to Prob. 12·7. If the phototube is replaced with one whose output is 5 ma at maximum illumination, what value of R_1 is necessary to fire the tube at 50 volts?

12·9   Draw the schematic of a thyratron half-wave rectifier as shown in Fig. 12·11a. If an 884 is used and the load resistor is 5 kilohms, $R_g = 100$ kilohms and the input to the primary is 110 volts rms. Assume a transformer turns ratio of 2:1 and $E_c = 10$ volts. What is the peak voltage across R_L? What is the peak load current?

12·10 Refer to Prob. 12·9. If the peak voltage across the load must be 200 volts, what value must the α of the transformer be?

XIII
SPECIAL-PURPOSE SEMICONDUCTOR DEVICES

13·1 INTRODUCTION

Following the discovery of the transistor and subsequent experimentation, many special semiconductor devices came into being. This chapter will examine three- and four-element devices.

13·2 THE SILICON CONTROLLED RECTIFIER

The silicon controlled rectifier (SCR) is a four-layer semiconductor device. Functionally it operates as sort of a solid-state thyratron. The SCR has greater efficiency but less current-handling capacity. For example, the SCR has about one-tenth the voltage drop of a thyratron. Its advantages are those of a solid-state component, including longer life, less power consumption, and smaller size. In addition the SCRs turn-on and turn-off time (comparable with ionization and deionization in a thyra-

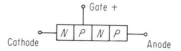

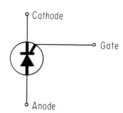

Fig. 13·1 Physical and schematic representation of SCR.

tron) are many times faster than those of the thyratron. Because of these advantages the SCR has replaced the thyratron in practically all recently developed circuits used in power-control, switching, and pulse-generating systems.

THEORY OF OPERATION

Figure 13·1 illustrates the physical construction of the SCR with its symbol. Bias polarities have been included to indicate normal operation. A better understanding of how the SCR works is possible if it is viewed as two transistors as in Fig. 13·2. Note that the equivalence is the same as an NPN and PNP transistor.

Figure 13·2b illustrates a schematic representation of the four-layer

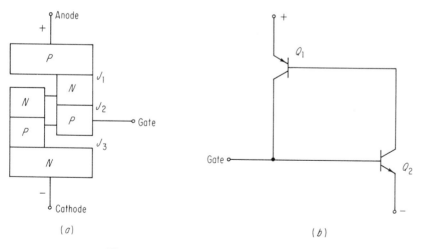

Fig. 13·2 Symbolic equivalent of SCR.

device. Assume that Q_1 has an α_1 and Q_2 has an α_2. Three junctions J_1, J_2, and J_3 represent the connection between the two equivalent transistors.

OFF *Condition.* Assume that the anode is at a positive potential and the cathode is negative with respect to the anode. If there is no signal applied at the gate terminal the device remains off. There is no bias between the base and emitter of Q_2 and hence no collector current at Q_2. With no collector current at Q_2, there is no bias between the base and emitter of Q_1 and hence Q_1 is off and the resistance across all four layers is high. The α of both Q_1 and Q_2 is zero.

ON *Condition.* If a positive voltage is applied between the gate and the cathode the base-emitter junction of Q_2 becomes forward-biased. This current is shown as I_1 of Fig. 13·3. This forward bias increases collector Q_2 current (shown as I_2). The resultant increase in collector current forward-biases the base-emitter junction of Q_1. This forward bias further increases Q_1 collector current (shown at I_3), which further forward-biases Q_2. This feedback loop quickly saturates the device ON. The SCR will remain on even after the positive voltage at the anode at the gate is removed.

In order to turn the device off either the positive voltage at the anode must be removed or a large negative bias must be applied at the gate.

Alpha Analysis. Note in Fig. 13·3, I_1 is a momentary pulse which turns on the device. Once it is on the current flowing into and out of the device is I_2. The collector current of Q_1 is

$$I_{c1} = \alpha_1 I_2 \qquad\qquad (13·1)$$

The collector current of Q_2 is

$$I_{c2} = \alpha_2 I_2 \qquad\qquad (13·2)$$

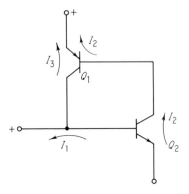

Fig. 13·3   On condition of SCR.

Fig. 13·4 Breakover characteristic.

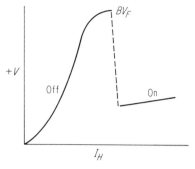

The total current I_2 through the device must be the sum of the two collector currents plus any leakage current I_{co}.

$$I_2 = \alpha_1 I_2 + \alpha_2 I_2 + I_{co} \qquad (13\cdot3)$$

$$I_2 = \frac{I_{co}}{1 - (\alpha_1 + \alpha_2)} \qquad (13\cdot4)$$

Note that when the device is off each of the alphas is zero and hence the current through the device is $I_2 = I_{co}/1 = I_{co}$, the leakage current. When the device is pulsed or forward-biased at the gate, the two alphas begin to increase. When their sum begins to approach unity the denominator approaches zero and the device offers a very low resistance.

Anode Turn-on. The α_1 and α_2 can be increased by increasing the voltage between anode and cathode. If the voltage is increased enough junction J_2 goes into avalanche breakdown and a reverse current will flow through it. The current through J_2 increases, thus increasing α_1 and α_2, causing the SCR to turn on. This avalanche voltage is called the *breakover voltage* BV_F. As long as the current through J_2 causes α_1 and α_2 to remain equal to unity, the SCR will remain on. The minimum current through J_2 necessary to sustain the on condition is called the *holding current* I_H.

The forward-voltage characteristics of an SCR in the OFF and ON states is shown in Fig. 13·4.

The bias at the gate controls the amount of current gain and determines the *breakover voltage* as indicated in Fig. 13·5. BV_{F4} is the lowest breakover voltage corresponding to the maximum amount of gate bias current. BV_{F1} is the highest breakover voltage corresponding to no forward gate bias.

If the gate bias has a forward bias from the start of the total-current total-voltage function, it will approach the dotted-line slope of OP similar to the forward-current curve of an ordinary PN diode.

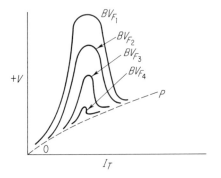

Fig. 13·5   Biased SCR characteristic.

SCR PARAMETERS

Peak Reverse Voltage (PRV). When the device is operated in the reverse direction the SCR acts like an ordinary semiconductor diode. Transient or temporary overvoltage can be withstood if within the PRV rating. The rating is given in SCR specifications. For example, the PRV rating for a 2N1595 is 50 volts when the junction temperature is between -65 and $+150°C$.

Forward Breakover Voltage (VB_F). The forward breakover voltage as identified in Fig. 13·4 is the maximum voltage applied to the SCR anode in the forward direction before the SCR "fires." B_F is sensitive to temperature and gate drive current. As the temperature increases VB_F tends to decrease since breakover occurs sooner.

RMS Forward Current. This is the effective value of anode current flowing from cathode to anode or to 7 percent of the peak forward current. Under ambient temperature conditions, medium-current SCRs like the type 2N1842 will have a 16 amp rms forward current rating.

Peak Forward Blocking Voltage. The symbol PF_V refers to the maximum instantaneous value of forward voltage applied between anode and cathode. If the VB_F forward breakage voltage occurs at a voltage higher than the PF_V, the SCR may be damaged. Typical values for medium-current SCRs are 600 to 700 volts.

Peak One Cycle Surge (or Fault) Current. The symbol I surge refers to the maximum allowable nonrepetitive peak current of a single forward cycle of not more than 8.3 msec duration in a 60-cycle single-phase resistive load system. The term nonrepetitive in this case means that this peak current value should not occur more than from 100 to 500 times during the life of the SCR.

SCR APPLICATIONS

Circuits formerly using thyratrons will now adapt easily to SCR operation. One SCR application is in the area of power switching. Current through the SCR is turned off or "switched" by reversal of a-c voltage. Figure 13·6 shows such a switching circuit for a-c loads. The circuit operates as a relay, eliminating contact, wear, and sticking. These characteristics are with relay operation. The circuit functions as follows: When the top of SCR_1 goes positive because of a change in the a-c input voltage, SCR_1 fires, drawing current through the load resistor. CR_1 and CR_2 control the gate firing potential for each SCR, with R_1 limiting gate current peaks. When the a-c input goes sufficiently negative, SCR_2 will fire, developing a voltage across the load resistor on input negative cycles.

Another circuit utilizes the 2N683, a 25-amp medium-current SCR, as a battery-charger regulator. Figure 13·7 shows the regulator circuit. CR_2 and CR_3 provide full-wave rectified d-c voltage. The SCR is in series with the battery being charged. CR_1 is a zener diode providing a reference voltage for the transistor Q_2. If the battery voltage is lower than the zener voltage, Q_2 will be cut off. At the same time, the emitter of Q_2 is sufficiently positive to conduct into the gate of the SCR, firing it and charging the battery. When the battery is sufficiently charged, Q_2 begins to conduct, reversing the voltage drop across R_1 and cutting off Q_1 and removing the gate signal to the SCR, thus cutting the SCR off. R_2 allows a trickle charge to be maintained across the battery while R_3 is desired. R_4 and R_6 are used for current limiting. R_5 and C_1 provide Q_1 bias and the RC time constant during SCR firing. This circuit has the advantage of automatic charge to trickle charge changeover with little power loss.

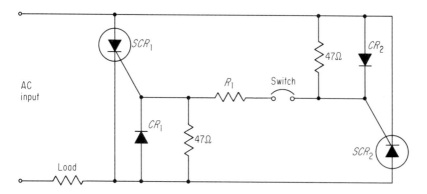

Fig. 13·6   A-C control.

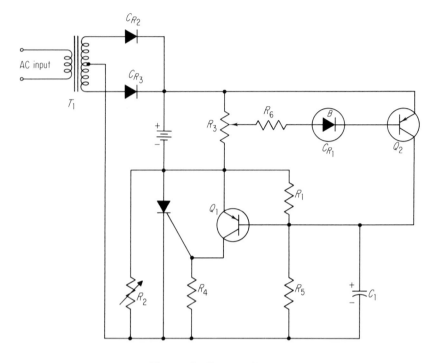

Fig. 13·7   Battery charger.

13·3 THE SILICON CONTROLLED SWITCH

The silicon controlled switch (SCS) is another four-layer semiconductor device quite similar to the SCR. One of the main differences, however, is that the SCS offers many operating advantages. Figure 13·8a shows the SCS block diagram and equivalent circuit.

Note that the trigger input, formerly the gate in the SCR, is now provided at either of the two center layers. The trigger input is used to switch the SCS on or off, dependent upon the circuit conditions. Figure 13·8b shows two schematic symbols.

Consider the two-transistor equivalent circuit of Fig. 13·8c. The collector emitter and base operate in the same manner as any ordinary NPN transistor. Assume that a positive-going signal is applied to the base of the SCS, thus causing the collector voltage to drop similar to normal transistor action. The loop gain rises very rapidly and a regenerative switching action occurs.

In general the SCS is very similar to the SCR. The advantages over

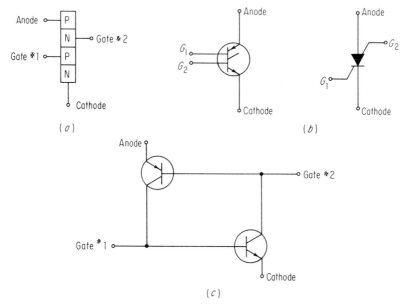

Fig. 13·8   Silicon control switch.

the SCR are faster switching, accurately predictable firing conditions, greater control, and low holding currents.

13·4 FOUR-LAYER DEVICES

Besides the silicon controlled rectifier and silicon controlled switch there are a variety of other four-layer devices.

TRIGISTOR AND TRANSWITCH

These two commercial names are actually the same device. Both are PNPN devices, capable of switching to on and off states. They can

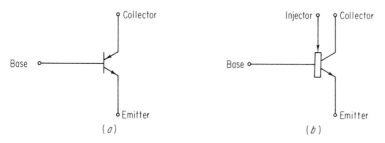

Fig. 13·9   Semiconductor bistable elements.

maintain the on or off state without a bias or holding signal. The schematic symbol for both the trigistor and the transwitch is shown in Fig. 13·9a.

BINISTOR

The binistor is a four-layer device very similar to the SCS, in that every layer is available electrically. Its circuit application is mainly in switching and computer units. The schematic symbol is shown in Fig. 13·9b.

XIV
TUBE
AND
TRANSISTOR
MANUALS

14·1 INTRODUCTION TO MANUALS

Almost every manufacturer of electron devices markets a manual or paperback handbook which lists all the characteristics of each device. The yearly issue of the RCA Tube Manual was for years a standard in the technician's or engineer's library. Today some 22 manuals are available to the electronics man. Some of these are free upon request to the company while others cost a nominal fee.

It would be impossible to present a complete list here. In most cases these manuals are as readily available in bookstores as they are at electronics-parts distributors.

14·2 TUBE MANUAL

The tube manual can be considered a useful tool to understanding vacuum tubes and putting them to practical use. It represents a compilation of data on practically all tubes in commercial and military use. Electrical and mechanical data are provided.

The tube manual seeks to provide all information necessary to satisfy questions on tube characteristics to problems of circuit design.

While the peak in receiving-tube technology has perhaps passed with more recent work in semiconductors, there have been additions to the vacuum-tube field. These additions require frequent revision of tube manuals in an effort to keep up to date.

No one manufacturer is engaged in the production of every tube type. For example, RCA, Sylvania, and others all manufacture the 6SN7. The tube manual produced by each of these companies will carry identical characteristics. The 6BK6 characteristics will not appear in the RCA tube manual because the company does not manufacture the tube. The characteristics for the 6BK6 can, however, be found in the Sylvania tube manual. In order to maintain a complete listing, it is necessary to have every manufacturer's manual on hand.

MANUAL ORGANIZATION

All tube manuals present tube information in alphanumerical order (numerically first and alphabetically second). A 5V4 would come before a 6A7.

Presentation of individual data is generally in a standard format. The tube silhouette and pin connections are given at the top of the page and are followed by the tube's use, such as "pentode amplifier" or "heptode converter." Mechanical data such as size, materials used in the envelope, and tube-socket type follow. The electrical data include typical operation and characteristics when the tube is used as an oscillator, amplifier, converter, etc. Graphs of operating characteristics are also provided. Careful consideration should be made to notes at the bottom of these graphs since electrical data depend on a given set of conditions. If these conditions are unusual and pertinent the notes will provide the necessary modifications.

NOTATION

Notation consists of two main types. One is the basic tube parameters: μ (amplification factor), g_m (transconductance), and r_p (plate resistance). The other consists of symbols referring to the various tube elements. Compare the following list with a tube manual:

$G_1 =$ control grid
$G_2 =$ screen grid
$G_3 =$ suppressor grid

H = heater
P = plate
K = cathode
Su = suppressor grid
F = filament (or heater)
E_{c1} = control-grid voltage (d-c)
E_{c2} = screen-grid voltage (d-c)
I_b = quiescent plate current (d-c)
I_{c2} = quiescent screen-grid current (d-c)
I_{c1} = quiescent control-grid current (d-c)
E_b = d-c plate voltage (measured from plate to cathode)

DATA SHEETS

The data sheets contain the heart of tube information; the mechanical and electrical data including maximum ratings for voltage and power dissipation, characteristics, and typical operation data.

Figure 14·1 is a sample of a typical data sheet. The mechanical-data section provides information concerning bulb and base types and base mounting. The tube described in Fig. 14·1 has three different bulb and base types depending upon its application. For instance, a metal bulb (outline 8-6) would be used in lower-power-dissipation circuits. The notations ST-14 and T-9 refer to different envelope varieties (glass) of the same tube capable of different heat dissipation.

Basing gives the proper socket diagrams showing pin connections. Figure 14·2 shows pin connections and tube elements. This particular tube can be mounted in any position and its operation will not be affected.

Electrical data list heater characteristics first with generally two important facts, heater voltage and current (at operating temperaure). Neither of these parameters can be varied.

Typical operation considers how the tube is to be used. The tube in question is a pentode. Since it can also be considered as a triode if its screen grid and suppressor are tied to the control grid these characteristics are also provided. A separate column gives typical operation data of the triode.

When plate voltage is given in typical operation data, the values are voltages from plate to cathode and not plate supply voltages, as is sometimes wrongly assumed. Thus, for the tube in Fig. 14·1, when connected as a pentode the voltage from plate to cathode can be 285 or 250 volts. Grid 2 voltage is the screen-grid voltage, which when connected in triode fashion, must be 250 volts. Grid 1 voltage, the control grid, can be derived from fixed or cathode bias. The peak AF grid voltage refers to the maximum (signal) voltage appearing between grid and cathode.

Bulb	Metal, Outline 8-6	ST-14, Outline 14-3	T-9, Outline 9-15
Base	Small Wafer	Medium	Intermediate
	Octal 7-Pin	Octal 7-Pin	Octal 7-Pin
Basing	7S	7S	7S
Mounting Position.	Any	Any	Any

ELECTRICAL DATA

HEATER CHARACTERISTICS

Heater Voltage	6.3 Volts
Heater Current	700 Ma

TYPICAL OPERATION

Class A Amplifier (Single Tube)	Pentode		Triode	
Plate Voltage	250	285	250	Volts
Grid No. 2 Voltage	250	285	Plate	Volts
Grid No. 1 Voltage[1]	−16.5	−20	−20	Volts
Peak A F Grid Voltage	16.5	20	20	Volts
Plate Current (Zero Signal)	34	38	31	Ma
Plate Current (Maximum Signal)	36	40	34	Ma
Grid No. 2 Current (Zero Signal)	6.5	7.0		Ma
Grid No. 2 Current (Maximum Signal)	10.5	13		Ma
Transconductance	2500	2550	2600	μmhos
Amplification Factor			6.8	
Plate Resistance (approx.)	80000	78000	2600	Ohms
Load Resistance	7000	7000	4000	Ohms
Power Output	3.2	4.8	0.85	Watts
Total Harmonic Distortion	8.0	9.0	6.5	Percent

Push-Pull Amplifier	Class A₁ Pentode	Class AB₂ Pentode	Triode	
Plate Voltage	315	375	350	Volts
Grid No. 2 Voltage	285	250	Plate	Volts
Grid No. 1 Voltage	−24	−26	−38	Volts
Peak A F Grid to Grid Voltage	48	82	123	Volts
Plate Current (Zero Signal)	62	34	48	Ma
Plate Current (Maximum Signal)	80	82	92	Ma
Grid No. 2 Current (Zero Signal)	12	5		Ma
Grid No. 2 Current (Maximum Signal)	19.5	19.5		Ma
Load Resistance (Plate to Plate)	10000	10000	6000	Ohms
Power Output	11	18.5	13	Watts
Total Harmonic Distortion	4.0	3.5	2.0	Percent

NOTE:

1. Maximum Grid No. 1 Circuit Resistance
   Fixed Bias   0.1 Megohm
   Cathode Bias   0.5 Megohm

Fig. 14·1   Sample data sheet.

Plate current (zero signal) is the quiescent (d-c) plate current flowing through the tube when no a-c signal is applied between grid and cathode. Plate current (maximum signal) is the plate current that flows when the signal voltage is at its peak positive value, between grid and cathode. Grid 2 current for maximum and zero signals has conditions similar to that of plate current.

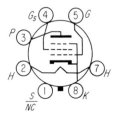

Fig. 14·2   Socket and element connections.

The three tube parameters μ, g_m, and r_p vary as the plate voltage and function of the tube. The amplification factor is not given for the pentode connection for two reasons. First, it is not customary to need to know the μ of a pentode because it is always hundreds of times higher than that of a triode; the pentode is a high-internal-resistance device analogous to a constant-current generator. Therefore, plate resistance r_p is more useful as a design value.

Secondly, the μ of a pentode can be computed from the equation $\mu = g_m r_p$. Thus the amplification factor of this tube is

$$\mu = (2{,}500)(10^{-6})(80)(10^3) = 200$$

The load resistance in ohms is also dependent upon whether the tube is pentode- or triode-connected, as is power output (the product of rms voltage and current across the load), and harmonic distortion is in effect a measurement of the nonlinearity of the tube, the distortion thus produced and imparted to the signal being amplified.

A circuit incorporating the factors discussed thus far would appear as in Fig. 14·3 (tube connected as a pentode).

PARAMETER TRANSFER CURVES

Parameter transfer curves present the following types of information graphically:

1. Average plate characteristics
2. Average transfer characteristics
3. Average operation characteristics

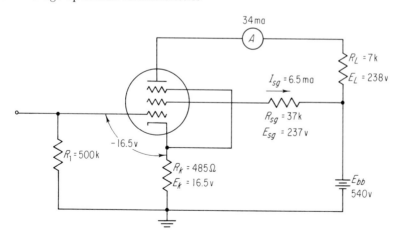

Fig. 14·3   Typical pentode circuit.

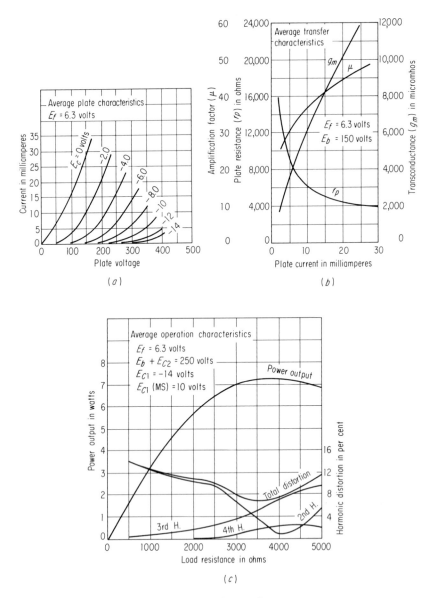

Fig. 14·4 Dynamic transfer curves.

264

Examples of these characteristics are given in Fig. 14·4. The curves of Fig. 14·4a represent constant values of control grid when increasing amounts of plate voltage are applied. The average plate characteristics are instrumental in projecting the effects of different loads on the tube-circuit voltages and at the same time graphically determining the tube's possible voltage gain. Figure 14·4b graphically represents the variation of the vacuum tube's three parameters as plate current is increased. Both Fig. 14·4a and 14·4b are static curves, that is, without a load applied to the tube. Figure 14·4c represents two output characteristics occurring simultaneously when a load resistance is in the plate circuit of the tube, power output and harmonic distortion. The block at the upper left of each figure specifies the operating conditions of the tube. In Fig. 14·4 the plate voltage E_b and screen voltage E_{c2} are each 250 volts. The grid voltage E_c is -14 volts. The rms signal voltage is 10 volts. The total distortion curve is the algebraic sum of the second, third, and fourth harmonic curves. The percentage is given as the right-hand ordinate.

According to the graph of Fig. 14·4c, maximum power output is approximately 7.4 watts when a load resistance of 3.9 kilohms is used. The plate resistance of the tube under the foregoing operating conditions must also be equal to approximately 3.9 kilohms according to the maximum-power-transfer theorem. Thus other information may often be obtained from a seemingly limited set of curves.

14·3 THE TRANSISTOR MANUAL

MANUAL ORGANIZATION

Recently published transistor manuals are divided into two sections, one dealing with basic theory and applications, the other a section devoted to transistor data. The latter is of primary interest. In the data section, the description of the transistor is divided into six categories. A description of the device is followed by information on absolute ratings, electrical thermal characteristics, mechanical data and general applications.

DATA SHEETS

Most currents and voltages on data sheets are d-c values obtained at an ambient temperature of 25°C.

The system of maximum ratings has been defined by JEDEC, the Joint Electron Device Engineering Council, and standardized by the National Electrical Manufacturers Association (NEMA) and the Electronic Industries Association (EIA).

Voltage ratings for transistors are always established with reference to a specified point on the device (e.g., collector-to-base emitter-to-collector). Maximum voltage ratings indicate maximum potentials that can be placed across two leads without causing material breakdown. Ratings for leakage currents are taken with the third lead open.

Transistor dissipation ratings consider heat dissipated at the collector. This power-dissipation factor is the difference between power supplied to the collector and that dissipated by the load. Semiconductor material is extremely temperature-sensitive. Therefore, dissipation ratings are dependent upon a given temperature. Many manuals provide a power-dissipation chart for different methods of transistor installation. This should be studied in detail and will not be covered here.

Transistor symbols are by no means standardized by industry. However, common usage has established familiar notation. Any good manual explains this notation, and therefore it will not be discussed in this section except for a few general symbols.

A glance at the transistor data sheet will tell the technician whether the transistor is germanium or silicon, PNP or NPN, designed for audio or high-frequency applications, etc. To choose a particular transistor for a special circuit design involves more than the foregoing, however. The transistor must be considered from given electrical ratings and characteristics. Careful study of these two descriptions will prove invaluable in determining performance and cost.

Ratings versus Characteristics. A rating is a value given by the manufacturer which, if exceeded, can result in component destruction. Characteristics are measurable parameters under specific conditions which illustrate regions of working performance. In most manuals maximum ratings are given at different temperatures. Design considerations must always be less than maximum rating. An example of both characteristics and maximum power rating is given in Fig. 14·5.

Collector-to-Base Cutoff Current. I_{CBO} is a common rating given to signify transistor quality. This current flows between collector and base with the emitter circuit open. A 2N139, for example, has an I_{CBO} of 6 μa when there is a collector-to-base voltage of 12 volts. Usually I_{CBO} is given with three different collector voltages, low, medium, and high, so that a range is established. Naturally, the lower the I_{CBO} the better the transistor as a useful device.

Collector-to-Base Breakdown Voltage BV_{CBO}. Though frequently specified, this rating is only occasionally considered unless the collector-to-base voltage is paramount in the circuit to be designed. For example, the 2N384 has a breakdown voltage of 80 volts when I_c is 50 μa and the emitter current equals zero. The same transistor in common-emitter configuration would have a rating for BV_{CEO}.

Emitter-to-Base Cutoff Current I_{EBO}. This is the d-c emitter current

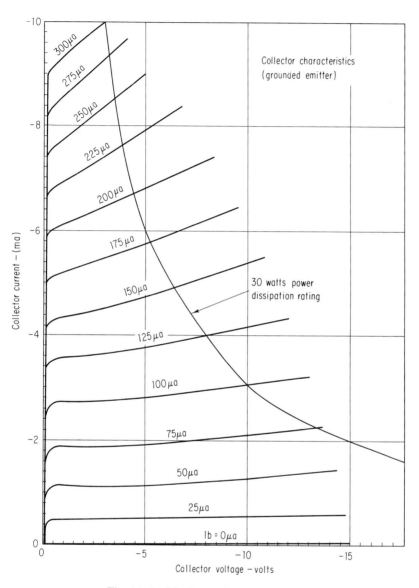

Fig. 14·5   Maximum-dissipation rating.

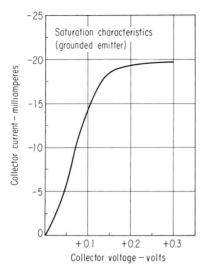

Fig. 14·6   Saturation characteristic.

when the emitter function is reverse-biased and the collector is open-circuited. This parameter is important in considering a typical design region. A 2N139 has an I_{EBO} of 40 μa.

Collector-to-Emitter Leakage Current I_{CEX}. This represents d-c collector current with the collector function reverse-biased and a specified base-emitter circuit connection. The rating is particularly important in considering switching-circuit applications.

Saturation Voltage $V_{CE\ sat}$. Saturation voltage represents the minimum potential necessary to induce transistor action at a particular collector current. Referring to Fig. 14·6, one notices saturation taking place at a collector voltage of approximately 0.2 volt when a collector current of about 20 ma is flowing. To the left of this point, the base-collector diode is forward-biased. Transistor efficiency in switching circuits is a function

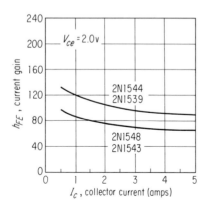

Fig. 14·7   Current gain vs. collector current.

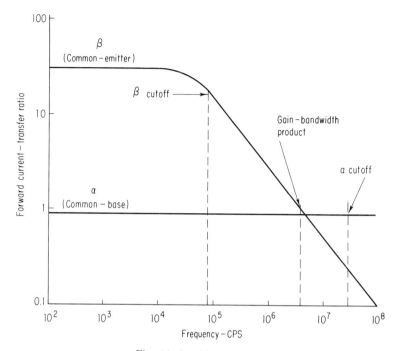

Fig. 14·8   Alpha cutoff.

of switching speed and power dissipated in the fully on condition. Therefore, a low saturation voltage is desirable. Saturation voltage will increase as collector current is increased and varies inversely as the gain of the transistor.

Current Gain h_{FE}. This parameter is a function of output current to input current with a constant output voltage as illustrated in Fig. 14·7. Another term used for this is the d-c forward current transfer ratio. As Fig. 14·7 illustrates, this is an especially arbitrary figure and dependent on a specific collector-to-emitter voltage and collector current. Figure 14·7 also points out that, as I_C is increased, gain decreases. Some manuals, incidentally, place a T next to the h_{FE} value, meaning that this is a typical or approximate value. A few transistors most usually used in common-base configuration have alpha or α in the h_{FE} column.

Frequency Cutoff. This characteristic is defined as the frequency at which alpha or beta drops to 0.707 times its value at 1,000 cycles. Figure 14·8 illustrates this. Frequently transistor data will give a figure for *gain-bandwidth product,* or the frequency at which beta is equal to unity. Both characteristics provide approximate indication of useful frequency range.

A

PERIODIC CHART

TRANSITION HEAVY METALS

LIGHT METALS

BRITTLE   DUCTILE

VIII

I A	II A	III B	IV B	V B	VI B	VII B		VIII	
1 H 1.0080	2 He 4.003								
3 Li 6.940	4 Be 9.013								
11 Na 22.991	12 Mg 24.32	21 Sc 44.96	22 Ti 47.90	23 V 50.95	24 Cr 52.01	25 Mn 54.94	26 Fe 55.85	27 Co 58.94	28 Ni 58.69
19 K 39.100	20 Ca 40.08								
37 Rb 85.48	38 Sr 87.63	39 Y 88.92	40 Zr 91.22	41 Nb 92.91	42 Mo 95.95	43 Tc [99]	44 Ru 101.1	45 Rh 102.91	46 Pd 106.7
55 Cs 132.91	56 Ba 137.36	57-71 See Lanthanide Series	72 Hf 178.6	73 Ta 180.95	74 W 183.92	75 Re 186.31	76 Os 190.2	77 Ir 192.2	78 Pt 195.23
87 Fr [223]	88 Ra 226.05	89-100 See Actinide Series							

LANTHANIDE SERIES (Rare Earth Elements)

57 La 138.92	58 Ce 140.13	59 Pr 140.92	60 Nd 144.27	61 Pm [145]

ACTINIDE SERIES

89 Ac 227	90 Th 232.05	91 Pa 231	92 U 238.07	93 Np [237]

(Based on *Fundamental Chemistry*, 2nd Edition, By H. G. Deming, Published by John Wiley & Sons, Inc.)

OF THE ELEMENTS

NON METALS

					2	2
						He
						4.003

| III A | IV A | V A | VI A | VII A | |

	III A	IV A	V A	VI A	VII A	
	2 3 **5** B 10.82	2 4 **6** C 12.011	2 5 **7** N 14.008	2 6 **8** O 16.000	2 7 **9** F 19.00	2 8 **10** Ne 20.183
	2 8 3 **13** Al 26.98	2 8 4 **14** Si 28.09	2 8 5 **15** P 30.975	2 8 6 **16** S 32.066	2 8 7 **17** Cl 35.457	2 8 8 **18** A 39.944

I B	II B						
2 8 18 1 **29** Cu 63.54	2 8 18 2 **30** Zn 65.38	2 8 18 3 **31** Ga 69.72	2 8 18 4 **32** Ge 72.60	2 8 18 5 **33** As 74.91	2 8 18 6 **34** Se 78.96	2 8 18 7 **35** Br 79.916	2 8 18 8 **36** Kr 83.80
2 8 18 18 1 **47** Ag 107.880	2 8 18 18 2 **48** Cd 112.41	2 8 18 18 3 **49** In 114.76	2 8 18 18 4 **50** Sn 118.70	2 8 18 18 5 **51** Sb 121.76	2 8 18 18 6 **52** Te 127.61	2 8 18 18 7 **53** I 126.91	2 8 18 18 8 **54** Xe 131.3
2 8 18 32 18 1 **79** Au 197.0	2 8 18 32 18 2 **80** Hg 200.61	2 8 18 32 18 3 **81** Tl 204.39	2 8 18 32 18 4 **82** Pb 207.21	2 8 18 32 18 5 **83** Bi 209.00	2 8 18 32 18 6 **84** Po 210	2 8 18 32 18 7 **85** At [210]	2 8 18 32 18 8 **86** Rn 222

2 8 18 24 2 **62** Sm 150.43	2 8 18 25 2 **63** Eu 152.0	2 8 18 25 2 **64** Gd 156.9	2 8 18 26 9 2 **65** Tb 158.93	2 8 18 28 2 **66** Dy 162.46	2 8 18 29 2 **67** Ho 164.94	2 8 18 30 2 **68** Er 167.2	2 8 18 31 2 **69** Tm 168.94	2 8 18 32 2 **70** Yb 173.04	2 8 18 32 9 2 **71** Lu 174.99
2 8 18 32 23 2 **94** Pu [244]	2 8 18 32 24 2 **95** Am [243]	2 8 18 32 25 2 **96** Cm [248]	2 8 18 32 26 9 2 **97** Bk [249]	2 8 18 32 27 28 2 **98** Cf [249]	2 8 18 32 28 2 **99** E [254]	2 8 18 32 29 2 **100** Fm [250]	2 8 18 32 30 2 **101** Mv [256]	**102** [253]	

B

CHARACTERISTIC CURVES FOR SELECTED TUBES AND TRANSISTORS

2CW4

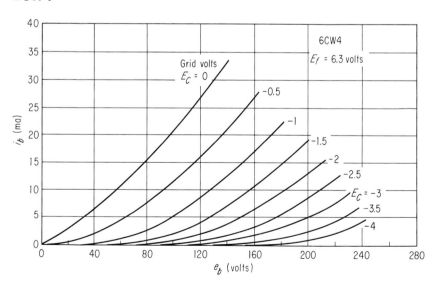

2N207 (Common base)

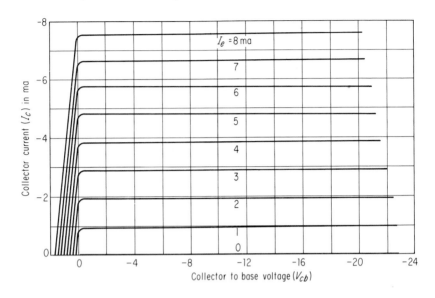

2N207 (Common emitter)

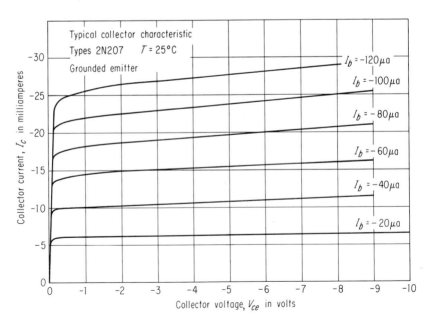

274

2N224   (Input)

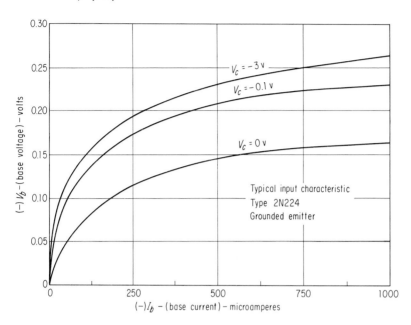

$V_c = -3$ v
$V_c = -0.1$ v
$V_c = 0$ v

Typical input characteristic
Type 2N224
Grounded emitter

$(-)$ V_b $-$ (base voltage) $-$ volts

$(-)I_b$ $-$ (base current) $-$ microamperes

2N224   (Output)

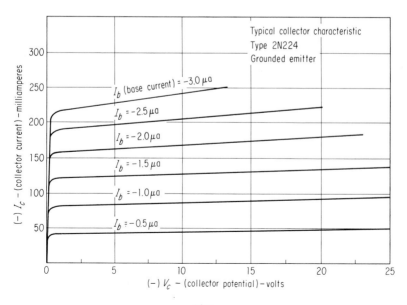

Typical collector characteristic
Type 2N224
Grounded emitter

I_b (base current) $= -3.0$ μa
$I_b = -2.5$ μa
$I_b = -2.0$ μa
$I_b = -1.5$ μa
$I_b = -1.0$ μa
$I_b = -0.5$ μa

$(-)$ I_c $-$ (collector current) $-$ milliamperes

$(-)$ V_c $-$ (collector potential) $-$ volts

275

2N1154

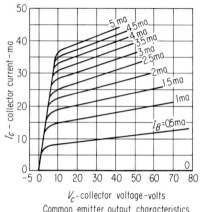

V_c-collector voltage–volts

Common emitter output characteristics

2EV5

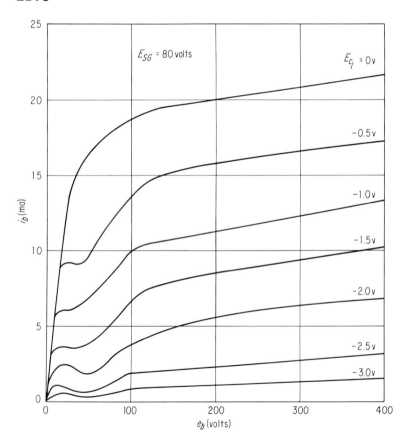

6AL5

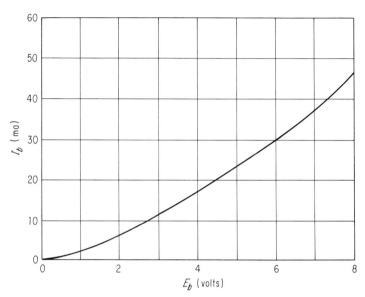

6AV6

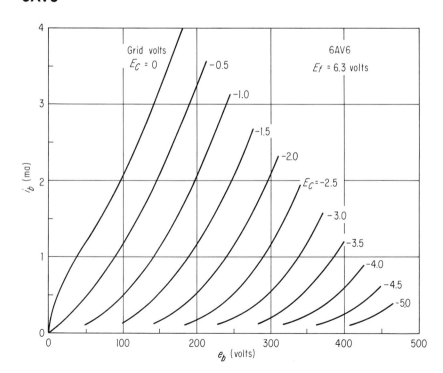

6BA6

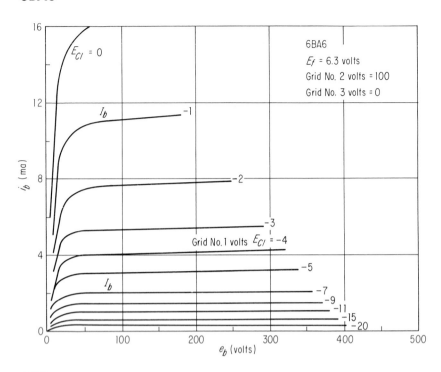

6C4

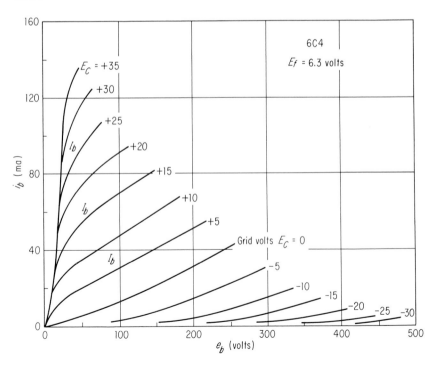

278

6EV5

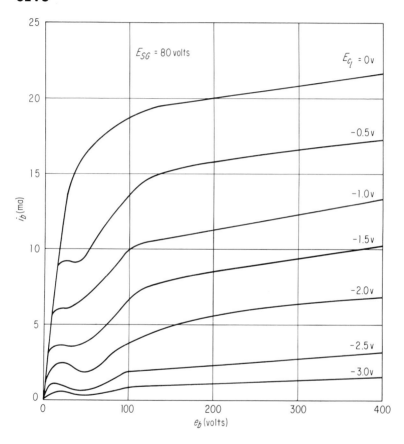

930

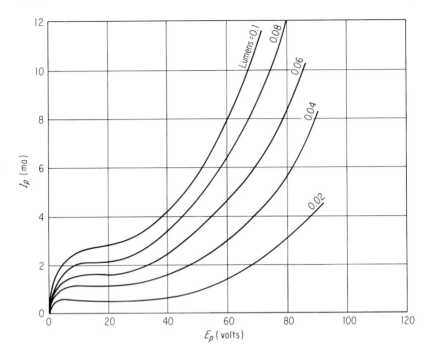

6J6

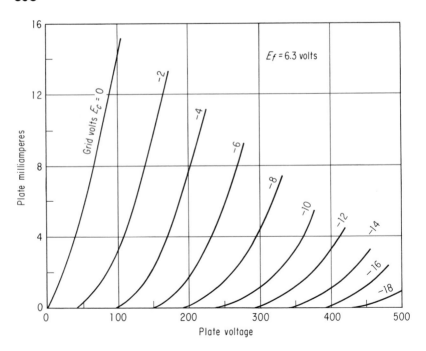

6SL7

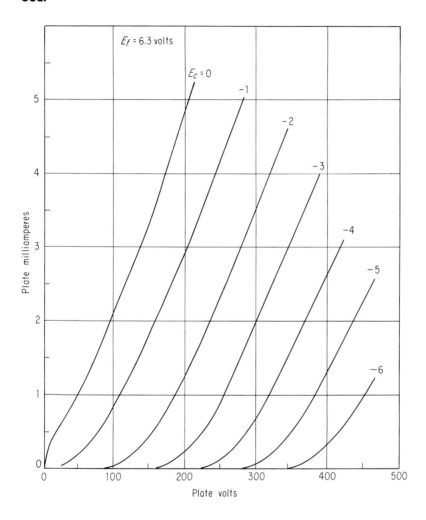

12AU7

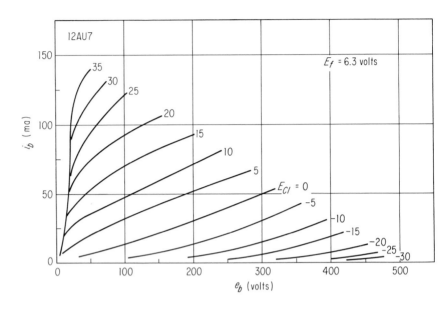

12AV7

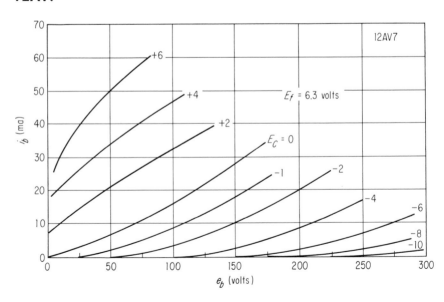

12BH7

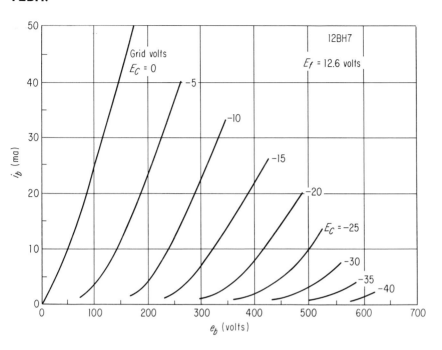

925

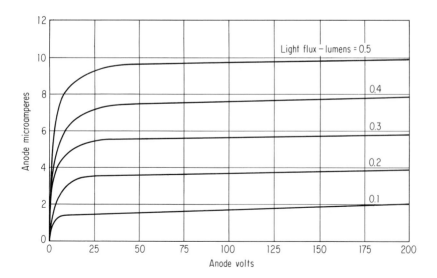

283

6H6

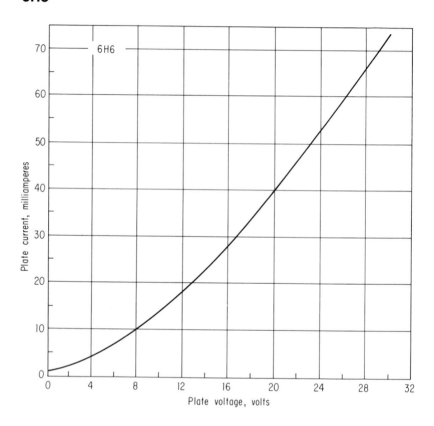

5691

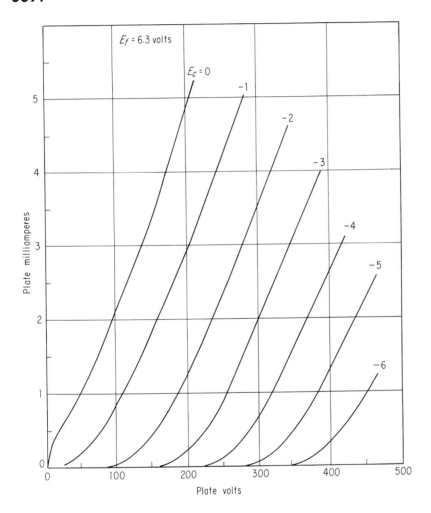

ANSWERS TO ODD-NUMBERED PROBLEMS

1·1	3.2 volts	1·3	24.3 mw
1·5	73.5 ohms; 2 watts	1·7	3.15 amps
1·9	As large as possible	1·11	17 ma, 0.2 watt
1·13	647 ohms at 20 watts; 40 ohms at 4 watts	1·15	730 ohms at 20 watts; 50 ohms at 4 watts
1·17	8 ma	1·19	6 volts
1·21	20 volts	1·23	25 volts
1·25	7.3 volts; 26.7 mw	1·27	1.25 mw
1·29	113 μsec		

2·1	25 kilohms	2·3	15 ma; 10 kilohms
2·5	7	2·7	75 kilohms
2·9	6 ma	2·11	7 kilohms
2·13	4.7 volts	2·15	R_p
2·17	1,000 μmhos; 95 kilohms; 95	2·19	2,000 μmhos
2·21	14 ma	2·23	10^9
2·25	22.5 volts		

3·1   1 ma; 40 volts

3·5   (a) 50 volts; (b) −6 volts; (c)
       0 volts

3·9   Between −2.5 and −3 volts

3·13   None

3·17   (a) 2.9 ma; (b) 35; (c) 70 volts;
       (d) 195 volts; (e) about 6 volts
       peak-to-peak

3·21   14

3·25   32.7

3·29   4.4 percent change

3·33   6 kilohms

3·37   (a) −4 volts; (b) 8 volts peak-
       to-peak

3·41   20.2

3·3   (a) 25 ma; (b) 262 volts; (c)
       35 ma; (d) 225 volts; (e) 175
       volts

3·7   20

3·11   7.9 ma

3·15   350 volts; −6 volts; 70 kilohms

3·19   The tube with a μ of 30

3·23   No change

3·27   2,000 μmhos

3·31   18.4 ma

3·35   (a) −5.5 volts; (b) −5.5 volts

3·39   4.75 ma peak-to-peak

4·1   (a) −3 volts, 12 ma, an increase
       of 10.6 ma; (b) 275, 16.4 ma,
       300 volts, 16.6 ma, 0.2 ma; (c)
       5,300 μmhos; (d) 125 kilohms

4·5   (a) 2 ma; (b) 2.8 ma; (c) 80 volts

4·3   (a) 115; (b) 6 ma; (c) 240 volts

4·7   (a) 100 kilohms; (b) 0.25 ma;
       (c) 0.15 watt

5·1   185 volts

5·5   56 pentode; 25 triode

5·9   100

5·3   70 volts

5·7   150 volts; 112.5 kilohms

6·1   400 volts

6·5   3.02 volts

6·9   No. −4.5 in.

6·3   1,409.7 volts

6·7   30 volts d-c per in.

7·1   100 kilohms

7·5   52 volts

7·9   1,100 ohms

7·13   5 ma

7·17   100 kc or 1.1 Mc

7·3   19μa per lumen

7·7   Tube v_2 cuts off at −14 volts. 0.1
       lumen will develop 14 volts
       across the 10-megohm resistor

7·11   (a) 375 volts; (b) 56 kilohms
       (i_b = 5 ma, e_c = 0 volts); (c) 75
       volts

7·15   Any voltage greater than −0.4
       volt

7·19   250 pulses per second

8·1   P type

8·5   0.125 eV

8·9   Increases

8·13   1.8 × 10^{-6} joules

8·3   Hole

8·7   Negative

8·11   Atomic, ionic, and molecular

9·1   166 ohms
9·5   (a) 162.5 ohms; (b) no
9·9   (a) 6 volts positive peak; (b) 1 volt negative peak
9·13 (b) 0.9 ma

9·3   1.2 megohms; 454 kilohms
9·7   100 ohms; 67 ohms
9·11 100 millimhos

10·1   PNP; emitter
10·5   Into
10·9   2.95 ma
10·13 49
10·17 83,300
10·21 9,000 μmhos
10·25 0.66 ma; 50.66 ma
10·29 (a) Grid; (b) plate; (c) cathode

10·3   0.75 volt
10·7   (a) 2.91 ma; (b) 32.3
10·11 90 ma
10·15 0.98
10·19 1,000 μmhos (Approx.)
10·23 PNP
10·27 (a) 0.977; (b) 44

11·1   100
11·5   43.8
11·9   1,400 ohms; 2,185
11·13 2.22 kilohms
11·17 (a) 0.99; (b) 136; (c) 134.6; (d) 36.2
11·21 A_{ib}, 0.99; A_{ie}, 82.4; A_{ic}, 82.4
11·25 4 volts
11·29 (a) 82.4; (b) 4.6
11·33 2.47

11·3   (a) 42.4; (b) 102; 432
11·7   43.7 kilohms
11·11 Decreases
11·15 48.9 kilohms
11·19 h_{ie}, 3.9 kilohms; h_{re}, 3.77 $\times$ 10^{-3}; h_{fe}, 110; h_{oe}, 0.111 $\times$ 10^{-3}
11·23 I_b, 0.51 ma; I_c, 42 ma
11·27 111
11·31 310 ohms
11·35 Decrease

12·1   26.67 ma
12·5 $R_2 = 6.25$ kilohms
12·9 E_L, 295 volts; I_L, 59 ma

12·3   (a) 3 kilohms; (b) 120 volts
12·7 $R_1 = 4$ kilohms, $E_{bb} = 85$ volts

INDEX